Most of the time the big k[...]t, the razor edge and tapering point of its ca[...]e protected by a cardboard sheath. But now he saw that it had been driven into the kitchen wall, pinning Sarah's apron. It was an I LOVE N.Y. apron, a bright red heart taking the place of the word LOVE. The apron's ties had been looped over a towel rack on one side and a cupboard door on the other, giving it a rough semblance of a human figure, a domestic scarecrow.

The knife's point has been plunged straight into the center of the red heart.

His pulse grew harder behind his temple. The arrangement was low on the wall, the knife right where his ten-year-old child's arm would have jabbed it.

'K. W. Jeter is one of the most versatile and uncompromising writers of imaginative fiction ... his tenaciousness deserves not only our admiration but our gratitude'
Ramsey Campbell

'Jeter has the brain-burning intensity of ... Philip K. Dick'
The Village Voice

'K. W. Jeter just keeps getting better'
Science Fiction Review

'*Soul Eater* reads to me like the work of a writer made ... eloquent by horror'
Ramsey Campbell

'Scary as hell ... wonderful and chilling read'
T. M. Wright

'An exhilarating writer!'
The New York Times

'Stunning'
Philip K. Dick

K. W. Jeter

SOUL EATER

PAN BOOKS
London, Sydney and Auckland

First published 1983 by Tor Books New York
This edition published 1990 by Pan Books Ltd,
Cavaye Place, London SW10 9PG

9 8 7 6 5 4 3 2

© K. W. Jeter 1983

ISBN 0 330 31682 6

Printed and bound in Great Britain by
Cox and Wyman Ltd, Reading, Berkshire

Lines on p 81 are from *The Secret of the Golden Flower* by Richard
Wilhelm and C. G. Jung, reproduced by permission of Harcourt Brace
Jovanovich, Inc.
Lines on p 205 are from 'We Must Bleed' by Darby Crash and Pat
Smear © 1980 Crash Course Music (Admin. by Bug). All rights reserved.
Used by permission.

To Geri

Mine is the voice one cannot hear,
That whispers in the darkened heart of fear;
From one shape to another without cease,
And thus my cruel power I increase.

—Goethe's *Faust* (Part II, Act 5),

BEFORE

darker in the forest

She woke up and felt for the knife under the pillow. Her fingers curved around the wooden handle between the sheet and the pillow's cool underside. Ghost light from the city's blue streetlamps flowed into the room. Her heart and breathing began to slow as the shapes of the room formed and became solid. Now she knew where she was.

Letting go of the knife, she sat up, hugged her knees and the covers close to her. Still dark outside. *darker in the forest* A pale coil of memory opened and twisted in the night. She brought her thumb to her mouth and kissed where she had scraped it across the knife's cutting edge. It was the biggest knife she had been able to find here. After everyone had gone to sleep, she had slipped out, padded barefoot in the dark to the kitchen, slowly pulled open the drawer so that no one could hear, and taken the knife back to her bed. She had been sleeping with a knife for a long time. It seemed as long as she could remember *darker in the forest with her mother* but she was ten now, and she had been nine back then, so she knew it had only been a year or so.

The rushing noise of the freeway was softer now, the sound stretched thin into cars swooping close and fading away one at a time, and the rumbling clatter of trucks. Just outside the window the bushy fronds of the palm trees said little hissing words as the wind rustled through them. And then under that she could hear—faintly—the sound of two other people's breathing in the apartment's darkness.

She sat curled up, her own breathing slowly matching time with the others'. That was something she had done before, too: huddled in the dark and listened for the sounds of someone near. But the knife had been ready in her hands then, not just tucked close by. And the dark space had not been sleeping, but instead tensed awake and waiting.

A motorcycle rasped and coughed in the quiet street outside. She leaned her face against her knees, hair breaking dark across the blanket and her nightgown's sleeve, and listened to the up-and-down whines of the small engine going through its gears. A city noise. That was fine; people made those. At this night hour, though, the silence beneath everything broke through, and that was the same here as anywhere else. *darker in the forest*

The covers fell away as she slid her legs to the side of the bed and reached down to the carpet with her bare feet. Her eyes had adjusted to the dark, and she could see everything in the room now, but she stood in the center with her hands spread apart from her, as if balancing on the sharpest point of a mountain. She was afraid to touch the table or the lamp or the chair, in case they should turn out to be really made of the fog that the blue light made them seem to be. They might dissolve like fog, and the room with them, and she'd find

10

herself someplace she didn't want to be, instead of here. *That's silly*. She tensed at the words in her head, then relaxed. It was her own voice; the other one was silent against the night's deeper silence. She reached down and grasped the chrome and glass of the table, cold in the night air. It stayed solid in her hand.

Her feet made no sound on the carpet as she walked down the hallway, listening to the breathing air as she approached it. A faint wedge of light slid around the bathroom door. She pushed it open; legs, pale and transparent, danced slowly in midair, a bisected ghost. Not really, she saw—just a pair of ballet tights that belonged to her father's girlfriend, Sarah. They were washed and hanging on the shower-curtain rod, the thin fabric fluttering disembodied entrechats in the breeze from the window. Another pair of tights, smaller, hung beside those. They were hers; Sarah had bought them for her, along with a pair of ballet shoes, at the Capezio store in the enormous shopping center with the waterfall flowing into a river of smooth stones right in the middle of it. And a dark blue leotard she'd wanted, just like one of Sarah's.

A handless arm drifted close to her. The sleeve of a white cotton blouse. Her father had bought that for her. The blouse and the tights seemed like the skin of some other girl that she put on when she was here, and shed again when she went home to her mother and aunt. She reached and took it, holding the light cloth against her face. She had worn the blouse home from her class, and then she and Sarah had washed their things out in the sink and hung them up. That had become a regular part of her weekends with her father. During the week, Sarah took the Advanced classes at the studio, but Saturday mornings she would take the Beginning along with her. He father would sit outside the classroom with the other parents—mostly mothers, but a couple like

11

him—his legs straddling a metal folding chair, hands and chin resting along its back, and watch the two of them at the barre and in the middle of the floor. She could see him, and would smile, but Sarah couldn't unless she fished her glasses out of her dance bag and put them back on for a second.

The blouse smelled of detergent and cold water. She thought she could smell a lingering trace of sweat: both she and Sarah came out of the classes with their hair in damp tendrils along their foreheads and the backs of their necks. This was just the sweat of moving, though. Not the other scent she remembered, of her own body in clothes that stiffened and grayed from never being washed, mixing with the fear in the cramped space, the not-sleeping and watching for the other that moved in the dark. *darker* She let go, and the breeze floated the blouse away from her.

Even quieter down the hallway, away from the windows that let in the scraps of the city's noise. The bedroom door was open just a crack. She pushed it—slowly; no sound—and looked inside. She could make out her father's hair, dark as hers, against the pillow. Sarah's, lighter, tangled on his arm, her sleeping face pressed against his bare shoulder. A fold of the blanket across his chest grew deeper, then shallower with his breathing.

She stood watching. Then it seemed as though the sound of breathing grew louder and louder, until it roared against the walls. It wouldn't stop; she had to lean against it like wind on the flat desert to keep from falling. Yet her father and Sarah didn't wake up. She realized it was her own breathing; she had walked through the apartment in a dream, and now she was awake. Quiet again, quiet enough to hear the other voice if it came. She looked down to her hands clasped against her chest and saw that she had brought the knife with her.

The pain woke her. The pain, and the night air sifting through the broken window. A few splinters of glass still dangled in the frame like jagged teeth. A wadded-up towel had been stuffed into the hole, but did nothing to stop the wind, carrying with it the sour smells—cooking oil fried into gray air, toxic sweats—of the city's inner streets. She clenched her eyes shut and twisted blindly on the cracked linoleum floor, trying to wrap the thin blanket closer around herself, until the pain throbbed again and brought her the rest of the distance to waking.

Some insulating chemical had filtered out of her veins; blood seeped back into her flesh, and the throttled-down nerves shrieked in response. Burns—the thought came through a haze as she pressed her face into the blanket's folds. This was nothing new. Scar tissue like wrinkled crepe already clung to the back of one of her legs.

This time it was in her forearm. It grew sharper with each pulse, a knife-edge shape moving closer in little steps, driving off the last of the concealing fog with its heat.

It became too large to hold inside. Her eyes opened, and a line of salt broke and traced the hollow curve of her cheek. She didn't wipe the tear away; it would dry where others had, the wet paths crossing to form the X's of words that couldn't be spelled out but stood for the mute pain of an animal watching the stages of its own death without understanding.

She saw the marks now. Small red circles where the fire had bit into the pale flesh of her arm. The burns were so small that her fingertip completely blotted one

13

out as she touched it. The pain sang even higher with the contact. Whatever it was that had burned her—she had no memory of it and was grateful, remembering the other hurting things that had gone before on her flesh—it had come at her again and again: random constellations of the marks dotted the skin.

If she held herself very carefully, balanced on a thin wire over the black, then the pain and the chemical nausea could be endured. Each breath held, and released; silence inside. No voice but her own barely shaped thoughts. The aftermath, the object left behind by the receding tide—the marred skin held no one but herself.

The wind through the broken window became sharper. She sat up, wrapping the blanket tighter around herself. She didn't recognize the dress that she had on. The thin, cheaply shiny fabric smelled of smoke and sweat, as did her hair, dangling in matted strands down her neck.

No idea where she was, whether she had been in this collapsing room before—the dark walls were overlaid with memories of other rooms, other pain-filled wakings—or how she had come here. She whispered her own name, as she had done before, the sound barely brushing past her dry lips: "Kathy." She knew that much, but sometimes another voice would speak with her mouth. That voice said other things.

A shape moved on the floor, roused by a human sound. She was not alone in the room. A man, deep in sleep. His thick-muscled arm flopped onto the linoleum as he rolled onto his back. An unreadable tattoo lay tangled in the bicep's dark, bristling hair. His chest moved with slow breathing from the mouth of a face that she didn't recognize.

Maybe she could get away without waking him. She watched the man carefully, gauging the depth of his sleep from the slow, dragging breaths. There was

14

nowhere for her to go, nowhere but whatever street lay outside. But that would be at least a few moments' respite from this room and the others like it. The farther she ran before the other voice spoke inside her head, the longer it would take for her unwilling legs to carry her back here. Enough time for the wounds to heal at least a little bit.

She leaned forward onto her hands and knees. Still watching the sleeping man, she raised herself from the floor. Pain, duller than the burns on her arm, ground through her spine as it unknotted from the ball she had formed of herself on the cold linoleum. She stood up and turned. Before she even saw the other figure in the room, she felt the hand clamp on her wrist and shove her backward.

In the middle of the room there was enough light from the street so that she could see the other man's thumb digging into the stringlike tendons of her wrist. Beyond that, his arm. And his face: a short fringe of hair falling toward the top of mirror-lensed glasses, the skin tight against the bones underneath, as though it had been gathered in back and pulled taut. Small, even teeth—for a moment she thought they might have caused the marks on her arm—lined up in a grin as he held her motionless. "Leaving?" he said. "Party's just started."

She said nothing, could say nothing as she looked into the dark silver lenses perched on the drumhead skin. For a moment she recognized the face, knew his name, but then pushed it away as impossible.

The man's eyes, dimly seen behind the lenses, shifted away from her. He nodded his head toward the sleeping figure. "How long's he been out?" He waited for a reply, got none, then pulled her closer to himself, the point of his gaze paring her skin away. Cold amusement in his voice: "What's your name?"

15

She started to speak. Her lips parted, her own name forming on her tongue. Then she heard the other voice, but not inside her head this time. "Renee," it said with her mouth. "My name's Renee."

He let go of her, and she felt herself falling backward. She looked up at him from where she sprawled and watched him fish a cigarette from his coat pocket. From behind her eyes, another thing watched as well. He exhaled gray smoke, nodding to himself. When he looked at her, the smile was no longer cruel.

"You made it," he said. Admiringly.

She was held from inside—there was no way to tear her eyes from his hidden ones. The glasses reflected the broken window across the room, so that two identical sharp-toothed mouths gazed at her. Her arm raised— she watched, helpless—and lifted her hand to him. Then she felt the sharp bite of the cigarette as he pressed its glowing end to the center of the palm, etching another mark like the ones on her arm.

"I knew you'd make it back," he said softly. "I've been waiting."

The wind pried at the apartment's roof, and the bad dreams seeped in. Under the weight of sleep he dreamed of his daughter, and his heart hammered the breath out of his throat. There was a field he ran through, the edges expanding in every direction as his feet stumbled and caught on the uneven earth. It was night in the dream, but different: only the same dry wind laid its soft hand over his face. The dark shapes of mountains along the horizon were edged with pale light, as though the moon had dissolved and spread behind them; he could see the thin ribbon of his shadow twisting and breaking over the furrows as he ran. His daughter was nowhere in the dream. He shouted her name over and over, then stopped, trying to hear more than the echoes of his own voice answering. Nothing but the wind, and his panting breath mingling in it. Then he fell in another direction, searching for her on the field stretching away beneath his feet.

When he woke, gasping for air, his eyes swept across the dark ceiling. Its mottled points came into focus. Another second, and he felt a warm weight beside him in the bed. His hand brushed under the covers and touched a curve of flesh. It's all right, he told himself as his eyes closed to the deeper black where the last traces of the dream were fading. He swallowed the sour taste in his mouth, his tongue dry from the shouting that had sounded only in the dream's dark field.

For a moment he lay listening to Sarah's breathing. Then he felt his other hand, dangling down the side of the bed, pressed by something. There was something holding on to it from which he couldn't pull loose. Something warm. Still confused with sleep, he rolled onto his shoulder and looked down beside the bed.

"Dee—" he said wonderingly. His daughter was huddled on the floor, clutching his hand. It was as if some fragment of his dream had persisted into his waking: the little girl, his child, whom he had called and searched for so desperately was here. Her cheek was pressed tight against his arm, the hair above his wrist bending with her shallow breaths. Her fingers, ivory against his coarser skin, were locked around his hand tight enough to cut the circulation. He realized how far he must have been into the rigors of his dreaming not to have felt her grip until now. Her eyes were tensed shut, the wrinkling eyelids matched by lines across her brow. Some dark landscape of her own held her.

Just a nightmare, he thought as he brushed a strand of hair from his daughter's sleeping face. That's all. He wondered if she got them often; what happened in them, on what night-lit ground she ran and from what shapes she fled. Maybe—the thought tightened around his heart—maybe there had been times before when she had reached for his hand and it hadn't been there. That thought saddened him as he watched his daughter's sleep. The past was in the room, faintly, like dust drifted in under the door by the wind.

Carefully he pulled his hand free from her grasp without waking her and laid her head against the side of the bed. He pushed the covers away from himself. Beside him, Sarah turned and murmured something, dimly sensing his movements. Sliding down to where he could swing his legs out of the bed without hitting Dee, he sat up and fished his pants from the floor.

Standing at the foot of the bed, he gazed at the two sleeping figures, the woman arched on the bed and the girl curled beside it, and felt the odd protective power that came from being the only one awake at a far hour of the night. He could hear their breathing, and the pulse of his heart, in the room's silence. The only sound from outside was the wind shearing against the building's corners. He listened and watched, guarding against nothing and everything. If there had been nights when his daughter's hand had reached and not found him, there had also been nights when he had lain awake, peering through the layers of darkness and wondering about her.

He bent down and lifted Dee up, her head against his shoulder, brown hair the same color as his but so fine that his breath stirred it as it fell along his arm. Her flannel nightgown felt damp with sweat against his bare chest as he carried her out of the bedroom.

The blankets on the sofa bed were tangled and thrown half onto the floor. He took Dee's weight into the cradle of one arm, and with his free hand pulled the covers straight. As he laid her down, her hands clung to his arm for a moment, then relaxed. He drew the covers up to her chin—an act that seemed oddly familiar to him, though there had been such a long time when he hadn't done it—and stood back. And watched.

She was falling away from him, deeper into sleep, her face releasing its tension. Whatever nightmares had brought her out of her bed to him had passed. His feet were bare on the carpet, his sweat growing chill across his shoulders. What can you do? he asked himself. Nothing; nothing, everyone's night was his own. Just be there, he thought. All that could be done. I'm here, he told his daughter without speaking. She burrowed farther into the blanket's warmth.

He went into the kitchen and fumbled for the wall switch. A slanting rectangle of light fell across the foot of his daughter's bed, but she didn't wake up. Padding quietly to the refrigerator, he took out a carton of milk and drank straight from it. A bachelor habit, Sarah had called that the first time she had seen him doing it. Something that men do when they're alone. The carton was still in his hand when something on the wall caught the corner of his eye. He turned and saw the knife.

It was Sarah's big kitchen knife. He had bought it for her, the largest German Henckels, but it was too big for her to use much. Most of the time it just lay in one of the drawers, the razor edge and tapering point of its carbon-steel blade protected by a cardboard sheath. But not now. Now it had been driven into the kitchen wall, pinning Sarah's apron. A Christmas gift from a friend back east, the apron had a large I LOVE N.Y. design, with a bright red heart taking the place of the word LOVE. The apron's ties had been looped over a towel rack on one side and a cupboard door on the other, giving it a rough semblance of a human figure, a domestic scarecrow. The knife's point had been plunged straight into the center of the red heart.

He stared at the knife and apron, feeling his pulse

grow harder behind his temple. The arrangement was low on the wall, the knife right where a ten-year-old child's arm would have jabbed it. That was easy to see, but the thought weighed so much in him that it could not move, but just lay in his tightening chest. The carton of milk grew heavy in his hand. Carefully, for fear of it sliding and falling from his grip, he opened the refrigerator door and put it back inside. When he switched off the kitchen light, the apron appeared a dim figure on the wall, a murdered ghost.

One of his daughter's hands was tucked beneath her cheek. Her mouth was slightly parted. He lowered himself onto the corner of the sofa bed, gently so as not to wake her. He sat and watched her sleep for a long time that he didn't measure, listening to the dying wind pass over the apartment building, until the dark changed to lead, then gray pearl outside. A few alleys away, in the first thin light of morning, a voice muddled with alcohol and madness shouted incomprehensible Bible verse. The streetlamps switched off, block by block. Then the night was over.

ONE

The off-ramp curved down from the freeway to the street below. The rushing wind of the Sunday evening traffic faded behind the small Datsun sedan as David Braemer steered it along the narrowing loop of concrete, the headlights sweeping across the guardrail and the slope of ice plant beyond.

He braked for the stop sign at the bottom of the ramp, and the change in motion woke his daughter Dee, curled up in the seat next to him. Her thin legs were tucked under her, and the seatbelt across her chest was all that kept her from falling forward as the car slowed. Braemer had snapped the belt's clasp together himself before they had pulled away from the apartment building in Los Angeles, drawing a familiar exasperated sigh and dramatic eye-roll from her. Now she lifted her head, the raised pattern of the seat's fabric printed in fading pink on one cheek, and looked at the metal light-posts slowing to a halt outside the car as if she had never seen anything like them before.

Braemer took one hand from the wheel and reached

across to brush away the web of fine hair tangled over one side of her face. "Hello?" he said. "Knock-knock? Anybody home?"

Scowling, Dee pulled away from his hand, her shoulders hunching up as if to put a shield between herself and the rest of the world. Sometimes, when she was awakened suddenly, it took a few moments for the last toxic layers of sleep to slide off her like a dry, clouded second skin. Braemer supposed that was something she inherited from him. Once, when he had been about her age, his mother had woken him where he had fallen asleep on the living-room couch, and with a child's fury he had reached down, picked up his shoes, and thrown them at her. Or so the family folklore informed him; he had no memory of doing it.

There was no other traffic coming off the freeway here. Braemer let the car idle at the stop sign for a few moments more, while Dee gradually came further awake. He watched her, the silence inside the car overlaid with the roar of cars and trucks above them.

She had his face, or the pretty version of it. As she grew up, he told himself that more often. Just in the last few years her hair had darkened, arms and legs lengthened from baby pudge. In her ballet tights and leotard, she looked like a colt with pink feet. The angles of her face had come up, high cheekbones and nose a little sharp. One time, getting ready to go to their class, Sarah had pulled Dee's hair into a classic dancer's chignon and called for him to come see, saying, "Hey! Look at Plisetskaya here, straight from the Bolshoi!" Dee had crossed her eyes at him and collapsed into giggles.

A few more years, and she would grow up to look like one of his aunts: his mother's youngest and prettiest sister, end result of Black Irish blood taking an Indian wife as it had moved west. The bluish lights arching over the freeway picked out the set of lines across her forehead, as though the world just outside the perimeter of her sleep were some infuriating puzzle to be worked out. In the corner of Braemer's eye a car's turn signal pulsed on the freeway. It made him flinch his eyes closed without knowing why. The red-plastic light had been the color of blood, like the red heart printed on Sarah's apron. White apron—he could see it just behind his eyelids. White kitchen wall beneath, white refrigerator with its door open, white milk in the carton his hand was slowly crushing. And the black-handled, gray-bladed knife sticking in the center of all he saw.

"Can I turn on the radio?"

He opened his eyes and saw a little girl. His. The scowl of dark sleep was reduced to the fleck of grit she was wiping out of one eye with the tip of her finger. The other image behind his eyelids faded into memory, with the thought *It doesn't mean anything, nothing at all, forget about it* drawn over it like an iron lid that he pressed all his weight against.

Dee was already reaching for the radio's buttons, knowing what he'd say. "Sure, go ahead. That's why I put you in charge of it," he said, hitting the gas and turning left. "You've got such good taste."

She made a face at him, nose wrinkling up under her eyes, as she switched the radio on. Some bright pop station bounced out, a chunky bass line rattling the speaker like a small animal trapped under the dashboard, fading a little as the car passed through the dark space under the freeway.

The current of light and noise on the freeway fell behind the car as he drove. Other fathers, other children, silent or talking as they went from one home to another. The great Sunday evening ritual in which Braemer had assumed his own small part: the return, from the weekend visit, to the "real" home, where the fathers, and a few mothers, become just voices on the telephone. Braemer saw those other divorced daddies on the street or in the supermarket, could recognize them even in the middle of the week when they didn't have their kids with them, pushing shopping carts stacked with TV dinners and kids' junk food. A fraternal organization that one didn't join but, except for those who had engineered it for themselves, fell into. The freeway sorted it out, sifting the children back and forth.

On this road the streetlamps ended just the other side of the overpass. The Datsun's headlights worked through the dark as the road narrowed and started to climb into low hills.

If Braemer had turned right off the freeway instead, the road would have cut straight into the community of San Aurelio, past a gas station, a brightly lit twenty-four-hour coffee shop, and the edge of one of the housing tracts surrounding the town, then on into the covered shopping mall at the center.

Before 1954 there hadn't been a San Aurelio, just green rows of orange and avocado trees. Then the suburbs had spilled a little farther, and the first tracts had been carved out. Every man's dream home: shake roofs and mutated Spanish Colonial nestling side by side on the cul-de-sacs. Schools to attract the families, the fathers having to drive just a little bit farther to work. Sewage district, master development plan; then it couldn't be just unincorporated county land anymore. One of the real-estate agents dreamed up a Spanish-sounding name, just as if it had been on the map since the days of the old ranchero land grants. By now it had reached the point where the Chamber of Commerce put on a yearly "fiesta," with the modern-dance classes at one of the high schools doing their version of a fandango in the open central area of the shopping mall, the concert band playing arrangements of Herb Alpert tunes that only their older brothers and sisters recog-

24

nized, and a piñata stuffed with merchandise coupons. Braemer had taken Dee to it one year, when she had been about seven. Bored, she'd tugged him over to the pet-shop window to watch the kittens scrabbling in a nest of shredded newspaper.

The farmland in the hills around San Aurelio had been owned by one family. Joseph Feld had come out from Indiana and bought the land cheap from a Mennonite offshoot group, made a success of their abandoned attempt to raise irrigation water with a wind-driven pump, planted orchards, prospered, and died. A few generations later, Braemer intersected with the local history: he met Renee, the youngest Feld daughter, at the local state college—a cluster of buildings with a token orange tree left withering in the center—married her, and begat Dee. By that time, the Feld clan had dwindled to Renee, her two sisters—one of them adopted—a brother, and their mother rattling away in the family house.

The old lady had died a couple of years after the marriage between Braemer and Renee had run its course. He had never seen her well. A gray, shuffling figure carrying about her a smell of illness overlaid with dusty lavender. He and Renee had driven down with Dee, just a newborn, to let the old woman see her granddaughter. Dee had screwed up her little red monkey face and screamed and screamed when she had been held in those mottled, slack-fleshed arms. The old woman had trembled so badly that Braemer had braced himself to catch Dee if she fell from the palsied cradle.

All that time ago, mused Braemer. The small flashback of memory played itself out—sometimes just a single scene running by, and other times dragged out to tiresome documentary lengths—every time he brought Dee back home to her mother and aunt. That smell of Dee's grandmother, which had always reminded him of hospitals—sickness not masked by disinfectant and powder—coiled in his nostrils as if the old lady were in the car's back seat right now, like some senile ghost of marriages past.

"Hey!" said Dee suddenly. She twisted about in her seat and leaned into the back of the car. "I think I forgot to pack my tights!" She pulled her bag from the rear seat and started to tug the zipper open.

"Tragedy strikes," said Braemer. His shoulder was jammed against his daughter's ribcage as she squirmed in the space between the front seats, digging through her bag behind them. "You probably left them hanging in the bathroom."

"Awww . . ." A little despairing wail sounded as Dee reached the bottom of the bag.

"Don't worry about them. Sarah's already put them away, I imagine. They'll be ready for you when you come back out next weekend." He brought the car to a halt at another stop sign, then turned right onto a street that climbed steeper into the hills.

"But how'm I gonna practice for a whole *week*?" she demanded, turning back around.

He shrugged, keeping his hands on the wheel. "Well . . . lesson numero uno. Real ballerinas don't lose their tights."

"Shoot." Dee slumped down in her seat in an agony of self-disgust.

The road passed by a sign, an elaborate construction of rough-hewn stone supporting a plastic rhomboid, with the name WINDHAVEN in dense black lettering. The last N was largely missing—some time ago, someone had thrown a rock through the sign, shattering the plastic and exposing the dead fluorescent tubes behind. Once the name had been visible at night all the way to the freeway. Now brown leaves, caught in the gap in the dusty plastic, spilled out across the knotted stone base.

The road leveled off, and the first of the houses came into view. Or what there was of a house: just the framework of a large two-story ranch-style, a skeletal assemblage of two-by-fours on a bare concrete floor, the lines of wood marking out the spaces that would have been bedrooms, kitchen, living room—the fireplace and chimney the broadest line, like a scrape of paint running down through a pencil sketch—if the house had ever been completed. No walls to stop the wind blowing the sawdust and wood scraps across the sills of nonexistent doors; the little stretch of roof that had been shingled before work had stopped now sagging with the damp that seeped into the bare wood.

Past the first house, then the others appeared. Outlines of the houses, with the night sky behind divided into segments by the spaces in the frameworks. Where the fertilized and neatly trimmed lawns would have run from sidewalk to front door, brown weeds rustled. Most of the lots were completely bare, marked out by faded rags on strings that had slumped to the ground, the house no more than a concrete rectangle with a pile of lumber stacked nearby, covered with black plastic tattered from the sun and wind.

The development company had had great plans, but shaky financing. They bought up all the Feld land from the old lady, stripped away the fruit trees, and began building what was intended to be San Aurelio's upscale housing tract. Scraped the land raw, laid out oddly winding streets on the bare ground, cut up the lots, and put out a massive sign of stone and back-lit plastic at the entrance to the tract, with an impressive-sounding, newly created name on it.

Their money had gone sour before the first house was completed. Ran out or never was; credit at banks that changed their minds. The work crews showed up one morning and sipped their coffee out of double-size

27

styrofoam cups from the place near the freeway off-ramp, warming their hands around the fires they built in a couple of trash barrels, until someone drove up in a car with the development company's logo on the door and told them all to go home.

That had been before Dee was born. She had grown up thinking that this suburban ghost town lined up on the way to visit her grandmother was a normal landscape. Somewhere, in bankruptcy courts and lawyers' offices, the scrabbling after the remains of money and the rights to the land, the slow untangling of mechanics' liens and claims and counterclaims was still going on ten years later. If it ever gets sorted out, Braemer thought nearly every time he drove past and observed the slow decay of the half-built houses, they'll have to bulldoze the land flat and start all over again. In the meantime the skeleton houses stood, the bottom transparency in a suburban anatomy book.

"Hey, there's Jess," said Dee, pulling herself up straight in her seat. The last street in the vacant tract had unwound and brought them to the old Feld house. Dee had spotted her uncle's pickup truck in the driveway, parked next to her aunt's veteran Chevrolet Bonneville.

Braemer steered around to the side of the two vehicles, tires crunching on the driveway's gravel, and switched off the engine. Dee had unsnapped her seatbelt and hopped out of the car before he had the headlights off. A faint smell of something burning traced across his nostrils as he got out and followed her across the unkempt lawn at the side of the house.

Jess was slouched in an aluminum lawn chair. One of the woven plastic straps had frayed loose and dangled beneath the tarnish-flecked frame. A few lumps of charcoal glowed dull red under gray ash in a shallow hole scooped into the ground. A rack taken from the oven in the kitchen and held up by bricks surrounding the hole completed the makeshift barbecue.

"What'd you have?" demanded Dee, pointing accusingly to the grill with its crust of carbonized grease.

"Burgers." Beer sloshed out of the can Jess balanced with one hand on his belt buckle as he put his other arm around Dee, standing beside the lawn chair, and pinned her arms in a hug. He set the can down on the grass, and raised his hand to shade his eyes from the house's back-porch light, and looked up. "Howdy, Dave," he said.

"How's it going?" Braemer worked his shoulder blades, releasing the cramp from the drive down from Los Angeles.

"Did you save me any?" asked Dee.

"You had dinner before we left." Even before his daughter had started up the dance classes with Sarah, Braemer had observed her ability to eat astonishing amounts of food and have none of it show up on her skinny frame.

"Maybe. Go ask Carol." Jess caught the square can of charcoal lighter as Dee, turning and sprinting to the house, hit it with her heel. He lifted the can to his lap and screwed the lid down tight on it. "So how's life in the big city?" His gaze, washed-out blue, rested quietly on Braemer's face.

Braemer shrugged. "'S all right. Hectic." Out here it was silent except for the shrill rasping of crickets in the hills' brush.

"Don't know how you can stand it." Jess rubbed at the dark spot his beer had left on his jeans. "Drive me nuts." He had an apartment in San Aurelio, and spent a lot of time here at the house where he had grown up, sometimes working on his truck, jacked up in the yard, and sleeping over on the couch if he didn't get it put back together. Braemer worried a little less about Dee being out here in the middle of nowhere without any neighbors because Jess was close by.

"Got to work someplace." He glanced over his shoulder to the house. Toward the front, Carol's assortment of overgrown hanging plants fringed the outline of the other porch, like a tame jungle hiding the front door's ornate brass knocker and insets of beveled glass. From one of the upstairs windows, above the overhang that sloped over the front porch, a slanting rectangle of light fell across the patchy lawn. The light never went off in that room.

"I'll catch you later," said Braemer, turning and heading toward the back porch. There were a few more things he wanted to do, stages of the Sunday evening ritual.

"Put that away for me, will ya?" Jess held the can of lighter fluid out to him.

Braemer stepped into the warm space of the kitchen, pulling the door shut behind him. Dee straddled one of the wooden chairs at the table, arms folded on top of its back. At the stove, her aunt prodded a hamburger patty in a black cast-iron skillet, grease sputtering over the blue gas flame. He opened the small doors under the sink and slid the square can into its usual storage place.

"Oh, hi, David." Carol left the spatula in the skillet and brushed a tendril of hair from her forehead. She reached over to the sink, took an upended cup from the dish rack, and filled it from the coffee pot on the back of the stove. Braemer sat down at the table as she put the cup in front of him, then went back to the sink to dig a spoon out of the pile of dishes and bring it to him.

"Thanks." He scraped sugar around the cup's bottom, watching Carol at the stove. The sleeves of her faded blue sweatshirt were pushed back, the faint hair of her forearms darkened in place by the sink's water. She slid the hamburger onto a paper plate and handed it to Dee.

"The buns and stuff are still on the porch," said Carol. Dee was already up from her chair and headed outside, her shouted thanks cut off by the door swinging shut. Carol lit a cigarette from the stove burner before turning it off, then slouched down in the chair across from Braemer. "You oughta feed that kid once in a while, you know."

He set his cup down and shrugged. "Nah," he said. "They tend to grow if you do that."

She smiled at the line worn smooth by repetition between them, and flicked a spot of ash from the grease-spattered front of her sweatshirt. There was not much else to say between them except old jokes, small passings of time. He mailed his child-support payment regularly at the beginning of the month, so that even the handing over of a check wouldn't cut into the silence-maintained fiction between them: that they were merely two people in a kitchen surrounded by night, without the past in the form of Carol's sister and his ex-wife upstairs. "How was the traffic?" she asked, delaying a bit the next stage in the process.

"All right." He had time. "It usually clears up once you get out of L.A." He sipped the coffee, then set the cup down beside a couple of unwashed dishes left from breakfast. A barely contained anarchy operated in the Feld house, broken by periodic spurts of cleaning in which Carol managed to get all the dishes washed at one time. She was overdue for one—a plastic cat dish with flecks of tuna dried hard and dark inside it had remained in the corner by the door more than a month after a gray tabby named Mischa had gotten out, disappeared, and been presumed eaten by the coyotes that lived in the far reaches of the hills. (The quick, loping shapes that Braemer sometimes glimpsed in the Datsun's headlights were rumored to be living up above Los Angeles, too, sneaking down for drinks from the backyard swimming pools and making off with the occasional poodle.)

It had been different when the old lady was still alive and doddering around the house. Carol had taken care of her—the changing of the urine-stained sheets every day, and the other duties that followed behind a sick old age—and kept the house clean enough to pass the inspection of the old lady's failing eyesight. The adopted daughter, grown up not as pretty as the two daughters by birth, with a jaw too strong and brow a little too wide, but still trying to earn her place in the family. The way she had put the coffee down in front of Braemer, like a waitress in her own home, was a holdover from that.

On the fireplace mantel in the living room stood a picture frame with a yellowed photograph—or part of a photograph; one side had been neatly cut away to reveal the cardboard backing—that Braemer always thought was a sad little human document. It showed a woman in early 1940's clothes holding a baby. Renee had told him once that it was Carol as an infant, just after she had been adopted by the Felds. Her new mother didn't look happy in the photograph. The whole future relationship between the two human creatures—the woman growing older and more bitter all the way into a withered, snapping-turtle senility, the baby growing into the family's ugly duckling, scrabbling for a place at the hearth and never quite making it, always pushed back into the cold —that had all been written in the expression of the woman's face, frozen in black and white.

Not that the old bitch had restricted her venom to Carol. The missing half of the photograph in the frame had shown the woman's husband, until some unspecified family scandal—the one part of the family dirt that Renee had been unable to fill Braemer in on—had caused the old lady to excise him out of history. A

32

domestic nonperson: every photograph of him had been destroyed, or his likeness cut out of the ones that remained. He'd died right after Renee was born, so that none of the children, biological or adopted, had more than the blurriest memory of him.

The house had started to slip into a comfortable sloppiness when the old woman finally died. Even more so when Renee and Dee had moved in after the divorce, setting up housekeeping with Carol on their combined inheritance of the land-sale money. A pair of Bert and Ernie handpuppets that Braemer had given his daughter, and which she no longer played with, had found a permanent resting place on the end table by the sofa. A collection of Dee's old crayoned school papers, curling at the edges, was taped to the refrigerator door like a fall of leaves. Signs of a child, something living rather than something dying in the house.

But now. Braemer tilted the cup, letting the last drop of coffee, lukewarm and bitter, ease onto his tongue. Past the doorway to the living room he could see, spilling down the staircase, the light from one of the upstairs bedrooms. The pool of light at the foot of the stairs was always there. Now the line between what was living and dying in the house had become dim.

Through the screened window he could see Dee talking to Jess, another lawn chair drawn up by his and the paper plate on her lap.

He pushed his own chair back from the kitchen table and stood up. "I think I'll go upstairs and see Renee," he said quietly.

Carol ground her cigarette out in one of the dirty dishes. "You know," she said, looking up at him, "you don't have to do that."

She had never said anything about it before, though he had been waiting a long time for it. He shrugged. "It doesn't mean anything."

Squeezing her eyes shut, Carol tilted her head back, her arms clasped across the front of her sweatshirt. "You're a nice guy, David," she said, opening her eyes at last, looking at the ceiling rather than him. "You just . . . shouldn't do it. That's all."

A ratchet gear clicked in his heart, driven by the mainspring of the past. "I know," he said. He knew he should go outside and hug his daughter goodbye, get in the car, and drive back to Los Angeles and the woman who loved him. But instead he was going to go upstairs and see his ex-wife. Or what was left of her.

He stepped from the kitchen into the living room, and started up the stairs, gripping the smooth-worn rail. The light from the open bedroom door fell across his face. Before he got to the top step he could hear the sound of her breathing.

His hand brushed the wooden ball at the end of the rail. He walked across the hallway and pushed the bedroom door open a little wider. The room was full of light and a hospital smell, disinfectant and the other, more cloying odor. He leaned his back against the doorway and looked. This was the last stage in his private Sunday evening ritual.

Renee was in bed, her body curling into a fetal position underneath the sheet Carol had drawn over her. Her face had become skin over bone, the feeding tube inserted in one nostril and fastened tight to her cheek with white surgical tape. Eyes turned unseeing to the light. Lips drawn back from dry teeth. Something rasped in her throat with each fierce, panting breath. A white-knuckled fist at the end of an arm drawn to a matchstick knotted elbow. A steel tint showed in the black hair, which Carol had cropped close to the emerging skull.

He leaned in the doorway and looked at her, his arms folded, eyes half-lidded, watching the remains of the face that had once slept on the same pillow as his, and the sleep that she had fallen so far into that she would never get out of it. He watched and felt nothing. Nothing at all. To feel that space blank inside himself, a space whose outline was that of the woman in the coma-deep bed, was why he had mounted the stairs, to where the room's endless light was full upon him.

She listened to her father's car heading up the driveway and away from the house. Onto the street that led to other streets, to the freeway, all the way back to that other place where he lived.

After their goodbye hug, his bending down and encircling her, lifting her onto the toes of her shoes, she had run back into the house. Up in her mother's room, she had watched him leave. The car's headlights swung around, lighting the trees stark for a moment, then faded and were lost in the street. When she could no longer hear the car's engine cutting through the night, the only sound was the scraping of crickets at the edges of the yard, and her mother's rasping breath soft in the room with her.

She turned and leaned back, her hands on the windowsill. The sheet over the coiled figure in the bed trembled slightly, as if the emaciated woman would any moment spring upright. Dee watched, but her mother stayed curled about herself, the ragged breathing the only sign of life.

She went over to the bed and looked down at her mother's face. Cropped hair; dry, cracked lips with tongue thrusting convulsively against the teeth behind; plastic tube snaking across the sunken cheeks—she had to lay a skin of memory over the skull before she could recognize her. With the face drawn so rigid, edges of white showing at the rims of the bruise-dark eyelids, she looked to Dee like that mother her own had changed into, the one that she hadn't been able to recognize, clutching a knife in the dark spaces of the forest. The one her daddy didn't know about.

As she looked at her mother's sleeping face—if this was sleep—the room's light dimmed, became dusty shafts filtering through pine branches. The weight of the trees towered above her. She whirled around, catching herself from falling into the sharp odor of the decaying needles matted on the ground. The room's outline, a spare drawing of a box, faded beyond the other space that closed about her.

A moment later, when she turned slowly around to look at the figure on the bed, the fear could no longer be seen in her own face. She smiled at the comatose body frozen in its slow writhing. But not the smile of a ten-year-old girl: another smile that traced her mouth into a line of knowing. A secret wrapped inside.

The child went to the window, and looked out at the night and stars. Something else inside her saw the cold pinpoints of light over the dark ground.

The sound of a key in a lock brought her eyes open. She had not been asleep, but keeping the dark squeezed tight inside her eyelids, wishing to fall back into the comforting haze. Then metal teeth sliding into its mate. The snap of a padlock opening. A door creaked apart from its jamb, and a flashlight's dim, slanting oval crawled over her. Her eyes followed it down across her body, blurred shadows outlining her breasts and the contour of her ribs.

Darkness again as the flashlight shut off, then another brighter light that filled the room. Her eyes winced shut and she tried to curl into a ball, but something caught her wrists, keeping her arms above her head as she lay on the cracked linoleum floor. The knots in strips of sweat-yellowed cloth cut into the base of her hands, tightening as she pulled against them.

The light's pain ebbed from her tearing eyes. She opened them and saw the figure standing in the center of the room, the light fixture's chain dangling by his hand as he drew his glasses back on. The mirror lenses held the bare lightbulb like two burning fists.

"Good evening," he said, looking down at her, voice soft through the smile that barely raised one corner of his mouth. He knelt down beside her, the hidden eyes searching for something in her face. She saw the two faces reflected back at her in the lenses' curves: hollow cheeks, eyelids like dark thumbprints under hair tangled across the forehead. A face she barely recognized as her own.

"It's just Kathy, isn't it," murmured the figure, brushing the hair from her face. He rocked back on his heels and studied her a moment longer. "That's all right," he said at last. "You'll do fine. Just fine." He straightened himself up and walked over to another corner of the room.

She turned her head against one pinioned arm, watching his shoulders hunch up under the creased brown leather of his jacket. "Renee," she whispered. "You wanted Renee. . . ."

He glanced over his shoulder at her, but said nothing. The face under the shining glasses blurred in her sight, a dream character melting in unseen rain. She knew who it was, but knew also that it wasn't true. She had gone crazy in the little room empty of everything except dirt and twice-breathed air—better that than to have the face be the one she thought she recognized. The face blurred even further through the wash of her tears.

Kneeling down again, he switched on a hot plate sitting on the floor, uncapped a plastic water bottle beside

37

it, and poured a little into a dented aluminum pan. While he waited for the hot plate's coil to heat to a dull red, he pulled a few items from his jacket pockets. Methodically, he unwrapped a needle from its sterile package and fitted it to a small syringe, then laid it on the floor and unfolded a square of crumpled silver. In the aluminum foil's last crease a powder glinted light like ice crystals across the room to her.

The water in the pan boiled, and his hands moved about, making preparations, fingers dipping the needle into the water with no sign of pain. He stood up and walked back toward her.

Bending down, he gripped her arm and turned the soft flesh up to himself. He moistened a forefinger on his tongue, then rubbed a patch clean in the crook of her elbow, the skin's embedded dirt rolling into thin black lines. The point of the needle sank into the rubbed-pink skin.

"Renee doesn't need to know, does she?" The voice crooned low in her ear as she closed her eyes, shutting out the face behind the mirror lenses. His breath brushed against her cheek as he leaned closer to her. Her heart began to race as the toxic blood, chemical-laden, reached it, a fire bursting under the skin.

"*She* doesn't need to know at all." His voice echoed distantly. Her eyelids fluttered open for a second and she saw the room's walls fall away, space lapping in waves over them.

"She doesn't need to know," he whispered. "But she will."

TWO

The alarm went off, but she was already awake. Sarah brought her arm from beneath the blanket, reached, and shut off the shrill clatter. The dial, faintly luminous in the gray light from the window, read six A.M. She closed her eyes for a few seconds against the pillow, poised on the edge of falling back into sleep, then drew a deep breath past the taste in her mouth and pushed herself up on her elbows.

Beside her, Dave was deep and away from her, his face buried in his arms, eyes squeezed tight against even the trace of light in the bedroom. She watched him sleep. Even if she had let it ring on, the alarm clock wouldn't have cut through. After the weekends, he was always further out of it than even the usual Monday morning jokes.

When he came back from driving Dee home to her aunt and mother—if you could call a breathing corpse that—he always stayed up well past two or three, bent over some project layout on the kitchen table, the stereo tuned low to one of the all-night classical stations.

Distance greater than yards separated them, even when she came in and kissed him good night on the back of his neck. He would lean back in the kitchen chair and circle his arm about her waist, but his thoughts would still be somewhere beyond his pen and the paper's inked lines. Then later, when he slipped into bed beside her, she could feel the shift of weight in the mattress, the other warmth, and knew without looking that he would be lying on his back, staring up at the dark ceiling.

On this and other nights, she would sometimes drift awake and find him finally asleep but pressed against her, arm around her shoulders to draw her tighter to him. She would lie there, quiet enough to feel the beat of his pulse, and think—oddly—of the six years she had been married: that other world where she and her husband had wound up sleeping with their backs to each other, a gulf of miles between their spines, and her pillow growing damp against her cheek as she bit her lip to keep him from ever hearing her crying. That was a long time ago, just a deep night memory now; she would go back to sleep curled into David's side.

Without switching on the lamp, Sarah got out of bed, tugged on the worn-out ballet shoes that she used for slippers, then padded out to the bathroom.

When she came out, toweling her damp hair, Dave had sprawled across the bed, as if trying to find her in the warmth and scent left behind. She picked up the alarm clock and reset it for three hours later, then reached across Dave and pulled the sheet up over his uncovered shoulders.

Half an hour later, dressed, with a carton of yogurt tucked into her shoulder bag, she came back into the bedroom and kissed him lightly on the brow. That brought a murmur from him, fragment of a dream conversation: a name, but not hers. She thought she had heard him say "Dee." For a moment she stayed bent

40

close to him, then straightened, turned and left for work.

"Hey, Braemer—you got a kid?"

He looked up from his drafting table and saw a sharp fox-terrier face, a fidgeting hand pulling a cigarette away from the mouth. For a second he couldn't remember the guy's name, then it hooked up: Stennis, the bookkeeper Rawling had hired a couple of weeks ago when he'd finally admitted that his graphics business couldn't be run out of a shoebox stuffed with bills and checks any longer.

Braemer dug the Rapidograph's cap from the tray mounted on the side of the table and snapped it on the pen. "A girl," he said. "About ten years old."

Stennis dropped uninvited into the faded canvas director's chair beside the cubicle's door and leaned his head, eyes closed, back against the thin wall partition. "I got a little girl, too. She's, uh . . . three, I think. Yeah, that's right. Three." He ran his cigaretteless hand through his hair. "Man, I don't know how you're supposed to do it. My friggin' child-support payments are just about killing me."

"Kids are expensive." He leaned his elbow onto one of the blank areas of the paper pinned to the table, careful not to smudge any of the layout's inked lines, and shrugged. "Everything's expensive."

"Christ, don't I know it." Stennis stared through a wisp of smoke, as if trying to look past his reflection in a bar mirror. His voice sounded as if it should be hanging over a half-empty glass, a tone of alcohol-loosened confidences to be traded. "Now my ex-wife wants me to up the support or she's going to drag my ass back into court."

Another shrug. "Your rent goes up, so does hers." The cubicle was a box small enough that Braemer could

41

smell the other's nicotine breath. He kept his answers clipped to increase the distance between the two of them. He hardly knew the guy. It was staring to sound like the warmup to a touch for money, a little loan until payday.

"I'm already moonlighting *this* job," said Stennis. That was probably true. Braemer had seen him a couple of times pulling out of the parking lot around three-thirty, in a Camaro with the dealer's ad still tucked in the license-plate holder. He remembered hearing something about a swing shift at the tax assessor's office.

Stennis brooded in silence for a moment, flicking ash onto the floor. "Your ex ever do that to you? Hit you up for more money?" His eyes squinted at Braemer.

It took him a second to reply. "No," he said. "Guess I'm lucky that way. If something like a dentist's bill comes up, I help pay it. That's about it."

"Really? I can't believe that. Man, once they got the hook set in you, they *all* love to just reel you in over and over. How come?"

"How come what?"

"How come your ex-wife doesn't ask you for more money?"

You little shit, thought Braemer, looking into the eyes reddened by nicotine and caffeine. The voice had hinted at wanting to be cut into whatever sharp little deal Braemer was in on. You asked for it. He laid the pen down in the groove at the table's bottom edge. "My ex-wife isn't going to be asking for anything. She's in a coma. And she's not coming out of it. Ever."

Stennis peered at him even sharper. "What happened to her?"

I hired guys to beat her up in an alley. He wanted to say that but instead told the truth. "She had a stroke. Massive." He let his voice broaden into barely sustained patience.

"How old was she?"

"Twenty-six. These things happen sometimes. I think there was a family history of it."

"Ah . . . I see." Stennis nodded sagely. "Then you divorced her, huh? Uncontested, as it were."

He felt like running the narrow face with its conspiratorial glances straight through the thin partition and into the corridor beyond. "It only happened about a year ago. We'd been split up for about five."

"Hm." Stennis looked up, puzzled. "So who's got the kid?"

"My ex-wife's sister. She'd been sharing a house with them before, so she just went on that way. I send her the support checks. And she'd done some nurse's training once, so she brought my ex-wife home from the hospital to take care of her." To die—the thought flicked past. "She doesn't need any respirator, or any other kind of life-support system." Too bad; it would've been over with by now. "That's pretty much how it is."

It had been that way for just about a year now. Almost exactly, Braemer calculated. About a year ago he had been in England. Some stuff he'd done a long time ago, in fact the last project he'd done while married—a set of poster designs for a foreign-film festival in Houston—had gotten picked up by a film distributor working out of Milan. From out of nowhere, in an envelope that looked like it had been walked on in every post office in Europe, had appeared a check for royalties. A month's worth of the salary he was making then as a night security guard, rattling shop doors on Wilshire Boulevard to make sure they were locked. He hadn't even spent any of the money when, second surprise, one of the glossy European graphics magazines bestowed one of its minor awards—a plaque, no money —on him for the posters. The royalties money was enough for him to quit the guard job, pay up a month ahead on his child-support, and fly to London for the awards banquet. A hollow honor: he hadn't put a pen to paper in five years. They had given their award to the artist he had been. What wound there was from that amputation had scarred over, enough that it had been a good excuse to go and spend a few weeks in England. He had never been out of the States before.

He had wound up being there for just three weeks, eating shawarma and yellow curry from stand-up bars in Earl's Court to stretch his money, when Carol's telegram had caught up with him in a cheap bed-and-breakfast hotel. RENEE IN HOSPITAL DEE OKAY RETURN SOON AS POSSIBLE. That had brought him back on the next flight out of Heathrow. To his daughter, and the living remains of his ex-wife, and the odd but functional living arrangement that had evolved in the months that followed.

"That's some setup." Stennis' voice broke into his thoughts. "You really lucked out."

He brought his gaze down, from where it had drifted to a corner of wall and ceiling as though searching for smaller vermin, and looked at the other for a few seconds before speaking. "I guess so. That's what you call luck, all right."

"Hey, now I get it." Stennis leaned forward, the cigarette in his hand now burnt out against the filter. He barked a quick laugh. "*That's* why Rawling called your ex-wife Sleeping Beauty."

Braemer turned around to study the drawing on his table. "When did he say that?"

"We were going over the payroll this morning, and it came up about your overtime making up for the hours you miss on Mondays. Rawling said you were always late on Monday mornings 'cause you'd been out visiting Sleeping Beauty. Now I get it."

Braemer turned back around to look at him. Stennis

44

swallowed the end trace of his laugh when their eyes met. He stood up and ground the dead cigarette butt under his shoe. "I'll catch you later," he said. Hitting on Braemer for a loan, or whatever the purpose of the visit, was forgotten for now.

He looked at the door's empty rectangle for a few seconds after Stennis had disappeared, then pulled the layout off the table and rolled it into a tube. Under the rubber band holding it tight he slipped the scrawled-on assignment tag. He slid off the stool and headed out into the corridor.

The building, one of the smaller units in an industrial park off the Harbor Freeway, echoed his footsteps in the quiet. Everyone else was still out to lunch, down at the sandwich shop at the corner or the bar across from it, depending on their tastes. The door to Rawling's office was ajar. He pushed it open with his shoulder.

"What's going on?"

Rawling looked up from his desk, a sheaf of color separations that he had farmed out to a photo lab spread out before him. "Nothing at all." His high-backed office chair creaked as he leaned away from the desk. "Same old B.S."

Braemer dropped the rolled-up drawing on the desk and lowered himself into the chair across from Rawling. "I was talking to what's-his-name. Your new book-keeper. Stennis."

Rawling folded his hands across his chest, a habit left from when he'd been fatter and there had been a comfortable soft ledge there to support them. He gazed out at the white-striped asphalt of the parking lot and grunted. "What can I say? He works cheap."

"I imagine so." He reached over the desk and pushed the color separations about with his forefinger, looking at them rather than Rawling. "He mentioned something you said about my ex-wife."

"Hm. That was something that just popped out. I'm sorry about that."

"Forget it." Braemer straightened the separations into a neat pile. The two of them went a ways back, long before Rawling had tracked him down through the notice of his award in the graphics magazine and had hired him, persisting over Braemer's protests that he hadn't done any work in five years. Rawling had been one of his instructors in college, before the collapse of a third marriage and the overlapping demands of alimony and child support had driven him to start hustling up more money than he could get from a faculty salary. Small coincidence: he'd also been the one who'd landed the poster assignment for Braemer by touting an ink-wash portfolio to the chairman of the festival in Houston.

"No, I really am," Rawling went on. "That little creep doesn't need to know about your personal life."

Braemer smiled. "Sometimes I wish I didn't know anything about it either."

"Jesus, mine too. Messes we can make of things." He continued brooding, eyes focused on nothing outside the window. "How is Dee? You had her this weekend, didn't you?"

"She's fine." He waited. "Something the matter?"

"Aww, I don't know. What am I supposed to do. It's Jeffrey."

That was his eight-year-old boy from his last marriage. "What happened?"

"He's started running away again," said Rawling. "Susan called me up Saturday and told me he didn't come home from school Friday, and then a janitor found him sleeping in a restroom in some shopping center out in Encino the next morning."

He seemed old to Braemer now, slumped in the chair

46

behind the desk, diminished by more than a loss of weight. "Any reason why?"

"Shit, who knows. I'd run away too if I had to live with Susan. Christ, I *did* run away." He shook his head slowly. "I drove out there and talked with him. He said he wants to come live with me."

Braemer said nothing. They had talked about this before, two absentee fathers hashing out life in the last quarter of the twentieth century.

"He's an eight-year-old boy, for God's sake," pleaded Rawling. "He'd wear me out in an afternoon. I love him, but he comes in the door, I gotta go get my heart medication out of the bathroom. I'd be dead in six months trying to raise him by myself. Where's the money going to come from then?" He swiveled around in his chair, his eyes locking into Braemer's, stating his case. "Who's going to . . . who's going to look after him then? Even from a distance." His voice had broken and fallen close to a whisper. He leaned across the desk, planting his elbows on the bright colored papers. "Wanna hear the latest horror story? This is good, this is real good."

"Sure." They had sat out each other's bleak patches before, sometimes sitting late at night in this office with a six-pack brought back from the bar, nursing old wounds. "Go ahead and tell me."

"The latest thing on the street." Rawling's voice was bitter. "Last year's drugs aren't good enough, there's always gotta be progress. This was in the *Times* last Sunday, plus I've been hearing some other stuff about it. You live in L.A., you hear these things, right? The new thing is to take these two prescription drugs—one of 'em is Talwin and I forget the name of the other; starts with a B, I think—and you crush 'em and cook 'em in a spoon like smack, then shoot it up. All the rage

47

with the street kids. Gets you loaded like heroin, plus it's cheaper and easier to score. Perfect, huh? Only problem is that the pills don't completely dissolve when they cook it up, so when they inject it there's this fine grit that goes right along into the veins. Like bits of sand. And the more you do it, the more of it in your blood, until it starts collecting at certain points in the body. Main one being the eyes. All those skinny kids you see standing around on the corners, and their eyes are slowly filling up with sand.''

You live in L.A., you hear these things. You got a kid, you worry about these things. Braemer met Rawling's eyes in silence. That's how it is, he thought. You bail out of your marriage to save your life, or you wake up in its ruins, and then you wonder when your kids will join that pale army stationed on the sidewalks. Filtering out of the suburbs, out of broken homes and ones that should be broken, to the place where dollars can be made. Like sloughing off layer after layer of dead skin. Selling pieces of oneself. The girls wind up on Hollywood or Sunset, the boys on Santa Monica. The boys were the worst. Slouching against the sides of buildings, hands deep in the pockets of grease-stained jeans or pushing their unwashed hair from their shoulders, the only color in their faces the reflection of the streetlights off the windshields of the cars crawling past to look them over. Slowing, then stopping: a little business transaction, the kid leaning in the rolled-down window, then getting in, and the car turning off the brightly lit boulevard and into the darker cross streets.

Braemer saw them all the time, everyone in Los Angeles did. Kids on the street, the boys and girls alike, until something happened to take them off. If enough bodies found in the bushes near the off-ramps were killed in the same way, then one of the anonymous vehicles cruising through the city would get a name to be used by the police and the newspapers. The Freeway Killer. The Trash Bag Murders. All the possibilities. So that if your kid bounced from the street scene to the Moonies, or the Children of God, or any of the other salvation-peddlers that specialized in taking in strays and burnouts, you only felt thankful that your kid was still alive—as you tried not to look at the eyes glazed with a fervor as rigid as death itself.

And Rawling's kid runs away from time to time. Braemer looked at the other man and saw him old and tired. Maybe one of these days Jeffrey would hitch a ride that would end up in the city, or somewhere else.

So what if a kid sticks a knife in the wall, thought Braemer. You watch and wait, and hope that it means nothing. A joke, and not the start of saying goodbye.

"What can you do."

They sat there in the office, two guys with kids, the heat from the L.A. noon seeping through the window onto their faces. Listening to the muffled noise of the traffic outside.

THREE

Braemer could feel the ache in his lower back, the one that came with the hours of leaning over the slanted drafting table. The poster design was nearly done now, the last of the series. He had kept the glossies the festival committee in Houston had sent him, production stills from an East German film of Hans Falada's Was Jetzt, Kleiner Mann? *stuck with masking tape to the curtain above the table. The design pinned to the table used a few thin lines to show the protagonist slumped in despair by a bare wooden table, the world outside the empty hut's door a dark mass, thick scrawls of trees coiling into the swastikas of Nazi Germany. A vacuum inside and swallowing menace outside.*

Almost done, and then he could wrap it up with the rest of the poster designs and send them off to Houston; then the other advance check would come winging back to him. Which would be the money for Renee's grad school. (A little, high singing note, a violin string pitched too high, always behind the pen's slow scratching on paper.)

He lifted the pen from the drafting table and sat back, feeling his spine straighten out like a knotted chain. This was just fussing work, not necessary at all. In fact, he knew he had better knock off before he spoiled the drawing, shaded in too much of that world outside that hut, made it banal instead of just the hint of darkness that one knew would always get darker. An alarm clock started to ring on the window ledge above the table, bringing him back to real time. He sat staring at it for a moment, listening to its piercing noise. He always set it for four P.M. when he was working, to remind him to put down his pens and go pick up Dee at the college's day-care center. Then the two of them would wait together for Renee's last class to be over.

For some reason the alarm clock sounded different today, as though the little machine-gun bell had somehow shifted into a different key. He stared at it, puzzled, wondering what it was that sounded false. For a moment there was something that he could almost remember, something just slipping past his grip. . . . He bent his head down toward the table, suddenly feeling hot and dizzy. The clock wound down and the alarm stopped. In the silence, he gripped the edge of the table and waited for it to pass. (What was it? Something wrong: the wrong time—Gone again, just out of reach.)

He stood up, the little puzzle still ticking away beneath his brow and at the base of his stomach, and started putting away his ink and pens. The figure in the drawing went on gazing in frozen apprehension at the world outside his hut.

He stopped, hearing the sound of a key in the apartment's front door. It was Renee letting herself in. "What are you doing home?" asked Braemer, standing in the hallway. Somehow he could hear the alarm clock still ringing, even though he had switched it off. She must have gotten a ride from someone in her class.

51

Come home early to celebrate his wrapping up the project. That must be it.

"I wanted to talk with you," said Renee. She left the door open behind her, and now he could see that there was someone else with her.

The false note of the alarm clock, which had gone on shrilling at the back of his mind, became the thin pitch of his thoughts racing. The other thing that he could almost remember seemed about to speak itself. Something was happening, but he couldn't catch it, tilting his head to shade his eyes from a sudden glare that filled the room.

The other person stepped into the apartment. The guy's name was—Steve; that was it, he remembered. (But not the other thing. He still couldn't catch it, though it was closer. The shrill note was now so loud that he could lean against it, seeing the room through a thin space between its whirling gears.) He'd met him at the college when he'd gone to pick up Renee; he was in one of her classes; and now Braemer knew why the two of them were here together and what they had come to tell him.

They told him, and he knew what they were saying even though the words were buried under the alarm clock's droning roar. He turned slowly away from them, wondering who was going to pick Dee up now that this was the way things were.

Renee caught him by the arm. She said nothing. He turned and saw that she looked different. Her hair was all cropped short, turning steely, and her skin was translucent as paper held to the light. Her tongue thrust spastically against yellowing teeth, her rattling breath deep in her throat. Eyelids that were about to flutter open . . .

He fell backward, but the grip at the end of the bone-thin arm held fast. She fell with him, fastened to him, *the eyelids fluttering against his face, breath that smelled of disinfectant and rotting—*

He woke bathed in sweat, the sheets in a damp tangle around his legs. On the table beside the bed the alarm clock was still ringing—an electric one, because Sarah slept so heavily in the morning that a wind-up model would stop before it cut through to her. That was the note that had sounded through the dream, the little wrong note that wouldn't stop. Lucky for me it didn't, thought Braemer grimly. That was a rough one. He reached for the clock, his slow fingers fumbling for the button on its back.

The dial read just past ten as he held the clock up, then set it back down on the table. Tuesday morning. Mondays he had an established excuse for going in to work late; today he'd have to hustle his butt out of bed, no matter how exhausted his dreaming had left him.

The harsh yellow sunlight of Los Angeles leaked around the bedroom's heavy curtain. Outside, he knew, the edges of the city would already be sharp and vibrating in the heat, like a photo transparency brought up close to a lightbulb.

The heat had been in the dream, too, spilling out of this world into that other. It hadn't really been a dream, but just old memory tapes playing back. Except for the business right at the end, with Renee's coma-withered face latching onto him; nice touch, that. A little fast forward to present time.

Wearing only his shorts, he padded out into the living room and switched on the box fan sitting in the window. For a moment its breeze chilled the sweat on his stomach and thighs, then was swallowed up by the apartment's muggy air as he headed for the kitchen.

In the light spilling out of the refrigerator he could see the faint, filled-in scar that the blade's point had left. Sunday morning, before Sarah or Dee had woken up, he had pulled the knife out and put it back in its drawer, hidden the wounded I LOVE N.Y. apron in the laundry hamper, and dabbed spackle into the tiny slit in the wall. Unless one knew where to look for it, it couldn't be seen.

All that was a day and a half ago now. Later, thought Braemer as he poured milk into his coffee. Still too soon to deal with it. He had filled the cup too full, and coffee slopped over the brim, stinging his hand as he carried it to the table.

This stuff is wearing me out, he thought. Not having Dee for the weekend—he wouldn't mind having her every day—but the driving her back to that house in San Aurelio, and leaving her with Carol and that thing that used to be her mother. Nearly every time he went out there, he looked in on Renee, wasting away in her sleep without end. For a long time, he hadn't been able to figure out why he did it; even now he wasn't sure. In some way, looking down upon her not-yet-dead face sealed another layer of scar tissue over an old wound. From somewhere else a deep exhaustion ate at him when he did, as though the weight of the past was hard upon his back.

On Monday mornings—and Tuesdays, and every other day—he wondered how much longer it would go on like this. A temporary arrangement, but already it had gone on for nearly a year. When Carol had brought Renee home from the hospital, they had thought it was for her to die there rather than in a cold, sterile—and expensive—hospital room. Yet she dragged on, wasting but not dying, with Carol doing nothing but bathing and turning her and feeding her through the nasal tube. Like that other one, that Karen Quinlan case: all that anguish to get a coma victim unhooked from the respirator, and the body went on living afterward. The persistence of the flesh, the blind animal's teeth locked onto the living.

And then Dee. Carol had been more of a mother to Dee than Renee ever had, anyway, Braemer knew. So naturally Dee had wanted to be with her, and he'd had no place to make a home for her then. So the little family in the rackety old Feld house had gone on with one woman, one child, and one vegetable. And one daddy, he thought, coming and going.

He sipped the coffee, cradling the cup in his hands. It was likely that he could get legal custody of Dee now; his ex-wife's coma surely changed the basis that all that had been decided on. But he didn't even know if Dee wanted that. He wouldn't have been surprised to find out that she wanted to stay with Carol rather than go with him, given how she only knew him two days out of seven.

Plus there was Sarah to think about. What she wanted was a factor, too. She had barely been able to crawl out of her own marriage intact. Getting married again was a subject that the two of them had agreed upon and labeled Not To Be Even Considered. Wanting to get permanent custody of Dee might look like a trap to Sarah: Let's Play *Real* Mommy and Daddy.

So for right now, he decided—not for the first time—it's just right out of the question. Maybe when Renee finally died, let go her clawlike grip on breath, something else could be worked out. That might be the time for it.

The half-empty cup was cooling in his hands. He took one more sip, then pushed it away. Going on eight-thirty by the kitchen clock—time to shower and dress and head on in to work. Once the morning was past, the day could be gotten through.

Things would have to change, he knew that; they

couldn't go on like this. For Dee's sake, and for his own. He just didn't know how. Or he did know, but was still an inch away from the verge of doing it. Just hold on, he told himself for the millionth time, until you figure out what to do. Just till then. He pushed the chair back and headed for the shower that would wash the night's sweat from him.

When he stood at the window stretching across one side of the room, he could see almost all of Los Angeles laid out at the foot of the hills. A dim haze that darkened to brown at the horizon smudged the buildings and grid of streets. Reflected in the glass, as if overlaying the city itself, was his own face: the pale skin sectioned by the dark silver of his glasses' mirrored lenses.

He dropped the half-smoked cigarette, one he had taken from the carved wooden box on the heavy marble coffee table, letting it burn a black mark in the sand-colored carpet before he ground it out with his heel.

The sounds from the other room had stopped. Now he could hear a shower running somewhere else in the house. He settled back into one of the chairs, an under-slung web of leather strips and chrome, and waited, flicking on and off a gold-filled Colibri lighter he picked up from the table.

The room was full of toys, all expensive and all abused. Tangled black tape spilled out of a video-cassette recorder sitting on top of a multilensed projection unit. The curved screen stood across the room, a brown stain splashed across its surface and dried into thin rivulets running to the bottom edge. An empty glass lay on its side underneath the screen. A few more cassettes with blurred typed labels in Dutch and Swedish were scattered over the rings on the table. The room looked like the aftermath of a party where adults had degenerated first into children, then into something else. A silver fork stood upright where it had been stabbed into one of the sofa cushions.

He heard the running water shut off, and a few minutes later someone's bare feet in the hallway. The lighter snapped shut in his hand, then slid into his jacket pocket.

The other man came into the room, belting a robe over a body whose exercise machine-bulked muscles were losing a war with the fat collecting around his gut. He dropped onto the sofa, bare legs splayed, and ran a hand through the damp hair at the back of his neck. "Whoa," he said, exhaling noisily. Every vein in his eyes looked as if it had been etched with a pin, the leaking collected in a red line along the bottom lid. "Quite a session."

"Glad you had a good time." He watched the other man, the sallow skin darkened by the tint of his own glasses, take a glass from the table and wipe it clean of cigarette ashes with the edge of his robe. The last brown inch from a bottle lying on the floor splashed into the glass, then trembled as the man's shaking hand raised it to his mouth.

"That's really a weird chick." He set the empty glass back on the table. "Where the hell do you find people like that?"

"Why don't we just say she's part of the family."

The other man giggled, a soft layer dancing across his chest. "That's right. You and your little buddies. Charlie Manson's got nothing on you, does he?" He smiled slyly, cocking his head to one side. "Just how is your little merry band these days?"

The rims of flesh around the nostrils flared and drained into bloodless ivory as the face under the mirror lenses tightened. "Maybe you should just shut up."

"Didn't think I'd heard about that, did you? About ol' Pedersen putting the kibosh on you guys. But I heard. I hear lots of things."

The man with the sunglasses pushed himself out of the chair and headed for the bedroom. "What you hear," he said, not turning his head, "and what you should remember are two different things."

Standing beside the bed, he reached down and thrust a hand into the tangled hair of the woman lying there. He turned her face up toward him. A red bubble formed on her lips with each shallow breath.

"Really got into it, didn't you?" He had felt the other man standing in the bedroom's doorway, watching him. Turning back to the woman, he saw something shiny and metallic glittering in folds of the blanket. He picked it up, studied it for a moment, then hurled it at the other man. The old-fashioned straight razor bounced off the front of the man's robe and fell to the floor. Against the carpet its mother-of-pearl handle caught the light, setting off the dull millimeter of dried blood along the razor's edge. "I told you not to use that fuckin' thing."

The owner of the sharp-edged little toy, and all the other toys in the house, prodded it with his toe. A smile spread across his stubbled jowls. "Saving the best for yourself, huh?"

Behind the mirror lenses his glare simmered. "The difference is," he said, "is that you don't know when to stop. You got no self-control. Someday you're going to wind up with a corpse, and I'm not going to drag it away for you. You're going to be on your sweet little own, asshole."

The beefy shoulders shrugged under the robe. "Whatever."

In the bathroom he wetted a hand towel, then brought it to the side of the bed. He pulled the sheet back. "Shit." Kneeling down, he began washing the woman's body. Fresh blood oozed under the damp cloth. The sting of cold drew a moan from her. He took the sheet's edge and tore strips from it, wrapping them into bandages over the wounds flowing worst.

"Hey!" A protest from the bedroom doorway.

"It's ruined already." He went on with his task, the hands moving quickly over the woman's pale skin. Old marks, healed scars in the flesh, showed where he had tended her before.

Several minutes later he walked back into the other room. "She's still out," he said. "You'll have to help me carry her out to the truck."

The man in the robe was sprawled on the sofa, meditatively watching smoke trail from the cigarette in his hand. "You know," he said, "she's really a very strange girl. I've never had one like that. I mean, she does this number, like right in the midddle of things—" He broke off, as if concentrating to see past the scrawl of gray in the air. "It's like . . . she *changes*. One moment she'll be *terrified*, and then, zap, she's somebody else who just loves it. And laughs. And she switches back and forth like that. Back and forth." His gaze swung over to the other, looking for some clue. "And the weirdest thing of all, it's like she's not acting."

"You don't say." The man with the glasses stood behind the couch, and rubbed his thumb and forefinger together in front of the other's face. "How about settling up."

A sigh preceded the other's lumbering off the sofa, pulling the robe tighter around himself, and heading for the desk by the windows. "You know, you take all the romance out of it." He pulled a checkbook from one of the drawers and started writing underneath the printed name of his production company.

"Cash."

The mirror lenses reflected the other's broad face, turning to look at him. Then the checkbook dropped back into the drawer, and the money slid note by note from a plain envelope.

His hand flicked through the bills and tucked them into his pocket, then straightened out again, grazing the robe's belt.

"Whattaya talking about—that's how much we agreed on."

The face under the glasses remained expressionless. "A little more. For depreciation."

"Christ, she wasn't in such great shape when you brought her up here."

"Maybe we won't come again, then. And then what'll you do for fun?"

Shaking his head, the man in the robe went back to the desk, dug in the envelope, and handed over the folded bills.

Once the money was out of sight, the broad face broke into a smile again. "You know," he said, "maybe we could work out an arrangement sometime. For like, an *extended* session? I've got some friends who'd really enjoy meeting your little, ah, companion there." His head bobbed toward the bedroom door. "Maybe you could see your way clear to letting me . . . *borrow* her for a weekend up at my place in the mountains."

The shielded eyes studied the other man. "No," he said finally. "Sorry. You see, weekends are something special. For her." The thin edge of a smile. "Very special." He turned his head toward the windows, and the hazy sunlight over the city darkened in the lenses.

She could hear them talking in the other room, but she couldn't move. Something had hurt her, taken small bites, leaving the muscles of her legs and arms as fibers stretched beyond their limits, and torn.

In her memory, clouded by pain and the needle, she

could see a man's face poised over her. Broad, with the smile of a child that had learned to excite itself by hurting weak things. A different face, not the one with the shining glasses, the one that she knew but would not believe.

Squinting against the light, she managed to open her eyes. A different room, too, not the cold, bare one where she was usually kept, which the voice inside her brought her back to again and again. She had memories of other rooms like this, softly lit and carpeted, a smell of quiet money brushing against the walls. They all blurred together into one, the one where she was brought, the dazing chemical in her blood leaving her limp as rags. The room where she was left splayed on the bed, the mirrored lenses disappearing as he pulled the bedroom door shut. Sweating faces and smiles that ran together into one. Their slow fun beginning again.

Which one am I now? she wondered dully. Her name, the last scrap of who she used to be, dimmed, a spark fading on wet ground. Then it came back, feebly, then growing a brighter red: Kathy. I'm Kathy. Not that other one—not my sister Renee. I'm still Kathy.

The room started to darken, eaten by the little point of light inside her thoughts. Then it faded into black as well.

Sarah rinsed the dish under the faucet and set it in the drainer. Braemer leaned back against the counter, the damp dish towel in his hands, waiting for the water to run off the plate. The air in the kitchen was still strong with the scent of a basil-and-tomato sauce; tangled bits of pasta had collected in the holes of the drain cover.

"What time are you going down to pick up Dee tomorrow?" Sarah's wet rubber gloves squeaked across another plate.

Thursday night—tomorrow would start the weekend

cycle over again. "Um, about six-thirty, I guess. Let some of the rush-hour traffic get off the freeway." He set the dried plate on the stack in the cupboard.

"You're going to have to take her to her ballet class. I've got to work Saturday."

"How come they want you there on Saturday?"

"Closing files," said Sarah. "A couple of the attorneys are going to come in and go through some of the backlog."

He shrugged. "I suppose I can take her over to the studio. But she might not want to go without you."

"I don't know about that. I think she's got the bug."

"Great. Cost of toe shoes alone will break me."

"Yeah, but you get to throw flowers across the footlights at her big debut."

He picked up his glass with the last of the dinner wine in it. "You think she really enjoys it?"

"Sure, are you kidding? She does *grand jetés*—or her version of them—down the sidewalk when we leave the studio."

"I mean . . . I don't know. Does she seem happy to you?"

The scouring pad stopped in Sarah's hands, and she looked up from the skillet in the sink. "Dee?" she said. "We're talking about the same kid here?"

The wine slid lukewarm across his tongue as he set the glass down. "You know, you have to worry about these things sometimes. She's in kind of a weird situation for a kid."

Sarah watched the suds drying on her gloves. "Lots of kids are in weird situations now," she said. "It's like they've all got their parents in two different places. Look at the statistics."

"Yeah, but they don't all have their mother upstairs doing some kind of stiff act."

She started scrubbing the pan again. "She seems

okay. How are you supposed to tell, anyway? Kids adapt to a lot of things. They have to. It wasn't all that great for me when I was a kid, and I didn't wind up in the rubber room."

He drained the glass and set it down in the sink. "I know, I know. Maybe I just worry too much." The words telling about the knife he'd found stuck through her apron were pressed against the gate of his teeth. From where he stood he could see the faint scar on the wall by the refrigerator.

"There was the one time, though," mused Sarah as she rinsed the pan and set it in the drainer.

"What time?"

"Nothing much. I'd just about forgotten it completely, until you started talking like this. Seemed spooky when it happened, though." She went on picking silverware out of the suds and passing them under the faucet's stream. "It was at the dance studio. Back when I first started taking her. We were in the middle of the Beginners' class, and I was standing right next to her. And all of a sudden she just walked off. She went over to the window and just stared out at the street. I went over to her because I thought she might be feeling sick or something. When I touched her she jerked around and gave me this look. . . . She didn't even seem like the same kid. Then she ran out of the studio, and I found her on the stairs. She seemed fine then. That was that afternoon we came home early."

He didn't remember it. The story settled in his stomach, a small knot. "What kind of look?"

"Hm?" She frowned, trying to describe it. "It was like . . . she didn't recognize me or something. And like she was furious about it, too. Something like that."

Silent, he gazed at the rows of glasses in the cupboard, the dish towel wadded in his hands.

"It's no big thing, Dave." She lifted the sink plug,

and the water began gurgling away. "One-time occurrence. She was probably pissed off about something, a spat with one of her friends at school or something like that. Something reminded her of it, and she went into a snit fit. Kids have personal lives, too, you know. I've seen you stomp around and glare out windows. You get a look that would freeze blood."

"I suppose." The little nagging thought behind his other thoughts wouldn't go away. He unwound the twisted rope of towel and picked up one of the dishes from the drainer.

Dee got off the school bus where it stopped below the hill. Carol was waiting for her. Together they walked back up to the house, past the weedy would-be lawns and the stick houses you could see through, while she showed Carol a week's worth of schoolwork in a folder made of green construction paper. B's in English and something called Media, where you wrote about some TV program you had watched—dumb; but a big star scrawled by the teacher on a map of California she'd drawn, complete with an elaborate compass rose copied from the encyclopedia in the hallway at home. She'd show that to her dad.

When they got home, she went upstairs and packed the big shoulder bag with CAPEZIO stenciled on it in letters made of little stars. Sarah had given it to her last Christmas. Carol had stitched DEE on the webbed strap. Clothes and stuff she needed for the weekend. No need to pack her dance tights—those were still at her dad's place, where she'd (boy, dumb) left them last weekend.

She lay on her bed, paging through *Balanchine's Stories of the Great Ballets*—another Christmas present, already well thumbed—spread down on her pillow. She could hear Carol in the kitchen downstairs, and smell a warm edge of last night's macaroni-and-chili being heated up, something for her to have before her dad came and picked her up. Faint clatter of the pan against the stove's burner, plates and bowls thumped onto the table.

Under the noises from the kitchen she could hear that other sound, so small that you could almost forget it, like a mouse nibbling on spilled oatmeal in the darkest corner of the cupboard. Just a whisper, coming and going. It was the sound of her mother's breathing, sliding out from under the door of the room down the hall. Seeping out like the fringe of light that was always under the door, no matter how late at night. If you paid attention to it, or woke up in the dark of your own room unable to hear anything else, you could tell when air was rasping into her throat, when it held for a couple of thumps of your own heart, and when it hissed back out past the dry, cracked lips.

Suddenly she couldn't hear that sound, her mother's slow mouthing of air. It was gone; all sound was gone. She couldn't hear Carol rattling around the kitchen, or even her own hand trembling the next page of the book. A forest's silence spread over like a wave, depths of interlaced branches towering above her.

darker in the forest The book's white pages faded *into the darkness.* Underneath her, the white nubbly bed-spread became *damp: layers of moss and pine needles rotting warm. Her own breath panted loud in her throat, choking past her racing heartbeat. Her hands dug through the matted tangle. Fingers closed at last on the handle of the knife. She pushed herself up from where she had fallen and ran. Past the trees standing dense around the open space, her shoulder aching numb from colliding with one of the rough trunks. The knife blade glittered in her hand, catching the thin shafts of moonlight that broke through the knotted branches above. Glittering like the other knife, the one in her mother's hand as she had stood rigid in the camper's doorway, hair tangled like the trees' black branches around her bloodless white face.*

She ran, her breath hot salt in her throat. Stumbling in the banks of dead needles, their points scratching toward her eyes as she ran past. Then the pine smell changed, to disinfectant, and something sour and sick.

Dark to light. Light filled a room to its corners. She wasn't running but lay curled on her side in a bed. Through eyelids whose fluttering she couldn't stop, she could see in hazy focus the flowered wallpaper of her mother's room. The sound of breathing was louder now, filling her head with wind in dry leaves.

She tried to lift her head but couldn't. She wanted to get out of the bed with its odor of slow decay, to find the knife wherever she'd dropped it, run outside where she'd be safe, into the darkness.

Her fists stayed clenched against the sheet, legs coiling toward her breast. Then she heard the laughing inside her head, and the scream in her throat was nothing but air rasping in and out, a pulse of life wrapped in a corpse. . . .

She heard Carol calling her. The sound of her mother's breathing was still loud, but outside her now. She blinked and found herself in her mother's bedroom, standing so close to the bed that she was staring, inches away, into that face of hollowed cheeks and tongue thrusting convulsively behind the cracked lips.

She almost fell backward as she jerked away. Back until her hands found the cool glass of the window. She broke her gaze away from her mother's face. Dark outside now, but no sign of her dad yet. She wanted to fall through the dark glass and start running, until she could see his bright headlights coming for her.

"Did you get the name of that cat?" asked Braemer.

"What cat?"

"The one that got your tongue."

"Ohhh . . ." Dee rolled her eyes in mock exasperation.

It was true. She had been quiet since she had waved goodbye to Carol. Braemer glanced away from the Friday-evening traffic heading for Los Angeles and watched her slouched in her seat, listening to the radio and staring out her window.

"Anything wrong?"

"Nope." Gaily, she pursed her lips and shook her head, a few loose strands flinging straight out. "Just thinking."

"About anything special?" As he turned his gaze back to the traffic, he caught the edge of the gaze his daughter leveled at him, serious and distant.

"No," she said. "Just . . . things."

He drove, feeling her eyes turn from him to the darkness outside the windshield.

FOUR

On the way home from the dance studio, traffic was blocked for a few minutes by a Krishna Consciousness parade. Dee leaned close to the windshield, not asking her father any questions about what was going on, but just watching the skinny devotees leaping and dancing about as they chanted, beating small hand drums and cymbals. The incongruous white middle-class faces shouted in ecstasy, heads shaved except for the thin ponytails whipping from side to side. After they had all crossed the intersection and the cars moved again, the voices could be heard from blocks away.

Braemer glanced at his daughter beside him. Her calm interest in things sometimes unnerved him. It's like nothing rattles her, he thought. He didn't know if that was good or bad. There were worse things on the streets than the Hari Krishna kids.

The city still held a few sinister vibrations, leftovers from the spooky '60's. One could drive down Beverly Boulevard and casually notice the Mexican restaurant where Sharon Tate had had her last meal, before she and her friends had gone back up to the house in the hills for a rendezvous they hadn't known was planned for them. The Hollywood streets where Manson had recruited teenyboppers into his acid-dipped schoolbus were filled with a new generation of loitering teenagers looking for a little chance excitement.

He wasn't sure if Los Angeles was a good place to have a kid, but the suburbs ticked off the same uneasiness. The dark things that had danced out into the open back then had now retreated beyond the city limits, into ragged communes tending their gun collections and sinsemilla patches. Evil hadn't been extinguished with the '60's, just spread thinner and closer to invisible. Until another time to dance came.

Braemer pushed the dark thoughts away as he drove through the city. There was a limit to how much worrying one could do.

At the apartment building, as he and Dee were walking from the car parked at the curb, Braemer heard a rustle in the trimmed oleander bushes. He turned and saw a hunched-over figure pushing the stiff branches away from itself.

One of the local street loons, a demented creature in a child's ragged baseball jacket and a knit cap, both nearly black with the same grease and dirt staining the skinny arms to dull magogany. Braemer had seen him (her? impossible to tell) shuffling on daily rounds of trash dumpsters behind supermarkets, pawing through the garbage for anything still edible.

Their approach had roused the vagrant from the little nest he had scooped in the dirt under the bushes, close to a heat vent from the basement laundry room. Braemer stopped and pulled Dee behind himself as the vagrant sidled toward them, the lopsided face breaking into a yellow Punch-and-Judy grin.

"Devil's a *beast*," he crooned. With the first words

Braemer recognized the voice as the one he sometimes heard shouting fractured Bible verse in the early morning hours. A crumpled paperback New Testament, entitled *Good News for Modern Man,* was clutched in one grimy hand. "*Devours* ya—eats you all *up!*" The vagrant laughed as he crouched and pointed a black-rimmed finger at Dee, looking out from behind Braemer. "And Devil's in *you!*"

"Get out of here," said Braemer. He knew the character was harmless, but didn't want him scaring Dee. "Go on, beat it."

The vagrant scuttled away, looking back with a sly animal face at the little girl.

"Come on, honey." He squeezed Dee's shoulder. She watched the stooping figure's retreat for a moment, then glanced up at him, a somber expression that he couldn't read on her face.

"What do you do?"

The question caught Braemer by surprise. He tried stalling with a joke. "Fine, thanks. And what do *you* do?"

Dee dug her sharp little elbow into his ribs. "No, stupid! what do you do for . . . you know, a job?"

"Don't call your old dad stupid, or I'll tell you all about heredity." She was leaning up against him as they sat on the couch, the back of her head against his chest, her thin legs sprawled out toward the empty hamburger wrappings and soft-drink cups of the lunch they had brought home. Her T-shirt was damp with sweat from the ballet class he had taken her to that morning. "I work," he said.

"At what?"

As interrogations went, Braemer knew this was pretty mild. The questions that divorced fathers wait for, chewing and rechewing their answers, hadn't shown up yet: *did you love Mommy? Did you love* me? *So why did you leave?* "I'm a commercial artist. Sort of. Draw things, that's all."

"I know *that.* But what kinda things?"

He shrugged, the motion making her head nod forward. "Buildings. Lots of buildings. What we call architectural renderings. Some of what we call layout work. A while back I did some logos—you know, like fancy lettering—for a couple of rock bands. Nobody you've heard of, but one of 'em did get signed to MCA, and they kept the logo I drew for them, so Rawling—my boss—is trying to see if he can get some more money out of them for it." He paused to think. "Helped design the menu for a place out in Culver City. It folded, though."

Dee considered this new information from her father. Then she twisted around to look up into his face. "D'you draw people?"

"Used to. Not anymore." That was true—the last human form he'd drawn was for the film poster design, the poor guy staring out of his hut at the darkness. Years ago, back when he was married to Renee. His daughter's questions were coming a little too close to a buried nerve of memory (*pen snapping in his hand*), like a dentist's probe toward a tooth that would be fine if one could just keep from touching it. *Ink spattering across the paper.*

"You could draw me?"

"Naw, sweetheart. Out of practice."

"You could, though."

Braemer sighed, resisting the urge to push the probe *that pen then the others splintering in his fist* away with any harsher words. "Someday. When you're the star of ABT. Do you as Giselle for the cover of the souvenir program."

Dee scrambled off the couch and disappeared into the

71

hallway. He could hear the zip of her Capezio bag, then she came back a moment later with something in her hands. "Here," she said, dropping it into his lap.

It was a large spiral-bound pad of sketching paper, the kind found in the stationery sections of supermarkets, and a little brown paper bag. He looked inside and saw a blue Magic Marker and a couple of nylon-tip pens. "Where'd you get this?"

"I bought it," said Dee. "With my money."

"You've been talking to Sarah." He lowered his eyebrows and glared at her accusingly. "You knew all this stuff already. Christ, you're coy." He drew his thumb across the edge of the pad. His heart was beating a little faster, trembling inside his chest. "So, uh, now what do you expect me to do with this stuff?"

"Guess."

"Yeah, right." He brought the paper bag up close to one eye and peered into it. "You know, Michelangelo didn't do the ceiling of the Sistine Chapel with no Magic Marker." Reaching into the bag, he felt the smooth, tapered cylinders of the pens. If he drew them out, he'd have to sketch her, and the memory that kept unfolding behind his forehead made that scary. He closed his eyes for a moment and felt clock time fall away into silence. "All right," he said, pulling out the pens. "Strike a pose, Pavlova."

Dee smiled and bounced into the other corner of the couch, then turned her profile to him, stretching out her neck as far as she could.

"Okay, Swanilda, hold it right there. Glad you don't want a three-quarters." He flipped open the sketch pad, uncapped one of the nylon-tips, and set its point to the top sheet of paper. "Dee Braemerovskaya, in the grand style. Stop giggling." He looked away from her and suddenly saw that his hands were white and trembling, one buckling the pad in its grip, the other pressing the

72

point of the pen too hard against the paper, a little dot of ink bleeding into the white. It wasn't all right, he realized, it was still wrong. The brittle shell covering the nerve had broken, and the pain was singing inside his head, higher as he knew his daughter was turning her face toward him, her eyes wide as

the empty apartment too quiet. Silence filling the rooms, empty except for him, silent except for the sound of his breathing, his footsteps padding on the carpet from one room to another, always circling back to the bedroom and the drafting table set up in one corner. Two days since that day, the one when Renee had come home early with her new boyfriend and had made her little announcement, quick twist of the knife, and he hadn't been able to do anything at the drafting table since then, just sit at its smooth, tilted surface, not even think, just gaze at the blank paper like the negative of a hole into some other world. He'd already lived through that day, had already come back to the empty apartment after sending off the film poster designs, wife and child and wife's boyfriend gone now, and nothing left but the empty apartment and him pacing through its rooms until he forces himself down into the chair before the drafting table. The chair can't hold him, and he stands up and leans over the table, his hands gripping its sides until the knuckles are white rivets of bone. A little pile of trash is growing on the kitchen counter, hamburger wrappings and dark pools at the bottom of the paper cups, coffee grounds staining the sink, the debris of somebody living by himself. So draw already, he tells himself furiously, you've finally got it just as nice and quiet as you could want, you blew the fucking marriage, wife gone, kid gone, all gone; so draw already. Anything. It's all that's left. He sits back down at the table, picks up a pen, sets its point to the paper, and can't draw. He can't draw because a little circuit has been etched into his brain and cuts deeper every time the needle goes around: *To Draw Is To Die.* To draw is to set yourself up to be kicked in the teeth, sitting in your little corner while everyone else is out there beyond the walls laughing at you. Until you finish drawing and show it to them, saying, There, aren't you proud of me? And they laugh and say goodbye, nice of you to keep yourself busy while we've been fucking around on you. Fool.

It goes around and around in his head, just below the surface where he can't really see it but just feel it tightening harder with every turn. Loosen up, he orders himself, just relax. He stands up again and goes to the kitchen, jerks a beer out of the six-pack in the refrigerator, and takes a long, cold, sour pull from the can. Another gurgling swallow, and the can is half-empty. What's one beer? Nothing. A whole six-pack is nothing, your arms and legs and face feel heavier, and you have to piss a lot, that's all. He tilts his head back and drains the can and, breathing heavily, takes another damp cylinder from the fridge. He carries it back to the table in the bedroom, sipping at it as he goes. The little circuit in his head starts to spin faster, faster with each can he fetches from the kitchen and then drops with the other empties beside the chair while the paper on the drafting table stays blank, just the one dot of ink on the whiteness. The last can is drained, and the circuit breaks loose from its tracks and spirals down inside him toward the dark trigger that's already been hit by each swallow of beer. For a moment he's dizzy and wants to lay his head on the cool, blank sheet of paper, wondering what's wrong with him, then he pulls himself up straight in the chair and picks up his pen. *To Draw Is To Die.* He watches it tremble in his hand, and then it snaps, ink spraying from the point across the paper, his fingers coming together on the splintered plastic and metal inside like rigid claws. The pieces drop from his hand as the chair jerks away from the table and he can't see anything now.

He comes to lying on the carpet, his mouth sour from his own breath. He manages to get himself onto his knees and pushes himself up with his hands. Crouching there, he sees the drafting table turned over on its side, ink spattered in dark constellations across its top. The chair is toppled over, too, and ragged-edged scraps of paper, torn in half and crumpled into balls, scatter across the carpet. There are other things on the floor, his pens, each one broken in half, the metal nibs bent and splayed from being jabbed against something hard. At the bottom of a dark splash trailing down one wall lies a shattered bottle of India ink. He sighs and lowers his head, feeling drained. At least he managed to keep from breaking a window or doing something else that would have alarmed the neighbors enough for them to call the police.

Unlocked by just a few beers, his little personal demon had been vomited forth to batter about the scraps of the life he used to have, and all in perfect privacy. Dim shots of memory slide away from him as he stands up, fuzzy images of himself breaking the pens one by one as something boils out of his heart. His hand stings, he looks at it and sees red mingling with the smeared ink. A splinter of plastic had gouged deep into the palm.

His toe scuffs against something, and he bends down to pick it up. One pen, unbroken, that had somehow escaped the bleak spree. Carefully, knowing exactly what he is doing this time, he takes its ends in his hands and bends it, slowly because his muscles feel so weak, until it snaps as his hands gripped the pad and nylon-tip pen too tightly. Dee looked at him in silence, and Braemer felt how dry his mouth was, as though the uncoiling memory had drained him completely. The nylon-tip was still frozen, unmoving, against the paper. Feeling his daughter's eyes upon him, he took a breath and quickly scrawled a heart on the paper, a sloppy valentine, a little V for an arrowhead slanting out at the bottom, big V's for the feathered shaft in the corner above. Then he lettered DEE + DADDY inside it. He turned the pad around and handed it to her. "That's . . . all I can do right now, sweetheart."

Dee looked at it for a moment, then the pad was against his shoulderblades as she wrapped her arms around his neck. "That's the best," she said as she pressed her cheek harder against his chest.

"Someday, though," he said. One hand, trembling, stroked her hair. She said nothing, but tightened her grip on him. He closed his eyes and let all memories fade.

Dee had fallen asleep. The Saturday afternoon had gotten hotter, the air heavy in the apartment. Braemer caught his head nodding toward his daughter resting against his leg. He pulled his eyes open wide. Hours yet until Sarah came home.

He took one of the pillows from the end of the couch and slid it under Dee's head as he drew his leg free. She went on sleeping, face against her arm. Carefully, he stood up.

His foot brushed against the pad and pens lying on the floor. The heart he'd scrawled for her was tucked inside the pad somewhere. That had been a strange thing—a tight moment when the past's teeth had sunk deep into the present. Several seconds passed as he just looked at the bright-colored cylinders on the carpet, before he gathered up the pens and stacked them on the table with the pad.

In the kitchen, the drowsiness made lead of his arm as he sipped a glass of water. He leaned back against the sink. Eyelids heavy, he saw that the drawer next to him had been left partway open. The rows of silverware and shining knives inside caught the light.

He reached over and pushed the drawer in.

On the way to the bedroom he stopped by the couch, unfolded an afghan, and covered Dee with it. The whole apartment seemed to be submerged in sleep as he laid himself on his own bed.

darker in the forest

Her hand closed on the handle of the knife. She drew it out from under the sofa cushions.

The forest was in the room. She could see the deep shade blotting out the afternoon light streaming in the windows. No city beyond, just the endless tangle of moss and pine needles.

She watched her white-knuckled hand bring the blade up before her eyes. Not the same knife, but one almost as big, and made from gleaming stainless steel. Twisted in the metal's shine, her face was rigid, the lines pulled by a tightening fist inside. Not her face any longer—now it was her mother's, the last time she had seen it over her shoulder as she ran into the battering forest.

Silence. She stood listening, knife poised in front of her. Then the sound of someone breathing, in the apartment underneath the dark layers of branches. Someone close. Someone asleep.

Her voice cried, but nothing broke the silence. It went on screaming inside her, beating against her lungs and skull, as her feet moved, one slow step after another.

Toward the bedroom.

The hallway's floor was thick with the matted tangle,

77

damp and rotting. She felt herself sinking into it, the strawlike needles clutching at her bare feet. The wall's rough bark leaned closer to her as she passed.

The knife glowed before her, a tapering light against black, the sharp point like an inverted candle flame pointing down.

Behind the bathroom door something wet dripped. A slow faucet or rain drizzling from a branch.

The bedroom door was ajar. Her father's breathing, slow and regular, sounded inside. Through the thick scrawl of branches she peered into the bedroom.

She saw her father, sprawled on his back on the bed, his head resting on one forearm. The forest darkened around him, the massed trees swallowing the room's space.

Silence.

Her own voice inside her head changed to pleading, whispered with the last of her strength. Bleeding fists against a mute wall. *Please . . . not him. Not*— But the other voice said nothing. This time, her mother's voice was silent. It moved in her arms and legs, and her hands clutching the knife.

She pushed the door open, wide enough for her to step into the bedroom.

Feet soft upon the matted needles.

Then she was at the side of the bed. She looked down at him. His chest rose and fell with his breathing, stretched by the one arm brought under the back of his head as he slept. Frayed light filtered through the branches and spattered across his shirt.

Suddenly the brighter light was above him. The knife, flashing brilliant in the sun, the blood squeezed from her upraised fists clutching the handle.

She felt herself raised up on the balls of her feet, a trickle of sweat creeping down her wrists.

Whisper to a scream. *No no please no*—

A slow pulse under her father's breastbone.

The light, blade filled with the sun like fire, cut down. through the air toward his chest.

"Dee!"

He caught her wrist in his hand. Her grip sprung open and the knife, with no weight behind it, bounced against his chest and fell on the bed.

His eyes were wide open now, not just slitted enough to watch her coming into the room. He had seen the knife missing from its spot in the kitchen drawer, and the worrying thoughts it had sparked had kept him awake, feigning sleep to see what she would do with it, what other wall would be stabbed.

Their eyes locked into each other, his and his daughter's, though he could hardly recognize her with her teeth clenched tight, lips straining back into a wolf's grimace. Then her other hand, nails like claws, swung down toward his face.

"*You motherfucker!*" The words were clear, a wire strung too tight for a child's voice. "*You should be dead, you shit!*"

The hard knob of her knee jerked up and caught him in the ribs. He gasped for breath, fighting the nausea climbing from his stomach to his throat. The voice out of his daughter's mouth battered against his ears, the room echoing with every obscenity. Sweat seeped through his clothes as he strained against the ten-year-old's body, her spine arching like a bow. The muscles and cords in her arms slid apart from each other and writhed, snakes underneath the white skin.

Her face, like something being peeled back from her teeth, began to disappear underneath the black spots swimming in his eyes. He couldn't get his breath. The spots grew larger, merged, a shaft of darkness that drew him, gasping for air, closer to his daughter's face. So close that he could hear the ragged intake of breath that preceded each scream.

Her arms went limp in his grasp. The body coiling like a fist weakened, a child's body again. Above him he saw his daughter's face, open mouth silent and trembling, eyes wide with fear.

She burst into tears, sobbing muffled in her throat. He let go of her wrists, pulling back from her, and watched her curl into a ball, shoulders heaving as she buried her face into the bed.

Then he was holding her, cradling her against himself, her tears wetting his neck.

"It wasn't me, it was her, it wasn't me, *it was her—*"

He rocked her back and forth. "It's all right, it's all right."

"—and it was so *d-dark,*" the words breaking through her sobs, "and she had a knife, and I kept running and running *but you weren't there!*"

"It's all right, everything's okay now." He held his daughter and felt the hollow space inside himself grow. Whatever he was supposed to have done, he knew, he had waited too long.

"It's all right," he said again, stroking her hair. But the sharp point of the fear he had seen in her eyes had broken off inside him.

But if, during life, the primal spirit was used by the conscious spirit for avarice, folly, desire, and lust, and committed all sorts of sins, then in the moment of death the spirit-energy is turbid and confused, and the conscious spirit passes out together with the breath, through the lower openings of the door of the belly. For if the spirit-energy is turbid and unclean, it crystallizes downward, sinks down to hell, and becomes a demon.

— *T'ai I Chin Hua Tsung Chih* (The Secret of the Golden Flower) by Richard Wilhelm and C.G. Jung

FIVE

It was darker in the bedroom than in her dreaming. She opened her eyes, lashes tangled with sleep, and saw nothing, just felt the hand gripping her shoulder, shaking her awake.

"Mommy—?" That's who it was. Now Dee could make out the face leaning over her, set against the darkness.

"Shhh." Her mother bent so close that their breaths mingled as she whispered. "Get dressed, honey. We're going on a trip."

"Huh?" She pushed herself up on her pillow. The fog of sleep slid away, but she still couldn't figure out what was going on. "Where? Where's Carol?"

"Be quiet." The whisper's edge sharpened, then went soft again. "Carol's still sleeping, honey. She's going to meet us there later."

"But where are we going?" Outside the window the night was completely black. Her dad was somewhere far away, she remembered, farther away than where he usually lived. In England, that's where he was. She'd

gotten a postcard from him yesterday, a picture of a big square tower with a clock in it and a bridge over a river, and a lady with a little crown on the stamp on the back. She wondered if her dad was asleep in the same thick darkness.

"We're going on a camping trip. Like I promised you —remember? Now come on, get dressed." Her mother switched on the lamp on the table beside the bed.

She had talked about going camping, a couple of months ago when she'd bought the camper, a used VW van with a top that lifted up like a tent, and beds, a tiny sink and fridge, and a folding table inside. It had seemed like a neat idea when she'd driven it home, a surprise to everyone, and Dee had wanted to camp out in it right in the front yard. Instead, up in her bedroom that night she'd been able to hear her mom and Carol arguing about that money taken out of the bank to pay for the camper. The talk of a camping trip had dwindled away after that, until she'd thought that everyone but her had forgotten about it.

Now this, in the middle of the night. She pushed the blankets away and swung her feet out to the floor. As she lifted her nightgown, the striped one her dad had bought her, over her head she brushed the lamp's shade, rattling it against the table.

Her mother gripped her shoulder, hard, the pain driving out the last traces of sleep. "Quiet."

Dee looked up, the nightgown tangled about her elbows, and saw her mother's face set tight as the fingers clamped onto her shoulders. She felt her bare skin prickle all over with goose bumps, as though a door had been left open somewhere in the house, and the cold night air had crept in and found her sitting here uncovered on the edge of her bed.

The hand loosened, and her mother's voice softened. "We don't want to wake Carol up, honey. Okay?"

"But—why?"

"Because I said so." Hard again, breaking past the thin layer drawn over like cotton wool.

Nothing more was said while Dee quickly pulled on the jeans and sweatshirt handed to her. Her mom had already packed a bag full of her clothes. She pulled on her faded red sneakers and stood up, her mom lifting the bag with one hand and taking her hand with the other. She tried to grab her nightgown, but her mom was already pulling her toward the bedroom door. The red-striped flannel lay crumpled on the bed as she looked back over her shoulder.

Sitting in the camper's passenger seat, she watched while her mom switched on the knob of the dashboard. The headlights cut out ghost-white sections of the yard. Her mom didn't turn the key all the way around to start the engine; she let go of the parking brake, and the slope of the little rise at the side of the driveway was enough to roll the camper slowly out onto the street. She watched her mom hunched over the wheel, steering in silence.

Past the fence, her mom switched on the engine, its coughing sputter loud in the cold night air. She glanced back at the house's unlit windows as the engine choked, died, whirred, and caught again with a roar. Then the house was gone, replaced by the empty stick-figure houses whose bare timbers were picked out by the headlights sweeping around the curving streets.

"Where we going?" Part of her—most—wanted to be back in her bed, shoulder pressed tight into her pillow until with light she would hear the sounds of Carol downstairs in the kitchen. Another part of her was leaning forward, peering down the road.

"Oh, pretty far away." Her mom smiled at her. *"That's why I wanted to get an early start. You'll love it —there'll be all kinds of trees and stuff. A real forest.*

And we'll go way inside. Way, way inside."

Something that wasn't excitement shivered through her arms. The little trailing softness at the end of her mom's words scared her. It made her think of the look her mom got on her face sometimes, like when she'd gone out to the front porch to call her for dinner and her mom had stood right there looking at her as if she didn't recognize her. Or like when her mom would come back home, leaving the car askew in the driveway, and lie on her bed upstairs staring at the ceiling, at nothing but the ceiling for a couple of hours.

She stayed quiet past the ghost houses, the edge of San Aurelio, and onto the freeway, rushing with traffic even at this hour. Her mom headed north, the same way her dad went when he picked her up on Friday evenings. For a moment she thought maybe that was where they were going now, her mom was taking her up to him. Then she remembered again that he was in England, far from here. She curled her legs up under herself and laid her head on the back of the seat, watching her mom's face as she drove, the taillights from the other cars ahead washing smudges of red across her face.

Sunlight woke her up. She blinked, eyelids gummy, and saw deep orange light filling the front seat of the camper. She raised her head. Outside her window, green rows stretched away from the highway to the low hills the sun was breaking across. Farmland. She had never seen so much, the neat parallel rows running far in front of them alongside the highway and—she pressed her face to the glass—as far back as she could see. The leaves were all sparkly, and their green, damp smell filled her nose.

"Where are we?"

Her mom jerked straight behind the wheel, startled by her voice. Then she smiled. "Not far now, honey."

"Yeah, but where?"

"Getting hungry?"

"Yeah, I guess. A little."

From a grocery sack under the dash her mom dug out a box of doughnuts and a carton of milk. "Here you go. Breakfast."

She opened them and ate, the chocolate frosting on the doughnuts melted and sticky, the milk lukewarm. She wanted to ask again about where they were, and where they were going, but knew she shouldn't. Sometimes her mom didn't talk about things, like where she went and what she did on weekends, while Dee was with her dad. She knew her mom was always gone for most of the weekends, because she had phoned from her dad's place and always been able only to talk with Carol. Carol didn't know where her mom went either, or else just wouldn't talk about it when Dee asked. Better not to keep asking—sometimes her mom would get mad, with a silent stare that made her run outside to get away from it. But now she was stuck in the camper with her mom. There was nowhere to go.

"I have to go to the bathroom."

"Okay," said her mom. "I have to stop for gas in just a bit. Wait till then?"

"Sure."

They drove and drove. Sandwiches and cans of Pepsi for lunch, which they bought from the little store next to one of the gas stations they stopped at. Her mom gave her money to buy something to read, but all she could find interesting was a copy of Newsweek with photos of the American Ballet Theatre's new season. She leafed through the magazine a couple of times, then let it slide off her lap onto the camper's floor. The air was heavy with sun and dust. Watching the fields go by, row after row, made her drowsy.

When she woke up again, the flat acres of farmland were gone. The sun was slanting through close-set masses of trees, as her mom pulled the steering wheel to one side and the other, following the narrow road's switchbacks. Now the air, thinner and colder, smelled sharp with pine.

"Almost there now." Her mom had seen her wake up and lean forward to look out the windshield. "Just like I told you." She steered the camper to the side of the road to let a jeep, tent and inflatable boat strapped on top, go by them.

"Uh-huh." She peered out, trying to see the tops of the trees. She couldn't remember having been in a real forest like this before. It wasn't like you saw in pictures in books at school. The spaces between the dense trees were darker, hiding the other trees behind.

"Not much farther. Not much farther . . . at all," said her mom in a little crooning voice.

The road went on twisting and climbing. A few other cars or camper vans went by them in either direction. Once a pair of motorcycles roared past, the riders leaning far over into the curves. The bits of sun breaking through the trees became lower and redder, and her mom switched on the camper's headlights.

Then her mom pulled off the paved road onto a dirt path so narrow that Dee hadn't even seen it coming; when her mom turned the wheel, it seemed like she was steering them straight into the trees. The camper bounced so hard in the path's ruts that Dee held on to the seat with both hands.

The camper jerked to a stop. Her mom peered into the rearview mirror as if searching for something, then got out of the camper, leaving the engine running. Through the windshield, Dee watched her lift and push open a wooden gate—PRIVATE ROAD NO TRESPASSING barely readable through the rusted brown pocks of rifle shots—across the path. She closed it behind them after she had driven the camper through. On either side of the *path, Dee could see wide stumps of trees where they had been sawn off clean, now almost obscured by the tangled new growth above them.*

Slowly, the camper went on picking its way upward, until the path widened into a little cleared space. Her mom steered the camper into the center, set the brake, and switched off the engine. Sudden quiet, deep as the darkness between the trees, welled over them.

"Here we are," said her mom.

Dee looked at her and saw her smiling. But the smile seemed cut from some other face and pasted below the watching, measuring eyes.

Outside was a circle of ashes and charred sticks where somebody had built fires before. But her mom opened a can of soup for dinner and heated it on the little stove inside the camper. Dee put on both the sweaters her mother had brought for her, and still felt the night's cold seeping in the curtained windows. She'd come back in after looking, head tilted back, at all the stars she could see inside the ragged circle of treetops. After the sun was down, the forest was completely black, but not so quiet as before. She could hear, or imagine hearing, soft rustling noises in the matted needles covering the ground.

Her mom left the pan and bowls unwashed in the little sink. "Time to go to sleep, honey."

"I'm not sleepy," said Dee. "I slept too much during the day."

"Time to go to sleep." Her mom's voice was soft and insistent. She pulled a rolled-up sleeping bag from under one of the benches alongside the table, undid the ties, and shook it open. A clatter of metal fell on the floor.

Startled by the noise, Dee watched as her mom dropped to her knees and scurried in the camper's narrow space, picking up the bright objects that had dropped out of the sleeping bag. She caught just a glimpse of them as her mom snatched them up: knives, big ones that she recognized from her aunt Carol's kitchen at home, and some others with different-shaped blades that she had never seen before. Her mom stood up with them clutched to her breasts, turned, and carried them away to the front of the camper.

She came back a moment later without the knives, her smile now just a thin line. "I said, time to go to sleep."

"But—"

Suddenly her toes were against the floor, her mom's face leaning close into hers as she dangled from the hand gripping her under the arm, the fingers pressing tight into her flesh.

"Now, you little shit." *A string of saliva lashed from her mother's lips.* "I told you now, goddamnit."

Her mom dropped her, and she caught the small of her back against the edge of the table. She watched, breath like a small animal trapped in her throat, as her mom flung the sleeping bag across one of the cots. Without being told to, Dee slid between the table and her mom's rigid, trembling form, crawled into the sleeping bag still dressed, and drew it up to her chin.

"That's right . . . that's a good girl." *Something drained out of her mom, leaving her voice a whisper. She reached up and switched off the camper's overhead light. Dee watched, the blood flowing back into her numbed arm, as her mom went to the front of the camper and sat down heavily in the seat behind the steering wheel. Something small, a crumpled square of aluminum foil that her mom dug out of her pocket, rustled in her hands as she unfolded it. She cupped her palm to her mouth and threw her head back, then sat hunched over, hands gripping the wheel.*

Dee listened to her own heartbeat fluttering her chest. Faint silver light from the sky outside glinted off metal almost hidden under the cot: one of the knives that had dropped out of the sleeping bag, which her mom hadn't found and taken away.

Up front, her mom leaned forward and stared at the sky as if searching for something in the moon's circle. Carefully, keeping her eyes on her mom, Dee reached down, wrapped her hand around the knife's handle, pulled it from under the cot, and brought it inside the sleeping bag with her. A big kitchen knife, with a tapering blade and sharp point.

Inside the bag's close darkness, warmed by her own breath, her fingers slid along the blade, as if they could trace a message there, one that she couldn't read yet...

... moving in the darkness. She could tell where her mother was by the sound of her breathing. Slow, dragging in, a catch of silence, then the hiss of her exhaling.

Her mother had drawn the curtains separating the driver's seat from the rest of the camper, so that the only light Dee could see was that leaking around the edges of the curtains over the cot. Dee drew her legs up under herself to stay out of the frayed lines of light, so her mother wouldn't be able to pinpoint where she was.

"Honey . . . come on now, sweetheart . . ." Her mother's voice, barely louder than her breathing. ". . . I won't hurt you."

Dee gripped the knife tighter in her hands, sweat sliding between the handle and her fingers. She said nothing, keeping her own breath small and silent. The stickiness along the knife's point, where she had nicked her mother's arm, had dried to a scaling crust. A panting scream, of pain and surprise, went on sounding somewhere deep inside her ear, though it had been two days ago that her mother had reached for her, one hand holding one of the other knives she'd brought.

The air inside the camper was stale, smelling of the sweat that seeped out of Dee's clothes no matter how cold it got. She had been unable to hold her bladder, and her urine had spilled warm though her jeans, then dried them stiff against her skin. That smell was strong inside the camper, too. Underneath, she could trace her mother's scent, acrid as if some toxic chemical were oozing out of her pores.

"Dee . . ." The voice crooned with idiot cunning. " . . . you don't want your mommy to die, do you, honey? . . . not die, honey . . . not die . . . can live forever . . . come on, honey . . ."

Her empty stomach gurgled. She tensed, clamping hard to quiet it. The box of saltines she had tucked inside the sleeping bag was finished—she had scraped up the last of the crumbs yesterday. She had washed them down with some of the warm Pepsi that she had filched out of the cupboard over the stove, before her mother had cut her off from the rest of the camper, boxing her into the cramped rear section where she couldn't get out.

Her mother, or whatever it was that her mother had become—Dee could scarcely recognize the crouching figure with tangled hair like a black halo—had stationed herself, knife in hand, right in the middle of the camper, barring Dee from the big sliding door along the camper's side. Only the knife in Dee's own hand, jabbing out of the dark, had kept her mother an arm's distance away—kept her from finishing the slow, half-sideways crawl she had started toward her daughter.

The darkness pulsed in Dee's eyes. She hadn't slept in all this time, since the moment when she'd been able to read the spark in her mother's eyes. A fragment of the moon filtering silver into the camper, catching the eyes held wide open. A full moon, and a private ritual uncoiling from her mother's heart, emerging snakelike from her throat and the point of the knife in her hand.

No sleep, just sitting curled up on the ledge at the back of the camper, her own knife ready to slash her mother's hand whenever she reached for her again. The world had shrunk to the dark space, herself at one end and her mother at the other. Her muscles trembled from the waiting.

"Dee . . . Dee, honey . . . Mommy won't hurt you . . ."

The voice sounded soothing now, far off, like something sung to her when she'd been just a baby. The only sound in the camper. The only sound anywhere. Nothing but the forest outside, far from anybody else. She felt her eyelids sink, the perfect darkness behind them swimming up over her like ink. The cold cut through her sweaters, draining the strength from her muscles. Wake up, wake up—she's coming at you; the last waking part of her brain screamed at the slackening arms, but they grew heavy and fell, and she fell with them.

She woke with a start, only seconds later. The knife was still in her hand. It flashed in the darkness in front of her. It met nothing but empty air. She pushed herself into a ball against the back of the camper, scanning the black space for her mother. She couldn't tell where her mother was, and the fear beat against her ribs like a fist.

No sound of breathing. The camper was empty except for herself. Another edge of light showed where the door had been slid open, then closed almost all the way again.

She waited a few heartbeats, then reached up and pulled back a corner of one of the curtains. Outside she could see nothing, only the outlines of the surrounding trees, black against deeper blackness.

Still clutching the knife, she slid off the ledge. Blood tingled in her legs after having been cramped for so long.

As she crept through the unlit camper, her elbow brushed something off the folding table. It clattered to *the floor, before she could bend down to silence it. Just her mother's keyring.*

She slid the door open a few inches. Cold air that didn't stink of sweat and fear surged against her face. The ground was silvery with moonlight. Her shoes whispered in the dry pine needles as she stepped down.

Silence outside the camper. Dimly, she could see the break in the trees' circle that marked the dirt road they had come up. Downhill there would be the paved road, and in the morning other cars, other people. Her breath clouded in front of her face as she turned, searching the quiet and dark for any sign. She pushed herself away from the cold metal of the camper, and started for the dirt road.

"Dee . . ."

She spun around, feet slipping in the needles, and saw her mother coming around the front of the camper. The moonlight made a silver line of the blade at the end of her upraised arm.

Her feet slid out from under her when she tried to run. She landed on her ribs, breath knocked from her and her own knife spinning out of her grip into the strawlike needles.

She rolled onto her back, gasping, and saw her mother leaning over her, spine twisting to bring the knife clutched in both hands down to the pale throat below her.

No breath to scream or beg or cry. Dee gripped her mother's wrists, but she was too weak. The edge of the blade bore down, pressed into the soft flesh under her chin.

Her mother lowered her face against hers, as if trying to drink in every sharp gulp of breath. " . . . you don't want Mommy to die . . . do you, honey . . . now she'll live for—"

The whisper bent upward to a scream as Dee sank her teeth into her mother's cheek.

She tasted salt spurt into her mouth as her mother jerked backward, hands pressed to her face. Dee scrabbled out from under her, got to her feet, and ran.

She couldn't find the gap in the circle, the end of the dirt road. When she reached the edge of the cleared space she pushed herself in among the dense trees, shoulders bruising against the rough bark. Her hands fought aside the branches clawing at her face.

Behind her, her mother screamed her name. Dee looked back and saw her through the web of branches, the blood streaming a dark patch on one side of the moonlit face. She was staring past her hands to the knife at her feet. Then she was lost as Dee ran farther into the darkness between the trees.

SIX

"So then what happened?" said the therapist.

Braemer leaned back in the chair and gazed out the window before replying. Across the clinic's parking lot and the traffic meshing on the street, the steel framework of a new building was going up. Sparks from a welding torch splashed from one girder to another. His face followed them down for a few seconds, then he turned back around.

"From what I was able to piece together," he said, "from what my daughter and her aunt told me, Dee managed to get downhill to the road. When it was light, a car stopped for her. She apparently wasn't suffering from anything more than hunger and a little exposure. Physically, that is. The park rangers came out, and found the camper and my ex-wife."

The springs of the therapist's chair creaked. On the wall behind his desk the framed certificates—MSW, MFCC, specialties in children's disorders—were neatly arranged. A thin fellow with spaniel eyes and not enough of a mustache to be worth bothering with. "You said her mother had had some kind of a stroke?"

Braemer nodded. "They found the last of the booze, and traces of the drugs she'd been taking, inside the camper. Plus in her bloodstream, when they took her to the hospital. Some of the stuff they could identify, some they couldn't. After Dee got away from her, she must've gobbled up everything she had left. She had a whole stew inside herself. Some combinations drove the blood pressure in her brain up so high that the major vessels ruptured. It's like what happened to that other woman—what was her name?—Quinlan; that's it. Except hers was supposedly caused by just a tranquilizer and a glass of wine. Considering what my ex-wife was doing up, it's a wonder she had any head left on her neck at all." Braemer lapsed into silence, brooding sightlessly out the window, hearing again his daughter's voice as she told him, past her racking sobs, of all that had happened, all that had been kept secret from him. The story had flowed out of her as if the knife she'd brought into the bedroom and tried to bring down into his chest had instead slit open some membrane holding back the dark memory.

Now it was in his memory, too. A spot of blood that deepened the closer you looked at it. He could see it if he closed his eyes: the trees at night, the cramped interior of the camper, his ex-wife crouched in the darkness with a knife just out of reach of his daughter—

". . . Mr. Braemer?"

He turned back to the therapist behind the desk. It took a moment for the clinic office and present time to become real around him again. "I'm sorry," he said. "What did you say?"

The therapist let the point of his pen rest on the notebook in front of him. "You confirmed your daughter's story with her aunt—" He searched his notes for the name.

"Carol. Carol Feld." Braemer nodded. "Soon as I had Dee calmed down, and she'd told me everything, I drove down to San Aurelio, down to where her aunt and . . . her mother are. I had to take Dee with me; there wasn't anybody to leave her with. And I hit Carol with it. Everything, Dee coming in with the knife, her story about what happened out there with her mother, the whole bit."

"And Carol did say your daughter's story was true?"

"Yeah. Apparently Renee—my ex-wife—had been planning it for some time, that was why she'd bought the camper and everything. Then, as soon as I was out of the country, she split with Dee. I guess she figured that I'd be able to find them somehow if I found out they were gone." He drew a deep breath. "Maybe I could have."

The pen tapped against the notebook. "Were you aware of the problems your ex-wife was having?"

"Jesus Christ." Braemer glared at the therapist's face with its sandy little mustache. "Do you think I would've let my kid stay with her if I'd known she was this fucking crazy? Look, I didn't have a very high opinion of my ex-wife—all right? If I could go there every weekend and pick up my kid without ever seeing her, that was fine by me. The only person I'd ever talk to out there was Carol, and she didn't tell me any of this crap that was going on. How the hell was I supposed to know?" His hands gripped the chair's armrests as if about to push himself upright.

The therapist's expression didn't change. "Carol did know, however. Or she might've suspected something. Did she say why she never told you anything, why she didn't tell you the truth about what happened with your ex-wife and your daughter?"

"She was afraid she'd lose Dee. She was afraid I'd be horrified about what had happened, and I'd take Dee to

98

get her away from all that. So she waited a few days after the police brought Dee back to her, then she sent the telegram to me in England, and when I got back she fed me the line about Dee's mother having a stroke, no reason for it, just one of those things that happen. And I bought it. I mean, I didn't go down to the hospital to look up the goddamn blood tests. Nobody called me up to say, Hey, your ex went off her rocker and chased your kid around with a knife. It might not even have gotten into the papers up north where it happened—I imagine the park service isn't exactly hot to publicize loonies with knives running around the forest. If anybody thought about filling in me, the kid's father, they probably thought Carol—responsible adult, right?— would tell me all about it." He relaxed his grip on the armrests, anger ebbing out of him. "So I just didn't know, okay?"

The therapist studied him. "And your daughter went along with this. She kept quiet, too."

Braemer leaned his head back and let his sight wander across the pattern of holes in the acoustic ceiling. "Yes." Softly. "That's what I don't understand. Why she didn't tell me."

"Your daughter undoubtedly had her reasons. Good or bad, logical or not, she had them. She may have responded to Carol's fear of losing her if you found out with an equally strong fear of her own about losing Carol—the stablest adult figure in her life, the one who's apparently been more of a parent to her than anyone else. It's not that she doesn't love you, it could just be that she doesn't know what would *happen* if you took her. And she'd just gone through a pretty unsettling experience, to put it mildly. It may be a child's logic to want to hold on to the security that Carol represents, and to join in a conspiracy against her own father to protect that security, but it's still logic." The therapist drew a small circle on the notebook and frowned at it. "There may be deeper reasons as well. Ones connected with the . . . traumatic incident."

"Like what?"

The therapist smoothed the paper with his hand. "Your daughter was attacked by her own mother, Mr. Braemer. She may have formed a reaction to that. A denial that it happened. She may not have been concealing the truth from you so much as she was suppressing it in her own memory. There are other possibilities. Your daughter fought back against her mother's attack, and, in a sense, her mother *died* as a result. There may be a sense of guilt over that. A desire to conceal what she herself did. And—a desire not to abandon her mother. Your ex-wife's coma is a cruel situation—all of the disadvantages of her being dead, without the advantage of your daughter being able to start forgetting her." He shrugged. "This is all top-of-the-head stuff, though. It's not worth much without my actually talking to your daughter."

Braemer nodded. "That's what I figured."

"Your daughter's still with you, I take it?"

"Yeah. When I went down to see Carol, I told her I was going to keep Dee, and see about getting some help for her. Right now a friend of mine—the lady I live with —is looking after her."

"When you say *keep*, do you mean permanently? Take custody of her, that is?"

"Uh, we kind of left that up in the air. It was the only way I could get Carol to agree to it."

The therapist made another small mark in his notebook. "Well, it should be decided pretty soon. As a stabilizing factor in your daughter's life. And frankly, I don't think living in that rather . . . macabre household, after all that's happened, can be doing your daughter any good. Maybe you should start making whatever arrangements are necessary to get custody of her."

"Right." *Should've done it a long time ago, you stupid shit*—inside Braemer his voice snarled at himself. "I guess so."

"The clinic does legal referrals in matters like this."

He shook his head. "My boss already recommended a lawyer to me. I've got an appointment set up." He pushed himself up from the chair, as heavy as coming out of a weed-choked pond. Telling a shrink all that he'd learned from his daughter had wrapped the darkness tighter around himself.

At the door of the office, the therapist laid his hand on Braemer's shoulder. "Don't worry about it. There's a lot can be done."

"Really?" Braemer looked at the other's bright professional face. Past the door and the clinic's lobby he could hear the traffic. Under the street dark tar had bubbled up and cracked the asphalt. "What can you do about . . ." He let the sentence drift and went to the counter to schedule an appointment for his daughter.

Empty room and daylight. The same room as before, cracked linoleum floor, smell of stale grease in the air. Light through the dust-clouded broken glass. She lay on her side on a thin mattress and watched the bright rectangle from the window creep toward her hand. In an hour or two it would reach the torn edges of her fingernails, then her whole hand would be as warm as if she had dabbled it in blood leaking from under her breast.

Or else she'd lie here and slide back across the blurred edge of sleep. Into the dream that kept tugging her downward into a comforting darkness. Her father would come, stepping through the wall like a painted curtain, and pick her up, holding and rocking her in his arms until every bruise and stiffened scar tissue was soothed. In the dream she knew it was her father, even though she couldn't see his face. There was no face to give him from her memory—he had died when she was a baby, and her mother had cut him out of all the fading pictures in the house, a prim little madness with a pair of sewing scissors. Nothing had been left of him but a faint remembrance of being cradled safely in air.

Waking meant leaving the protection of his arms in the dream. Her father would call her Kathy in the dream, and she'd smile and nod, no other voice clawing into her mouth to spit out her sister Renee's name, laughter shrieking like an animal caught in her teeth.

The square of light was an inch closer to her hand, sliding across the floor with the sun's motion. Sleep was locked someplace away from her, and remembering the dream about her father wouldn't take away the pain clamoring under her skin. Old wounds healing, torn open again, festering under a dark crust of blood, muted cry under flesh that had died to everything but the small bite of the needle, and the flame that would surge up her arm and meet the tide of her racing pulse.

The chemical had drained away again, leaving her in the empty room with muscles drained of will, watching a square of sunlight crawl across a dirty linoleum floor.

Maybe the door would open and the sunlight would bounce off a pair of mirror-lensed glasses looking down at her. He would pull the stained sheet away from her, the cloth catching where it had dried against bloodied skin, and coolly inspect her, wash her with something that stung wet and cold, bandage whatever wounds wouldn't stop flowing, feed her from a white paper bag turning translucent with grease at the bottom.

There had been a time when she'd tried to ask him why, pleading and sobbing against the torn strip he'd knotted around her wrists, but the sight of him smiling, that face she knew as well as her own—KathyRenee-kathyrenee—and never answering unless her sister's voice was in her mouth, had killed those nerves inch by inch. Until there was no question any longer, just the pain battering her.

It was better when he dressed her, tugging the clothes over her limp arms and legs, and took her someplace else. To the ones who paid him for her. They got excited, as if they'd never been in a room where a woman's body could be cut apart and eaten like candy. It was over quickly with them, their hunger stuffed full as if their hands could claw at her and put it in their mouths.

Better that, those hands and sharp teeth, than the face with the mirror lenses leaning over her as she lay spread-eagled on this bare floor. No excitement trembled in that face above her, just the slow, methodical rituals of his hands. Motions tender as a lover's. The small cuts that loosed waves of pulsing red underneath the fevering chemical, lapping red across her own eyes until she screamed in both her own voice and her sister's.

Quiet now, the square of sunlight just touching her finger. She wondered how far the warm light would slide across her hand and arm, whether it would be in her face when he returned, blocking the window as he looked down at her, glasses dark in the shadow of his own body. The waiting would be over then, and her life—what her life had become—would begin again.

Something tugged in her memory. All her remembering had become a red piece, but something now stood out, like the light on the dirty linoleum. Something bright. The room faded as she let the image work upward out of the darkness.

A girl. That was it, a little girl. She could see her now in her mind. Long, dark hair pulled back, thin legs in dancer's tights, serious face reflected in a mirror that

103

ran the length of a wall with a wooden barre mounted on it. She could recognize her, even though the girl was older than the last time she had seen her, years ago. Dee —the image in her memory was that of her niece Dee. Her sister's daughter. She smiled at the picture in her memory, her own face pressed against the gray mattress on the floor, then wondered where she could have seen the little dancer.

Then the rest came into light. And she knew that the memory of the girl wasn't her own, but was in her mind the way her sister's voice would be in her mouth. The image had been left in her memory by the passing of the thing that came inside her and spoke and laughed with her sister's voice.

Memories of that voice came, sounding in her head. The voice from the face with the mirror glasses was there in her memory as well. They were talking about the little girl Dee, while she listened, trapped in her own body that was no longer hers alone. In her memory the talking and laughing went on, wouldn't stop, went on until she snatched her hand from the burning sunlight on the floor and jerked upright in the crumpled sheet, fists trying to beat out the sounds inside her head.

The voices stopped. Even memory was silent. She stared around the empty room. Clothes—a dress and jacket, clean enough for her to be taken to one of the customers in, shoes—were piled in one corner. The sheet slid off her as she stood up. The air was chill against her pale, marked skin as she stepped slowly to the corner.

She dressed as quickly as her numbed fingers could pull the clothes onto herself. The blurring fog had lifted enough so that she could remember all she had thought and planned on doing. If she hurried, there would be time before her sister's voice came back inside her, turning her back to this room where the eyes hidden behind mirrors would be patiently waiting for her return.

"What did you want to do today?" Sarah set her coffee cup down.

"I don't know." Dee shrugged, gazing at a half-eaten sandwich on a plate in front of her. "Nothing."

The kid looked miserable, face still a little puffy from crying. Sarah had found her this morning trying to muffle her sobs in her pillow. Plus the weekend's long siege: all the talking, with Dee and without her, then Dave taking Dee down to San Aurelio to talk to Carol, then their coming back with him even more grim-faced than when he'd left, phone calls to his boss and then to some psychiatric clinic and a lawyer to make appointments. It made Sarah tired just to remember it all.

When she'd come back to the apartment from working overtime on Saturday, it had been like stepping into a storm with Dee at the center. This Monday morning, with just her and Dee in the apartment, Dave off to see the shrink and the lawyer about the kid, seemed like the quiet after the storm. She had called in to the law office and taken a sick-day to look after Dee.

"Well," said Sarah, "I called the dance studio, and there's a Beginning class at two. Would you like to go to that?"

Dee looked up from the nibbled sandwich. "Would . . . that be okay?"

"Sure. Your dad's not going to be home for a while. And I think we need to get out of here for a while. So what d'you say—feel up to it?"

"Sure. I guess."

"Go get your stuff, then. I think your tights are still hanging in the bathroom."

Dee scooted from the table. Alone in the kitchen,

Sarah stacked the plates from the table and carried them to the sink. Her gaze darted to the faint scar on the wall beside the refrigerator, the filled-in mark left by the knife that David had pointed out to her. That was Saturday—that day when explanations and hidden pieces of the past had all come rushing at her. All that to take in, and to try and arrange in her own mind, the worrying about what was going to happen next. Plus all the practical details that had to be taken care of. What do you do with a kid that's flipped out (once, twice, how many other times?) and does things with knives? Only a wounded apron and a close call so far, but what do you *do* with the kid? Turn her over to the police? Tie her up in a chair?

She and Dave had wound up pulling the mattress from the sofa bed into their own room and making it up there for Dee to sleep on, so they could keep an eye on her at night. Dave had gathered up all the kitchen knives and anything else with a sharp point or edge—screwdrivers, can openers—and stashed them in the locking toolbox he'd brought in from the car. She finished rinsing off the table knife with which she'd spread the peanut butter on Dee's sandwich, then put it back in the toolbox sitting on one of the top cupboard shelves, locked it; and put the key back into her pocket.

Even as she did it, she felt stupid for it. She could feel that the moment was past, that the wound inside Dee, which had worked its way to her skin and her hand closing around the handle of the knife she'd brought down toward her father's chest, was gone for the time being. Now she was just a little girl again, her father's daughter, scared by something that had come out of the darkness that had been planted in her by her mother. Something that had betrayed her, as though her own small hand had been someone else's. *Her mother's,* thought Sarah as she mechanically rinsed the plates.

That psycho. Even all but dead, she just kept reaching out of the past.

So even keeping watch over Dee that Saturday night, neither she or Dave catching a minute of sleep, she hadn't worried about Dee finding another knife, sneaking up on them in the dark, any of those new possibilities. What mattered was Dee tossing against her pillow under the heavy point of her nightmares. And Dave staring out the window, watching the streetlamps flick off and turn gray against the morning light, while every mistake he'd ever made with his daughter—and a worldful of them opened up by the knife's cutting edge—turned darker still inside him, one by one.

"I'm ready."

Sarah turned and saw Dee standing in the kitchen doorway, the shoulder strap of her Capezio bag in her hands. "Okay," she said, shutting off the water. "Let me get my makeup on, and we'll take off. All right?"

Dee nodded, looking back at her with eyes that—Sarah could see it in them—would now always be sadder than those of a little girl.

"All right, Braemer." The lawyer's name was Layton. He rocked back in his chair and ground out a cigarette in an ashtray already mounded with butts. He was probably only a few years older than Braemer, but a hairline thinning to the back of his head made his frozen scowl seem like that of an old man. "Now I suppose you want everything fixed up all neat and tidy, don't you?"

"What do you mean?" One of the chair's armrests wobbled under Braemer's elbow as he drew away from the snarl across the desk from him. The beat-up chair had creaked all during the past half-hour of telling the situation to the lawyer.

"You know, I really like Rawling." Layton studied a brown spot on the ceiling. "He pays his bills."

"I can write you a check."

"And that'll make it all okay, won't it?" Layton brought his gaze back down to Braemer. "Better than new. That's what you figure, isn't it?"

"You know, I really don't see what you're getting at."

"Guys like you, Braemer, you screw up royally and then you expect someone like me to put it all back together again for you. Nice going."

Braemer stiffened in the chair, almost rose, then forced himself to stay sitting. "Do you get a lot of business with this approach?" he asked.

Layton shrugged. "Some people appreciate a lack of bullshit when dealing with a lawyer. Like your buddy Rawling—he comes in with something, one of his fly-by-night Hollywood clients won't pay up, and if it's a shit case I tell him so. Saves him money. Frankly, Braemer, you have a shit case."

"I'm the girl's *father,* for Christ's sake. Her mother is . . . incapacitated, to say the least. Don't you think I should get her automatically?"

"It doesn't matter what I think. It's what the judge thinks. This is a very enlightened, progressive state, and the court doesn't have to just hand custody of your daughter over to you. The court's supposed to look to what's best for the child. If the girl's aunt, this Carol Feld you talked about, decides to sue for custody— and from what you told me, she probably will—she could argue a pretty good case for herself."

"But I'm—"

"Yeah, right, you're the father. Big deal. You also sat on your butt for a whole year while your ex-wife was in a coma and your kid's aunt continued to be the responsible adult in the whole setup, taking care of your kid while you wrote your measly child-support checks and played weekend daddy. You know, that just doesn't cut it. Especially when your kid is suffering some weird psychological trauma from her mother flipping out and coming at her with a knife."

"But I didn't even know about that—"

"Oh, that looks good. That'll look real good to a judge. *Reeks* of a father's concern for his child." Layton shook his head in disgust as he fumbled with his cigarette pack. "You're off fooling around in London, Mr. Jet Setter, while your ex is chasing your kid around in the forest with a meat cleaver, the aunt cleans up the mess, and your kid doesn't even want to tell you about any of this. Right, that indicates a real close relationship between you and your kid. The judge'll love it."

"Great," said Braemer. "You don't want to take it on, I can find another—"

"Sit down." Layton motioned him back into the chair. "I didn't say I wouldn't take you on, or that you wouldn't be able to get legal custody of your kid. Even if this Feld woman contests it, you got a case. I just wanted to point out to you that it's not some automatic thing where you go into the court, punch a few buttons, and your kid pops out of a chute for you. It won't be like that. We'll have to be prepared to argue that the best interests of your daughter are served by you getting custody of her. So you might have to clean up your act a little bit to meet the court's approval. You said you live with another person?"

"That's right."

"Female?"

"Yeah, of course."

"This is L.A., you have to make sure about these things. Getting married to her?"

"We decided not to."

"Hmm. Way it usually goes is, he decides, she goes along with it. Unless she's smart. Anyway, if you want to improve your chances on getting legal custody of your kid, you'll change your mind about that. You want to show the court that you can offer a stable home environment, not some shack-up. Yeah, I know, it's the twentieth century, more's the pity—figure on the judge being back in the nineteenth. If that. And while your legal right to your kid, or how good a home you can give her, doesn't depend on your being married, if you want to impress the court with what a good daddy you are, it's a good idea. It's like wearing a coat and tie to the hearing—appearances count for a lot."

"All right." Braemer nodded. "I'll talk it over with her."

"You do that," said Layton. "And I'll start getting things together at this end. I'll need a copy of your final dissolution of marriage, child-custody agreement, some kind of record of your support payments, cancelled checks, that sort of thing. That'll do for starters. Now, as to what it's going to cost."

They talked money for a few minutes, then Braemer wrote the first check.

SEVEN

The class at the dance studio, even if it was only a Beginners', had been enough to work up a good sweat. Going through the simple barre and floor exercises with Dee had been exactly the routine, mindless workout that Sarah had needed. Stuff that she'd learned so long ago, back when she'd been Dee's age, that the motions were grooved deep into her muscles. She could just turn off her overtaxed brain, and listen to the music and the teacher's voice.

"Did you like her better than the teacher who gives the class on Saturdays?" said Sarah. She and Dee stood on the sidewalk in front of the studio, the warm sun drying the sweat on their necks, waiting for the bus.

"She's okay." Dee squinted in the bright light, holding her dance bag's strap with both hands in front of her. All during the class, a mask had seemed to hide her thoughts.

Sarah adjusted the strap of her own bag on her shoulder. "You know, one thing I've never been able to figure out, is why dance studios always have to be up some stupid flight of stairs. It's like a tradition or some— Dee!"

Her hand reached to catch her but closed on nothing as Dee's bag fell at Sarah's feet. Dee was already yards down the sidewalk, running, her dark hair streaming behind her. One moment she had been standing beside Sarah, then had bolted without warning.

Sarah's bag fell beside Dee's as she ran after her. "Dee!" she yelled again. She didn't look back, but kept running. A couple of people on the opposite sidewalk stopped and watched, then went on their way.

Dee hit the corner and the traffic muddling together at the light. A car slammed on its brakes as Dee ran in front of it, catching herself with both hands on its fender to keep from falling. Other tires screeched and a horn sounded, then she had made it to the other side of the street.

"Dee!" The light changed as Sarah ran to the corner. She gasped for breath as she squeezed past the cars blocking the crosswalk. She could still see Dee running ahead of her, toward a freeway ramp branching off the street and the faster river of traffic swarming on it.

Shrink done, lawyer done, Braemer drove back out to his job. A quarter to four or so in the afternoon—he supposed he could get something done there, some project under way that would take his mind off his daughter and everything else.

He pulled into the driveway of Rawling Graphics' parking lot, stopped, and looked at the building over his hands gripping the wheel. It struck him that he didn't want to go inside. He didn't want to go inside and have Rawling ask how things had gone, what the therapist and the lawyer had said, what was going to happen now. He didn't want to talk about it, to make up something soothing to meet Rawling's concern. What I want, thought Braemer, is a drink. A nice dark bar, a door with padding tucked into diamonds on the inside to keep the daylight out. There wouldn't be anyone from Rawling Graphics at the one down the street at this hour. He backed the car out of the driveway and turned a U in the street.

Cooler in the bar. A click of cue stick against ball, a wispy-bearded kid shooting pool by himself at the table in the corner. No one else. Braemer left the change on the bar and carried his beer over to one of the booths, away from the glimmering mirror lined with glasses.

He became aware of a wedge of light falling inside the bar as the door to the outside was opened and closed. He didn't look up, watching instead his finger tracing a slow cross through the wet ring left by his glass on the table.

Footsteps halted for a moment, then came closer. The person, whoever it was, slid into the seat on the other side of the booth.

He looked up, saw it was a woman across from him, and held a sigh inside himself. Perfect timing for something like this to happen. "Not interested," he said, raising his beer.

"I want to talk to you." Her voice rasped out of the shadow cast by the high back of the booth.

Great, thought Braemer. Not even a healthy hooker. An odor of sweat curled in his nostrils. "Look—I know a girl's got to pay the rent and all, but I'm just not in the market. You're wasting your time. Okay? No hard feelings."

The woman's hands trembled and clasped on the table. "You've got to listen—"

"No, I don't," he said. "I don't have to do anything. I don't want to be rude, but why don't you hike it back down to Hollywood Boulevard and try your luck there with the rest of the ladies. You're not going to get much business in a place like this."

"David, you don't recognize me?"

If this is some fucking joke, he thought, I'm going to kill Stennis and the rest of those jerks. "All right, how do you know my name?"

"You used to be married to my sister."

"What—" He leaned forward as the woman brought her face into the faint light from the bar.

The last time he had seen Renee's sister Kathy was at the funeral of their mother. She had shown up late for the service and had sat in the last pew of the church until it was over. A trim figure in a frilled blouse and tailored suit, a handbag with some designer's initials for a clasp, shining hair pulled into a businesswoman's efficient bun. Outside she had said nothing to Renee, only a nod passing between them. Their sisterly hatred had remained perfect and unbroken, a family spat running back long enough for it to have curdled into permanence. Kathy had come up to him, though, as he had held four-year-old Dee, her head nodding against his shoulder. She had looked at the niece she had never seen before, smiled, and said a few words to him, then walked to her car without looking back, the points of her heels clicking on the church's cement path.

But this couldn't be the same woman. There's no way, he thought, appalled. Her hair was dirty brown straw, hanging forward to hide a bruise fading on her cheek. The bone under the skin seemed to be slicing up through the skin, the edges around her eyes sinking in dark flesh, sharp enough to trace with a finger.

It was her, though. There was enough left for him to tell, to make the connection with the image of her in his memory. Six years, he thought. A lot could happen to someone in six years. In L.A. that could be like sixty years. Drugs, hard tricks to get the money to buy more, boyfriends with needs beyond mere pleasure—anything was possible.

"Jesus Christ." He took a long swallow from his beer.

Kathy's pale, cracked lips smiled grimly. Her fingers fumbled open the buttons at the cuffs of her dress. She slid the sleeves past her elbows and slowly turned her arms in the light between them.

"Christ," said Braemer. An overlapping network of burns and scars, some old, some barely closed. Telltale red dots clustered around the veins in the crook of the elbow. A little horror movie carved in skin. She rolled the sleeves back down, her smile fading.

"It's really you, isn't it?" Braemer shook his head. "What the fuck must've happened to you—you look like shit. How did you find me here?"

"I knew where you worked," said Kathy. "I was watching across the street and saw you pull into the lot, then come over here. So I followed you. I've been waiting to talk with you."

"I guess . . . you want some money or something." He supposed that was how it went. People get this way and burn out everybody around them, then go looking up everybody they can dredge out of the past, no matter how remote the connection, how unlikely the charity. It was like a diseased version of having somebody you barely remembered from high school become an insurance agent and start phoning you up to hawk a policy.

Ordinarily, Braemer would have cold-shouldered any touch for money—he had lived in Los Angeles long enough to develop a hard shell for things like this— but he was still unnerved by the last few days' events. It was obviously part of the universe's grimly comic gearing that somebody like this would pop up on top of everything else going on. He reached for his wallet in his back pocket. A few dollars would be a cheap price to pay for cutting this short.

Kathy shook her head, the tangled hair sliding across the bruise on her cheek. "I don't want any money. I don't need anything anymore. I want to talk to you."

Braemer wrapped his hands around his glass. Whatever her pitch was, it was more complex—and tiresome—than the usual. "What about?"

"Your daughter. Dee."

That was the second surprise to catch him in the face. He stiffened, the beer nearly sloshing out of the glass between his hands. "What about her?"

"I know a lot about her, David. More than you do."

Insanity laid over insanity. Braemer looked into the dark-circled eyes across the table from him. Just what every father wants to hear: some loon, burned out on bad speed and the jittering city wavelength talking secrets in her fillings, has fixated her crapped-out brain cells on your kid. Wonderful, he thought. "Kathy," he said quietly, sadly, "you haven't seen my daughter in six years—"

"I don't have much time. Just listen to me."

Maybe it would be better if he did. Maybe it was something in her head that could be purged and gotten rid of, so there wouldn't be any phone calls in the middle of the night later on, or this scraggly figure haunting Dee's schoolyard. "Okay," he said. "Go on."

"Your daughter," said Kathy, "tried to kill you. She tried to stick a knife in you while you were sleeping. But you woke up, or you were already awake. And you caught her hand and stopped her."

Braemer rocked back against the booth's seat. "Who . . . who told you about that?"

"Nobody told me. I saw it."

"Carol told you. That's how you know."

Kathy shook her head. "I haven't seen any of my

family in six years. *I saw it.* I saw your daughter bring the knife down, right at your chest.''

"Look, I don't care who told you about this, or why they told you. Just tell me what you want—''

"David, it's true." Her fingers dug clawlike at the table as she leaned forward. "I saw it through your daughter's eyes. That's how I know."

He stayed silent. There was no answer to any of this. He took a thin sip of beer, knowing that it would just get worse.

There was no breath left in Sarah's lungs to call out Dee's name. A ribbon of fire stitched her ribs as she pushed through a knot of people blocking the sidewalk. She heard another flurry of brakes squealing ahead, but Dee was nowhere to be seen, already vanished on the other side of the traffic. The curve of the freeway ramp bent away from the street.

At the corner she could see across to one of the vendors who stood along the freeway ramps. But this man wasn't slowly moving up the line of cars backed up from the stop sign at the ramp's end, as he held up plastic bags of oranges, swapping them for dollar bills through the cars' rolled-down windows. He was staring past the cars to something up on the freeway itself. Sarah's eyes swept up in the direction of the man's gaze and caught a flash of Dee's jeans and bright red shirt.

The vendor shouted something in Spanish at Sarah as she ran past him, along the ramp's curb as it sloped upward, the drivers staring at her through their windshields. The noise of the freeway washed over her in a wave at the top.

A flow, almost bumper to bumper, the cars up to speed and over. The rush-hour crawl hadn't set in yet.

There was no sign of Dee when Sarah looked down against the traffic. She turned around and saw her, running along the litter-strewn freeway shoulder. Dee looked behind herself and caught sight of Sarah, just as her foot tripped at the slots of a metal drain cover. Sarah saw her fall against the bank of ice plant banking the shoulder, leaving a smear of crushed green on the concrete as she slid onto her hands and knees.

Dee scrambled back onto her feet, looking up at Sarah running toward her. A quick glance down the narrow shoulder, blocked several yards away by the pilings of a street overpass crossing the freeway, then Dee ran straight into the traffic.

A gap in the stream, as a car swerved from the closest lane into the middle. Dee's hair tangled in a web against her drained-white face, mouth open and silent in the roar of the traffic. She half jumped, half fell from the shoulder into the path of an oncoming truck, even as Sarah's hands were reaching for her as she ran, fingers just inches from the sleeve of the red shirt.

The bar's space was congealed darkness around the booth. Braemer closed his eyes as Kathy's frayed voice went on.

"When your daughter came at you with that knife, it wasn't her. Believe me, David, it wasn't her. It was her body, but something else was inside her. Something else, another mind inside her made her do it."

"And—somehow—you know this for a fact?" He didn't want to sound to skeptical. He didn't want to provoke some kind of screaming fit from her. In his exhausted condition—exhaustion deepened by the sight of the ravaged face across from him—it was easier just to let her go on with her brain-scrambled rap. The bar's walls seemed close around his shoulder. Now he wanted to be out in the sunlight and air again.

"I know it," said Kathy, "because the same thing comes inside me." One hand tapped the inside of the other forearm. "That's why . . ." Her voice softened to a whisper. "That's why . . . I'm the way I am. It's what *she* wants."

"She? The thing that . . . comes inside you?"

"It's my sister. Your ex-wife. Renee."

Family business. Braemer sighed, shaking his head. The hatred of one sister for another. It happens sometimes, in families less screwed up than the Felds. Planted in little adolescent jealousies, spats, feuds; and now blossoming in deranged fantasies about a comatose body. Maybe, thought Braemer, she doesn't even know what happened to her sister. It was like a low-budget version of an interlocking Greek tragedy. "Renee somehow . . . comes into your mind," he said, watching her eyes. "And takes you over. Makes you do things. Some kind of telepathy or something."

Kathy nodded.

"And she comes into Dee's mind, too? And does the same things. Made her come at me with a knife."

"Yes."

"For your information, your sister has been in a coma for the past year. There's nothing there. Just a body that Carol feeds through a tube and wipes. Renee's brain is *dead*. There's nobody home. Got it?" His anger had broken through his restraint. "She can't go creeping around into other people's heads, because she's *not there.*"

"She's not dead," said Kathy. "Not her mind. Something inside her is still alive. Something that still thinks, something that *wants.*"

"And just what does it want? This thing inside Renee?"

"It wants to go on living. Inside your daughter."

The last swallow of beer was flat on his tongue. "I suppose it—she, whatever—tells you all this. A little sisterly chat."

"When Renee comes inside me, I can see some of its . . . memories. Things she does when she's inside Dee. That was how I knew about the knife. When she came into me afterward, I saw what she had seen through your daughter's eyes, what she had made her do." Kathy fell silent, her own gaze focusing on some inner vision. "She talks when she's inside me, too. There's . . . a man. They talk and laugh together. And I'm inside somewhere, and I can hear it all. They talk about . . . what they want. And how they'll get it. How she . . . lives."

"And how does she go on living?"

Kathy shook her head. "I don't know. It's all confused. They know what they're talking about, but I don't. Something to do with a man named Pedersen. Something he did made it possible. And there were others like them, a group or something. But now they hate him. They want to do something to him, too. And they laugh about it. They laugh."

His temper simmered just below the surface. "And just what am I supposed to do about all this?"

The ragged edges of her nails caught at his sleeve as she grabbed his arm. "You've got to do *something!* You've got to stop her or she'll do to your daughter what she's done—"

"That's it. That's enough." He jerked his arm free and slid out from the booth. Trembling, he leaned down close to her face. "Look. I don't want to hear any more of this fucking crap. Ever." The solitaire pool game in the corner stopped, and behind him he could hear the bartender lifting the bar's hinged section, coming out to see what the sudden outburst of shouting was about. "You stay away from me, you stay away from my daughter. Crawl back into whatever hole you came out of and do whatever you do in there, but leave us alone. Got it?"

120

He caught sight of the glimmer of a tear welling along the curve of her eye before he turned on his heel and walked out of the bar. She didn't call after him.

The truck slammed on its brakes and swerved. Dee, her tennis shoes still slippery from the crushed ice plant, fell onto her hands and knees a few feet into the lane from the freeway's shoulder. The raised plastic dots dividing the lanes chattered under the truck's tires as its bumper missed a car in the middle lane by inches. The rush of wind whipped Dee's hair up and across the truck's fender.

Then she was in Sarah's arms. Her knuckles scraped against the concrete as Sarah scooped the small body up, then stumbled, almost falling, back up onto the shoulder.

She knelt by the bank of ice plant, pressing Dee tight against herself, the traffic's roar loud and unheeded at her back. "Why, honey . . . why did you—"

Dee's tears were wet against her neck. "I didn't want *her* to come back," she sobbed. "I d-didn't want my daddy and—and you to get hurt. . . ."

A silent chasm grew around them, and inside Sarah as she held the trembling little girl. "Sweetheart, she's not coming back. Everything will be all right." She couldn't think of anything else to say to her. "It'll be all right. But don't go running like that. Please. Just stay with us, okay?"

Dee nodded, face pressed against Sarah's neck.

"Hey." She pulled her face away and tried to smile, tasting the salt of her own tears at the corner of her mouth. "We'd better get out of here before the Highway Patrol comes along. They'll think we're trying to hitch a ride."

Another nod, as Dee wiped the sleeve of her sweatshirt across her nose.

"Can you walk okay?" The smell of gasoline and oil on hot pavement caught in her breath.

The knee of Dee's jeans was shredded open, but the skin underneath was scraped only pink and not bleeding. "Yeah."

Back at the sidewalk in front of the dance studio, they found Dee's Capezio bag kicked against the side of the building. Sarah's bag was gone.

"Great," she said. "I hope whoever took it has a thing for sweaty leotards—that's all he's going to find in it."

Dee held on to Sarah's arm and gave a small smile. "Maybe a bag lady took it. A bag ballerina."

"Very funny. Thank God the bus is coming." She picked up the other bag and draped its strap across Dee's shoulder.

The streets and the cars on them seemed like a movie projected on Braemer's windshield as he drove. A movie that he had no interest in. His own thoughts, moving in their rigid circles, rising and falling from anger to guilt, absorbed him, his hands operating mechanically on the steering wheel and gearshift.

When he became aware of time again, he saw that he had worked his way through the rush-hour traffic, back toward his job. He'd gone in a loop, or several of them, around Rawling Graphics.

No other cars remained in the parking lot. He pulled in, shut off the Datsun's engine, and sat for a moment. The setting sun glazed the building's windows in red. He slid out of the car and unlocked the lobby door with his own key. Inside the building, the overhead fluorescent light buzzed softly. He switched it back off when he had his bearings, and the tubes sputtered back into darkness.

In Rawling's office, where the comfortable chairs

were, he sat smoking a cigarette from a pack that Stennis had left by his adding machine. I should get back home, thought Braemer, watching the cigarette's end glow brighter as the light from outside faded bit by bit. Sarah and Dee would be waiting for him, he knew.

A ghost touch feel across his hand. The ash from the cigarette drifted onto his lap. Soon, he thought. He needed a little breathing space. The cigarette's heat neared his lip as he took·a last draw of smoke. Just a couple of minutes more, and I'll go home.

The bus let them off at the top of the street. Sarah and Dee, toting her dance bag, started down the three or four blocks to the apartment building. The traffic noise faded behind them as the street changed, block by block, into a residential area, the city's asphalt and concrete merging into trees and grass.

"Maybe your dad's home." Sarah shaded her eyes against the sun, turning orange beyond the houses and apartments. She didn't see Dave's car parked in front of the building.

She dug in her pocket for her keys as they stood on the building's front steps. Dee suddenly stiffened beside her. Sarah turned and saw a man getting out of a pickup truck parked at the curb, slamming its door, then striding rapidly across the strip of grass toward them.

"Jess," said Dee, surprise in her voice.

"Hello, Dee," said the man. He was already standing next to them, his pale eyes glancing cold at Sarah. His hand closed tightly around Dee's arm. "You're going home now."

"What?" Sarah reached for Dee, but her uncle jerked her behind himself. "What do you think you're doing?"

"She's going with me," said Jess. "I'm taking her back home where she belongs."

"The hell you are." Sarah grabbed his jacket, pulling herself across him toward Dee. The girl's bewildered eyes stared up at the man's face.

He pushed Sarah away with a jab of his free arm. She fell back, catching herself on the edge of the sidewalk with her hands. The man pulled Dee along with him to the pickup.

Sarah scrambled up and was on his back, trying to get her hands around his face. "You son-of-a-bitch, let go of her!" He shook her off again, picked Dee up, and pushed her into the front of the pickup.

She grabbed the door handle as the engine clattered to life and jerked away from the curb. She tugged, pushing with one hand against the window pillar, but it wouldn't open. Dee's face pressed against the glass, turning to look at her, eyes wide as if in shock. The door handle tore from Sarah's hand as the truck sped up. She ran behind it for a block, the exhaust hot against her, but it left her behind.

Panting, Sarah watched the truck turn at the head of the street without stopping for the light. The nearest freeway ramp was just a few blocks away.

"Shit." She pushed her hair from her face. The adrenaline in her arms and legs started to ebb, leaving her clenched fists trembling at her sides.

"Hey, come on." Jess took one hand from the steering wheel and reached across to touch Dee's shoulder. She was curled up against the door, arms wrapped around herself. "Everything's okay now. You didn't get hurt, did you?"

For a moment Dee went on staring out the windshield, then she shook her head.

"You want to see Carol, don't you?" said Jess. "If I hadn't come and got you, you'd never have seen her again. You don't want that, do you?"

124

Silence, than another shake of her head.

"And this is just for right now," he continued. "You'll see your dad again, soon as we all get some things straightened out. Then it'll be just like it was before. Okay?"

She nodded, still without words.

Jess put both hands back on the wheel, guiding the pickup truck through the freeway traffic. The setting sun bounced off the rear windows and chrome of the cars ahead, bright in his eyes. He fished in his shirt pocket for a pair of sunglasses, opened them, and put them on. The sunlight reflected red from the mirror lenses as he looked from the traffic to Dee.

"Everything's going to be all right." Voice soft, eyes hidden behind the mirrors. "Everything's going to be fine now."

EIGHT

In the underground parking garage beneath the Century City towers, a man in a Brooks Brothers corporate gray suit walked across the empty spaces. At this hour, well past five, his Mercedes 280 was the only car left.

As he bent to unlock the door he felt a hand grip his forearm, strong fingers sinking into the soft flannel of his sleeve. His face jerked around, eyes widening in a shock of recognition. "Pedersen," he managed to say.

"Hello, Evans." The other figure didn't let go his grip, just above a wrist with a pale band of skin showing where a Rolex had been pulled off for pawning. "I've been trying to see you for a long time now. You've become very devious."

The two men, alone in the garage's gray cement ramps and parking spaces, made an odd contrast: the one slim and well dressed, the other a bulky figure, broad face weathered as the plain cotton workshirt tight across his chest and thick arms. A concrete pillar hid most of an unwashed panel truck several yards away.

The young exec shrugged, a nervous smile twitching the corner of his mouth. "I—I don't know what to tell you, Pedersen."

"You can tell me you won't have anything more to do with Jess Feld." The other's calloused hand tightened its grasp.

"Hey," Evans' free hand spread open, placating, "I cut that off. Weeks ago. It was getting . . . just a little too scary."

"That's a wise decision. Wiser than you've been for a long time." He let go of the captured man.

Massaging blood back into the muscle, Evans nodded. "Yeah, well . . . I didn't know. I didn't know what that stuff Jess talked about really meant."

"Now you do." The larger man started to turn away. "Keep the decision you've made. I can always find you if you don't."

"Pedersen!" Evans called after him, across the empty parking spaces. His voice rang hollow against the bare concrete walls. "Is there any chance . . . of my coming back into the group? You know, picking up where I left off?"

A cold gaze studied him. "No," said Pedersen at last. "The damage has been done. The way I teach begins at a point higher than where you've brought yourself. You'll have to find your own way back."

The figure in the three-piece suit watched the panel truck's door slam shut, then stood leaning against his car's fender, listening to the engine noise fade along the curving exit ramp.

When Braemer got back to the apartment, there were two LAPD officers standing in the living room. Their badges shone against uniforms as dark as the evening sky out the window.

With the door key still in his hand, knowing at once

what was the matter, why they were there, Braemer turned to Sarah and asked, "Where's Dee?"

She was framed by the kitchen doorway with her arms clasped across her breast. "They took her," she said. "Dee's uncle—Jess—came and took her. I tried to stop him, but I couldn't."

"All right." He nodded, feeling the muscles across his shoulders tighten. In a way, he'd expected it. Or should have, he realized. His thought darkened: Carol agreed too soon. Shouldn't have trusted her.

"I'm sorry, Dave." Sarah's eyes were red-tinged.

"It's okay. I'll take care of it."

"Mr. Braemer—" One of the officers, holding a clipboard, turned to him. Red-haired, pale; his partner was olive-skinned. "Were you aware that your ex-wife's family would be trying to get your daughter back in their custody?"

Braemer shook his head. "No. Of course not." He wanted the police gone, out of the apartment. He had business to take care of.

"Miss Aceves here has told us that you were not, in fact, awarded legal custody of your daughter. Is that true?"

"My ex-wife," said Braemer, grinding out the words, "is incapacitated. She's been in a fucking coma for the last year. Got it? She's unable to take care of our daughter. I'm the girl's father, I've got the right to have her, and to take care of her."

The officer looked sad, a frown bending on his sandy face. He was the same age or a little younger than Braemer. "Miss Aceves filled us in on the background, Mr. Braemer. And you probably do have the legal right to custody of your daughter. That's going to have to be decided by the court, though."

"Screw that," muttered Braemer. He'd heard all this once today. "I suppose you'd like me to just sit here."

"We called down to the Orange County Sheriff's Department and asked them to send a car around to the Feld place, and make sure your daughter's all right. Other than that, nothing needs to be done right now."

"Do you have kids?"

"I don't think that matters, Mr. Braemer."

"What would you do if somebody took one?"

"What I would or wouldn't do doesn't matter. What I'm trying to warn you about is your doing something stupid. There are other—better—ways of handling this. Your daughter's okay right now. She's being taken care of by the same person who's been taking care of her for the past year. If you go down there yourself and try to get her back, you'll only make a bigger mess out of this. There's some free advice you don't have to see your lawyer for. You could possibly endanger your chances of having the court award you pemanent custody of the child. You could wind up charged with some heavy offenses—it can be a felony for a parent to steal his own child, depending on the circumstances."

"Whatever," said Braemer. He could feel the blood vessels at his temple grow harder.

"And you should think of your kid's welfare, too, Mr. Braemer."

"That's exactly what I'm thinking of."

"It doesn't do your kid any good to get yanked back and forth between the adults fighting over her. Whether it's by her father or anybody else, it's frightening. A lot of psychological damage can be done to a kid because of something like this."

"Damage, huh." Braemer shook his head, the skin of his face pulling tight against the bone. "You know, if you knew a little more of the story here, you'd think that was pretty funny."

The officer folded the cover back over his clipboard. "Mr. Braemer, the best thing you can do is to let us, and the court, take care of it. Go talk to your lawyer. These kinds of things are really messy, and they take time to sort out, but if you want to have your daughter, that's the way to do it."

"Right. You bet."

"I know how you feel." A glance, sympathy of a common brotherhood, passed from him. "My ex-wife took my kids back home with her. To Delaware. Some summers I see 'em."

"Yeah. Well . . ." Braemer looked away from the officer and to the window, with the scattered lights of the city set in darkness. "Thanks for the advice."

The officer turned to Sarah. "If you decide you want to press assault charges against this Jess Feld, just come down to the station on Wilcox."

She nodded, drawing one hand along her arm.

The officers left. The apartment was a set of connected rooms when they were gone, filled with dead quiet, and space large and empty.

"I'm sorry." Sarah leaned her head against the side of the kitchen doorway, her eyes filling with tears again. "I tried, I really did. But he was so fast—"

"It's okay." He pulled her to him, held her. "It's okay. Not your fault. And I'll get her back."

Her head was against his chest. "What are you going to do?"

"I'm going down there. And I'm bringing her back with me."

Sarah nodded, her face moving on his shirt. "Do you want me to come?"

"No. I can take care of it." He took her shoulders and stepped back so he could see her face. "Don't worry."

"What—what's going to happen then? After you bring her back? What did the lawyer say?"

"He's going to take the case on. So he thinks I should

130

be able to get legal custody of Dee. But he did tell me that if Carol fights it, she might be able to put up a pretty good case herself, what with her having taken care of Dee for so long. So he gave me some advice, about what I should do to help my case look stronger. And I wanted to talk to you about that."

"What'd he say?"

Braemer watched her eyes. "He thinks it'll be important to show to the court that I can provide Dee with a stable home. The squarer the better. So he thinks you and I should get married."

"Oh."

"I know what we agreed about that."

She looked up, catching his gaze with hers. "That's what I've wanted, though. For a long time now. Really wanted." She was silent for a moment. "But what do you want?"

"You," he said. "And my kid."

"Ours."

He nodded. "Okay. Uh, we'll start taking care of the arrangements tomorrow, then. License and stuff." He let go of her and turned toward the door. "I'll be back in a couple of hours."

"Be careful."

"Don't worry." He closed his fist around his keys, the toothed metal biting into his palm, digging toward the blood rushing under the skin.

The shambling vagrant in the child's baseball jacket caught Braemer outside the building. As he strode to his car, Braemer felt a tug on his sleeve, looked down, and saw the hunched-over figure loping doglike beside him. The thin face grinned up at him in ecstasy.

"I seen 'em!" the vagrant shouted. "Angel smote the whore!" The blackened fingers plucked at Braemer's elbow. "And—*took* the beast! Chained it in the pit!"

Braemer thrust him away, hard enough to knock the

babbling figure to the sidewalk. "Get the fuck away from me." He could already barely keep his anger inside himself.

Still grinning, the vagrant dug a forefinger into his skinny chest. "I *seen* it! Witness!" The trembling hand flung wide, pointing across the street. "And *he* saw it! He saw the angel chain the beast!"

Braemer glanced across the street in a reflex, and saw a panel truck parked on the other side. He could barely make out, in the darkness inside the truck, a man's face, broad and roughened with age and work, impassively watching the scene on the sidewalk. Their gazes met for a second—the other's eyes seemed like small, sharp points under a hooded brow—before the man inside the truck turned, started the engine and pulled away.

He looked down to the feral leer of the figure crouched in front of him. "Get out of here," said Braemer, his own voice trembling, a wire drawn too tight. "I don't want to see you around here again." He pushed past the vagrant and headed for his car.

The kitchen smelled like fried food. Hamburger or something. Dee ate the dinner that Carol had fixed for her, not tasting it. While she was pushing the last couple of bites around on the plate with her fork, someone knocked at the front door.

Carol came back with two policemen. One's gaze locked onto Jess, slouched against the kitchen door as if standing guard. The other, big freckled arms in the dark blue short sleeves of his uniform, stooped down at the table and talked to Dee. She made little answers that she could barely hear, let alone remember. The other voice whispering in her head was louder.

After the policemen had left, their small mission satisfied, Dee pushed herself away from the table and walked out of the kitchen. Behind her she could hear

Jess getting another beer from the refrigerator, and feel his and Carol's gaze upon her.

"Dee—"

She turned, partway up the stairs, and saw Carol, framed in the doorway, looking up at her. A smile trembled as Carol wiped her hands on her grease-spotted apron. "I . . . I'm glad you're home," she said. "I would've—"

"I know." . . . *yes* . . . The scent of pine was mixed up in the words crooning inside her. *Now you're home* . . . "I'm really sleepy. I'm gonna go to bed."

"Good night."

She heard Carol's words as a fading whisper. The other voice crooned, as though her mother's soft finger were gently tracing the curve of her ear. Little words and murmured phrases, the voice sighing to itself.

Then Dee's hand was on the doorknob, cold brass in her grip, not her room's door but the other one at the end of the hall. The light that never went off spilled across her as she pushed the door open.

She saw her mother, the slight motion of her rasping breath moving the sheet drawn over her. The face—white skin drawn over bone, with the long transparent worm of the feeding tube taped into the nose—stared up at the ceiling.

A field of white suddenly blurred her vision, fluttering at the edges. The ceiling—she was staring up at the ceiling and her eyes wouldn't turn away. Points of fire burned and sang beneath her body, red to white heat with the slow thunder of her pulse. A wire of acid sank deep into her face. She reached to tear the tube away, but her hand remained a knotted claw against the protruding bone of her hip.

Dee lay on the bed with its needle mouths piercing the burning sheets. She watched her mother's frozen writhing as she stood in the room's doorway, hand still

133

clutching the cold brass knob. The figure on the bed merged with the blurred white ceiling, a corpse in an ocean of milk. She saw it, and the other behind her eyes saw it.

Now the voice no longer spoke its soft words inside her head. Now it laughed.

Braemer pulled into the Feld house's driveway, as if on the same errand that had always brought him out here before, and shut off the engine. For a few seconds he sat gripping the wheel, trying to let the night air drain the heat inside himself one notch lower before he went up to the house. Keep it cool, he told himself, stepping out into the rectangle of light from the upstairs window.

Jess met him on the porch. The screen door creaked, then banged shut behind his silhouetted form. A single lamp lit the living room. Braemer thought he could see Carol watching the two of them.

Braemer halted on the top of the steps to the porch. Jess was a couple of inches shorter than he, so that now their eyes met straight across. Jess stood waiting with folded arms across his chest.

"Go get Dee," said Braemer. Even, quietly. "I'm taking her home."

"She's home now," said Jess.

Braemer sighed, tilting his head back as if to see the stars cut off by the porch's overhang. The engine of his anger ticked faster. "Come on, Jess. I'm her father."

"So what." The dark figure grew taller, Jess flexing onto the balls of his feet. "What's that mean."

"Come on, come on." Ticking faster, up a degree of heat inside, the cooling brake slipping away from him. "I don't want to talk, I don't want to argue with you, I don't want anything—except Dee. All right? So why don't you, or Carol, go bring her out here, and we'll leave. And then all this'll get settled later on, the way it's supposed to."

"Fuck off."

Through the screen door behind Jess, he could see a figure moving, Carol heading up the stairs at the end of the room. Dee was probably up in her bedroom, listening to the voices of the adults below her. "Look," he said. "I don't want to go inside, or screw around with you people at all. But if I have to go in there to get her, I will."

"No, you won't." Jess' breath smelled of beer, sharp and warm. "Just get the hell out of here."

It wasn't an engine inside him now. That had melted away in a sudden rush of heat, leaving the fire doubling on itself, feeding into white that spread across his chest and into his arms, eating up any part that might whisper of staying calm. Braemer stepped up onto the porch, one arm brushing Jess aside, his right hand flat on the other's shoulder as his left reached for the screen door's latch. He could feel his own pulse echoing in his tightening chest, and the anger felt good and hard inside him, the best thing he had felt in years.

Jess stepped back from Braemer's arm. He brought both his hands to Braemer's chest, gripping the jacket and shirt, pulling them upward and tearing Braemer's fingers from the screen door.

Braemer looked down at the top of Jess's head, as though the other were sinking into a hole at the edge of his feet. Then he knew that his own feet were no longer touching the porch boards. Then he fell, Jess's hands flinging him away.

His back hit against the post by the steps, his head snapping against the wood. Knees buckling, he slid partway down before his hands could grip the post behind him.

Jess grasped Braemer's shirt again, pulling him upright and slamming him once more into the post. The wood creaked, dry flecks of paint falling onto Braemer's hair. He managed to suck in a breath, a gulp of fire in his lungs, and brought his hands up, reaching across Jess's arms for the face.

Then he was sprawled in the dust at the foot of the porch. His ribs ached from striking the edges of the steps. He rolled onto his back and saw Jess loom over him, his face lit clearer by the light from the upstairs window. It showed his teeth bared in something other than a smile. He knelt down and brought his forearm around Braemer's neck, cradling the throat in the crook of his elbow.

Braemer's fingers scrabbled against Jess's stomach, but the muscles were hard under the shirt, metal softened only by an overlay of skin. The sweat on Jess's arms was sharp, chemical-like, in Braemer's nostrils as Jess brought Braemer's ear up to his mouth.

"That was cute." Jess's whisper rasped like bark torn from a tree. "You're real cute. You little shit."

Another layer of blackness started to slide over the night, blanking out the stars, as Braemer fought for breath, his hands tugging futilely at the lock of Jess's forearm.

"Dee's a pretty little girl," whispered Jess. "Too pretty for you." His fist knotted tighter, drawing the arm harder into Braemer's throat. "I'm not going to let you get your dirty hands on her."

He could feel the spittle of Jess's words, wet against his ear.

"I don't think she's your kid at all. She's too pretty. Whose kid is she? Huh? Whose kid?"

His fingers could no longer feel Jess's arm. There was just the voice crawling into his head. It stopped suddenly, and in the silence his breath swelled back into his chest. He gagged and, free now, turned onto his shoulder, spitting out a string of white saliva into the dust.

"Get out of here."

Braemer, drawing his sleeve across his mouth, looked up at Jess. Jesus Christ, the only thought forming in his mind.

Jess's eyes glittered, picking up the cold edge from the starlight. "Don't come back, either."

Panting, Braemer got to his feet. The Feld house was walled off from him by Jess, a shabby fortress and its dragon. Braemer stepped backward to his car. "All right." The words squeezed out painfully from his chest. "I'm getting her back. Just watch." It sounded like a child's anger in his own ears, the heat inside turned to the scalding salt at the edge of his eyes. "I'll be back."

"Come on back now, motherfucker." Jess's chin jerked upward, his shoulders hunching as his hands spread outward.

Braemer was in the car, fumbling the keys out of his pocket. The headlights swept across the front of the house, then lit Jess stark-white, as he swung the car around, gravel spitting under the wheels, and headed out into the street.

"That's taken care of."

Carol watched Jess walk through the kitchen, open the refrigerator, and pull out another beer. A light sheen of sweat was on his arms, and he paused between gulps to catch his breath.

"Did . . . did you hurt him?" After she had gone upstairs to see that Dee was in her bedroom, where she wouldn't be able to see what happened to her father, Carol had watched from the other room's window. Renee's ragged breathing had sounded an odd accom-

137

paniment to the brief struggle at the front of the house.

"Naw." Jess wiped his mouth with the back of his hand. "Just shook him up a little. That's all." A brooding contempt crossed Jess's face, as if the weight of the beer had settled like dark blood under the skin.

Sometimes Carol was scared of him. Sometimes they were just like real brother and sister, the legal bond of her adoption into the family thickening into almost one of the flesh. Then they were close. She'd cook for him, he'd fix the things that came loose in the house's slow decay. Brother and sister, she thought, watching him sip the beer. It had gotten better after that bitter, sick old woman—his real mother, her adoptive—had finally gone to join the husband whose face she had so methodically scissored out of the family photos and memories.

Sometimes she dreamed of him, the man who'd adopted her—it must've been his idea, his love, not *hers* —but he was faceless in her dreams as well.

But there were other times with Jess, when he seemed a stranger to her. He'd be gone for so long, days at a stretch, and she never knew where. Vague references to going up to Los Angeles, never any talk of what for. And sometimes he'd come back and be different, wouldn't talk at all, would sit brooding in a half-broken lawn chair outside, his mirror-lensed sunglasses on even after the last tint of the sunset had faded away. He wouldn't come into the house without the glasses, complaining that the light gave him headaches. Once, when he'd been like that, well along in a second six-pack, he'd accidentally brushed the glasses from his face, and she had seen his eyes, the whites pink turning to red, as if every small vein in them had torn loose.

And the strength that broke out from his brooding spells into violence—she hadn't been surprised at the way Jess had tossed David around. She'd seen him rip loose from its hinges a door that had dared to become

138

wedged tight on him. Later, when his temper had ebbed, he'd carefully planed the edge of the door down a fraction of an inch and remounted it.

"Do you think he'll be back?" Carol watched Jess standing by the back door, gazing into the dark and idly swirling the last bit of beer around in the can.

"Not likely," he said. "I put the fear of God in him."

Jess went on staring at the night outside, back into the private world where she'd never been able to follow. Renee had always been the one to go there with him, real brother and sister. Little conspiracies and whispers, first as kids, then as adults. Before the stroke that'd left her upstairs in a sleep that fed on itself like a worm coiling into its own blind mouth, Renee had frequently disappeared along with her brother, off into the night and the city, while Carol had stayed here at home with Dee. Any questions about where they went, what they did, had been unanswered. But the same reddened eyes that flinched from the light had begun to show in Renee's face as well.

"Don't worry," said Jess. The thin metal of the empty beer can dented in his fist. "I've got to leave for a while, but I'll be back." He pulled the door open and stepped out to the unlit back porch.

Carol said nothing, watching the darker silhouette of his back. She tried to hear the sound of a child's breathing under the other rasping movement of air that sounded upstairs in the quiet house.

Dee lay in her bed, listening. She knew, without having seen it happen, that her dad had come for her and Jess had made him go away. She'd wanted to run out of her room, past Carol, down the stairs to his car, and go back home with him. But it was better this way; she knew that. If she stayed here, in this house, maybe he wouldn't get hurt. The voice that came inside her, inside her arms and hands, wouldn't be able to do anything to him.

It's better, it's better. She went on trying to think that, lying in the dark with the blanket up to her chin, even when the voice started to laugh inside her and went on laughing without stopping.

He didn't get back on the freeway. When Braemer came to the on-ramp, curving off the street that led back to the silent tract—and his daughter captive like a fairy-tale princess—he saw the bright yellow sign of the coffee shop on the other side of the overpass. The black-lit plastic revolved slowly at the top of its metal post, competing against the streetlights that marked the edge of San Aurelio.

He drove past the ramp, under the freeway, and pulled into the parking lot next to a Peterbilt freight truck with its diesel engine still murmuring softly. The yellow light from the sign bathed his hands on the steering wheel. He didn't want to go back to Los Angeles— not yet. The memory of being tossed away from the house was a stone in his throat that he couldn't swallow. His heart was still racing, the adrenaline of frustration feeding what his anger had triggered. He wanted to be here, breathing the same night air his daughter breathed, just a little longer. Brooding, teasing the wound open with thoughts sharpened by the nearness of his daughter. Inside, he knew the coffee would be bitter on his tongue, darkened with hours of a slow heat.

The truck's driver was at the counter, working through a dripping hamburger. Braemer slid into a booth, and nodded when the waitress came over and asked if he wanted coffee. As soon as the muddy-looking cup was in front of him, he stood up and went over to the pay phone by the men's-room door.

He listened to the phone ringing in his own apartment. He didn't feel like talking to anyone right now, especially Sarah. Mingled shame and anger pulled his tongue back down toward his gut. But the explaining, he knew, would be tougher later than now, after even more hours of her worrying about him. Get it over with, he prodded himself.

"Hello?" Sarah, breathless, catching the phone in the middle of the second ring.

"I didn't get her back." His voice sounded flat and hard in his own ear.

"What happened?"

"Well . . . she's there at the house, but I just couldn't get her. Okay?" The last word spilled out with more anger than he wanted; he drew his breath and held it for a second. "I'll tell you about it when I get home."

"Oh. Is . . . is she all right?"

"I didn't even see her. But I suppose she's okay. Look, I'm going to be a few hours. I'm going to have some coffee and think about stuff for a bit. Okay?"

"What are you going to do?"

"That's all. Just . . . sit for a while."

"All right," said Sarah. "I'll see you when you get here."

At the booth, his coffee had cooled. The cream formed a ragged star on the black surface when he poured it. He stirred it, his eye traveling over the bright plastic menu the waitress had dropped on the table.

A figure slid into the booth across from him. Without looking up, Braemer could see a man's hands, rough-skinned and with dark crescents under the nails of the blunt fingers, come to rest on the top of the table.

He raised his cup and sipped, still looking at the menu. Twice in one day for this kind of thing was asking too much. "Why don't you find another booth?" he said. "I don't feel like talking."

"What you feel like doesn't matter." One of the hands lifted and signaled for the waitress. "You need to listen to me. Coffee, please."

Braemer looked up, his shoulders bending wearily. First that looned-out Kathy, now this. He'd lived in the city long enough to get hit on by Moonies and every other sort of evangelical flower-seller, and had learned to get rid of them before their addled pitches got started. This one didn't look like the usual glassy-eyed twenty-year-old thinned out on cold oatmeal rations and group chanting. Stockier, gray hair cropped over a seamed face, the sleeves of a faded brown workshirt rolled up on coarse-haired forearms, a plastic sheath with several ballpoint pens tucked into one of the pockets. Different eyes, too: points, not wide-eyed glass.

The eyes triggered Braemer's recognition of the face. He had seen this man before—just this evening, parked out in front of his apartment building, watching him shove away the Bible-spouting vagrant that had latched onto him. "You've been following me around," said Braemer, setting his cup down. "Look, I don't know what you want, but whatever it is, you're wasting your time."

"All your time is wasted, Braemer." The other's voice, deep, saddened. "Why don't you just listen?" One large hand folded around the cup set in front of him.

"Great," said Braemer angrily. "Everybody knows my name. I must be on some kind of list. Do they give it to you when they let you people out of the hospital, or what?"

"There isn't enough time for this, Braemer." The points sharpened under the thick brows. "My name's Pedersen."

"So? I never—Wait a minute." The memory of

words in a darkened bar came back to him. "You're the guy . . . the guy that Kathy mentioned. She said you . . . used to know my ex-wife or something."

"I know Renee."

"You do, huh? Well, that's nice. Maybe we can get together and exchange notes sometime." The surprise of the name connecting with Kathy's weird monologue had faded away. "But right now, I've got some more important things to think about. Why don't you just buzz off."

Pedersen studied him in silence for a moment. "Why do you think your daughter tried to kill you, Braemer?"

His own silence filled the space between the two of them. Then: "Look. I don't know how you and Kathy —and God knows who else—are finding out all this stuff. And I don't care. But I don't like people fucking spying on me. I want you, and whoever else is in on this, to knock it off, and get the hell away from me and my kid. Got it?"

The calm expression on the other's face didn't change. "Jess was a lot stronger than you expected, wasn't he?"

"What, you were in the house? Or you were hiding in the bushes, and saw me get thrown on my butt?" From the corner of his eye he saw the waitress glance over at his rising voice, and decided he didn't care any longer. "Good for you. Hire out as a detective. But leave me alone."

A slow sip of coffee. "Did you think Jess was insane," said Pedersen, "when he whispered in your ear about Dee not being your daughter?" He sat back, waiting.

The anger, then the skin over his spine contracted. "How do you know what he said? He told you?"

"Jess is insane. In a way. Everything he said to you was for you only—you know that, don't you?"

143

"He must've told you."

"Jess didn't tell me," said Pedersen. "I heard it right when he whispered it into your ear."

The night surrounded the coffee shop, and its interior of chrome, plastic, and light.

"What do you want?"

"I want to help you," said Pedersen. "And your daughter."

"How can you do that?"

"I know a great deal about you, Braemer. And about your daughter and your ex-wife. And I know what to do about it."

"What?"

"I'm not going to tell you here. In the open, where anybody can hear what we're talking about. You seem to set a great value on your privacy. My place is up in Los Angeles." He pulled one of the pens from the plastic holder in his shirt pocket, scribbled something on the corner of his napkin, then tore it off and handed it across the table. "You can meet me there. You might have trouble finding it, though. It'd be better if you left now and followed me in your car."

I don't have time for this bullshit, Braemer thought. There was too much that had to be taken care of, for him to go chasing around with every lunatic that button-holed him. No matter what they knew, or claimed to know. He glanced at the address scrawled on the scrap of napkin. What could the guy possibly tell him, anyway?

"I can help your daughter. She's in more trouble than you know."

He looked up, and the sharp points caught him. The small world inside the coffee shop receded: another world, darker, came closer. A hollow one, a cave with his daughter somewhere in its depth. And if he stepped across into it to look for her—

144

"There's not much time." Pedersen was standing up, laying some money down on the table. "Follow me, or don't follow me. Whatever you decide." He turned away.

The waitress, coming to pick up the bill and the money, blocked Braemer's sight for a moment. Then he could see Pedersen push through the glass door and out into the parking lot.

The cup trembled in his hands. He watched the dregs shimmering into circles. Then he drew his breath, stood up, and walked, almost breaking into a run as his hand reached for the door.

NINE

Pedersen's panel truck, the same one Braemer had seen parked in front of his apartment building, led him off the Santa Ana Freeway and into one of Los Angeles' industrial districts. Warehouses and loading docks butted up to the railroad tracks that jounced the car's wheels as Braemer drove over them. The Datsun's headlights caught dull sparks off the eyes of guard dogs in the darkness behind the chain-link gates topped with barbed wire. Pedersen drove on, winding the truck from one cross street to another.

He finally stopped, pulling into one of the driveways. Braemer watched as Pedersen got out, leaving the truck's engine running, unlocked the gate, and dragged it rattling aside. On the other side, under a yellow floodlight, a row of cars was parked, some of them up on cement blocks or low metal ramps.

Pedersen got back into the truck and drove it into the only vacant space. "Park it over there," he called to Braemer, pointing to the street curb. "It'll be all right."

Braemer locked the Datsun and walked back up to the

gate. Now he could see that the lettering on the side of the panel truck was the same as that on the painted sheet-metal sign above the building. PACIFIC AUTO RESTORERS. He watched, hands in pockets and shoulders hunched against the chill night air smelling of diesel oil, as Pedersen opened the door marked OFFICE and switched the lights on inside.

"Come on in," said Pedersen.

The office was a desk cluttered with papers—bills, parts lists—shining chrome tools, a ten-key adding machine with a tongue of numbered paper curling to the ground, a Rolls-Royce hubcap filled with cigarette butts. Polaroids of cars, in sad shape and then transformed, taken in front of the building. A Pirelli nude calendar, out of date. Through one of the glass panes that walled the office from the work space, Braemer could see an old Jaguar, no windshield, fenders covered with splotches of primer paint.

Pedersen turned from the coffee maker on a shelf behind the desk, already starting to hiss, and nodded toward a chair. "Have a seat." He went behind the desk and lowered his bulk, the swivel chair creaking as he leaned back into it.

Braemer glanced around the small space. "Why don't you just tell me . . . whatever it is you've got to say."

"It'll take a bit. Sit down." Pedersen's hands folded on his stomach as he watched Braemer drag the other chair up to the desk. "Kathy talked to you. What did she tell you about me?"

"I thought you were the one with the big mind-reading act."

"I do know what she told you. But I don't know what you remember of it."

Braemer shrugged. "Something about . . . some kind of a group. That you lead, or teach, or whatever. I didn't pay much attention. She looked pretty screwed

147

up. Strung out on something. That's about it.''

Pedersen nodded, looking away to the dark sections of the shop. ''Some things, Braemer, don't have a name. Types of knowledge. They're either just known, or unknown. And if they're unknown, for those people those things don't exist. So if I tell you things that you've never heard of, that doesn't mean they don't exist, haven't existed for thousands of years.''

''Like what?''

Pedersen's voice fell in pitch, as though climbing from some hollow space inside him. ''The things that we study here—the things that I have come to know and that the people come to me to find out—deal with the soul. A substance so fine that it cannot be detected. And the . . . *preservation* of that substance. Against death.''

Braemer shook his head, eyes closed. He'd been afraid it would be something like this. ''Well. Good for you. I don't see what that's got to do with me.''

Pedersen reached over to the coffeepot and poured into two cups on the desk. He pushed one toward Braemer. ''Your child is in danger,'' he said. ''There is an evil inside her. One that I helped to bring into being. That's why I sought you out. To make amends for my own sins.''

The coffee tasted thick and bitter. ''I don't know what the hell you're talking about.''

''The child's mother is alive.''

''Yeah, I suppose so, if you want to call that being alive. Alive as any other vegetable.''

''She lives inside your daughter,'' said Pedersen. An undercurrent of clenched anger darkened his words.

Braemer sighed. ''Look. Just tell me what you want. Okay? I really don't have a lot of time for this.''

Pedersen's gaze locked on him. ''You have hardly any time at all. Your ex-wife has gone too far on the *via sinistra* for you to delay any longer what you must do.''

"On the what? I didn't catch that."

The level gaze shifted to a point in space beyond Braemer. "The left-hand path,'.' murmured Pedersen. "I should have known when Renee first came to me . . . She and her brother Jess had the teeth of animals, to sink into something and not let go of it. Hunger that could never be sated. But I thought the animal in them could be tamed. The two of them had qualities that made them . . . *proficient* at the study. But the other parts were weak inside them. The temptations of the shorter way were too much for them. I should have seen that."

"What the fuck are you talking about?" Braemer's irritation began to leak out.

Pedersen looked back at him. "Renee studied with me. Jess found me and then later brought Renee into the group. After her divorce from you. That was the root of the evil that has come inside your daughter."

Braemer studied him across the desk, a face that age and sadness had lined, now set with rage that flickered barely visible, like electricity in air heavy with clouds. This wasn't the usual high-pitched weirdness, saffron robes and finger cymbals, that you ran into on street corners. Wide-eyed messiahs and the TV gospel in shining three-piece suits—all the stuff that one ignored every day, dimly aware of loose cogs spiraling away into their little Jonestowns and ashrams. If this guy Pedersen was cracked, the pieces were at least holding together in an appearance of sanity. Even if Braemer didn't buy any of the spiel, the impulse to stalk out of the building, get in the car, and drive had passed, replaced by something more than curiosity. "All right," he said. "Lay it on me. What happened?"

Pedersen leaned back and gazed at the ceiling. "The soul," he said slowly, as though searching for the words to translate from another language, "as it is found in man, is a very finely divided substance. It's like a cloud of light, small particles swarming about. Nothing solid and permanent about it, just as in most people there is nothing permanent in the personality that reflects the soul. Most people are this way or that way, happy or sad, angry or calm, the world's circumstances blowing them about like the wind to a cloud of gnats. The physical body contains the elements of the soul, like a jar holding a swarm of insects. When the body dies, the container is broken, the elements disperse into nothing. The dispersing is the true death. The soul is scattered, each particle drifting into the darkness. Then the person is no more."

Braemer shrugged. "I've heard stuff like this before."

"I dare say you have. This awareness of the soul's nature has been perceived in many places, many epochs. It is no secret. What is kept hidden is the knowledge of what to do about this condition, the technologies—spiritual and psychological exercises—that one can use to, in a sense, *crystallize* the soul and preserve it from dispersing at the moment of death."

"And that's what Renee and Jess hooked up with you for?"

"The diamond body. It can be created inside one. The way is possible. But there is more than one kind of permanence that the soul can achieve." Pedersen's voice went lower, brooding. "The immortality of light and air—and that of the dark earth. One path is long; it takes all of one's life to follow it, and only culminates at the moment of physical death. Then the soul becomes transparent and crystalline, and lives. The other path—the *via sinistra*—is quicker, but darkness is at the end of it. One's soul achieves permanence, but that of cold stone, heavy, sinking to the earth's core. Away from the light. And for those who follow that path, the damage begins long before the end is reached. The personality becomes deranged, vicious. The methods of the *via sinistra* are cruel. Pain, one's own and others', heightened by certain drugs. A food is produced from the soul; consumed, it accelerates the process of crystallization. . . ." He fell silent, one corner of his mouth curling at a sight held inside himself. Then he glanced up at Braemer. "This is what has happened to Renee. She followed the left-hand path."

The vehemence clenched in the other's jaws transfixed Braemer. Beyond the pool of light falling around the desk, he could sense the quiet building and the reaches of night past its walls. He drew back from Pedersen's gaze as though from the edge of a cliff. "Maybe you don't know it," he said carefully, "but my ex-wife's been in a coma for over a year now."

Pedersen focused on him, away from his own internal vision. "I know that. I know—and see—a great deal of what happens to Renee, and to Jess. They studied with me for two years. The natural abilities they possess, which made the work I teach so easy for them, also made possible a channel between their thoughts and my own. Moments when they are excited or aroused—then the connection becomes stronger, I see what they see, hear what they hear. The words from Jess's mouth—that's how I knew what he said to you tonight. That's how I've traced—and dispersed—the members of my group who followed him after I had discerned that he had embarked on the *via sinistra*. Lost to the light. The same with Renee's thoughts. I know the thing that she's become, and what happened to her. Out in the forest, with the frightened child. The drugs that Jess taught Renee to use—amphetamine sulfate combined with a German industrial solvent that acts to alter the synaptic gaps in the central nervous system—the overdose that she used in her suicide attempt caused the stroke and brain damage that put her in a coma. I saw it. I felt the blood bursting in her skull."

"Suicide?" Braemer peered at him.

"Her thoughts were so confused by that point I couldn't make out the reason. Perhaps a last flash of contrition for what she had tried to do to her own child. Perhaps despair at having come so close to what she'd thought was necessary to complete the *via sinistra*—the sacrifice of the innocent—only to have the lamb escape. Even now, when her thoughts come to me, that segment of the past remains clouded."

Braemer set his cup down, as he watched the other's eyes for the spark of insanity that would allow him to get up and walk without hearing any more. "But she's gone now," he said. "In a coma. There's no mind there for you to . . . pick up, or whatever."

"Something remains, Braemer. The dark soul that Renee created for herself with the left-hand path survived. The process was essentially complete when she triggered the stroke that put her into the coma. The soul is separate from the brain, and hers is still living, undispersed, inside her. And that's the source of the evil touching your daughter."

Get up, thought Braemer, and get out of here right now. This is just craziness talking. A small current etched under the skin of his arms with the thought below that one. Because what if it's not crazy, what if it's true? Then the deep shit starts here, whatever it is, and all the shrinks and lawyers in the world aren't going to help your kid now. He gripped the arms of the chair, felt the sweat between his palms and the wood.

"All right," he said. "How's this affect Dee?"

"Your ex-wife's soul," said Pedersen slowly, "is in the undispersed state it would have been in had she died. Yet because of her body being alive, that soul still exists here, in the sphere of the living. The soul is sick, twisted

152

—it wants to go on living in this world, beyond the day when the comatose body that houses it will eventually die. And the soul can do that, by penetrating and taking over the minds and bodies of those closest to her, those related to her by blood. Renee's soul has become like a virus that can travel over the link of a common blood and take over anyone related closely enough to her. You've seen Renee's sister Kathy-the pain and degradation she's undergone was at the hands of her brother, Jess. He body submits to it because of Renee taking control of her."

"She told me that," murmured Braemer. All the little pieces, with their own logic, were falling together. "She said her sister was still alive. That she was like a voice that came inside of her."

"That's right. I've seen some of the things that Jess, still following the left-hand path, has done to Kathy—fragments of what Renee sees through Kathy's eyes while inside her. And I've seen things through your daughter's eyes, too. Things that happened while Renee's soul had taken her over. I saw, from inside Dee, her hand stab the apron and the wall, and then later try to put the knife into your chest. Renee's soul has become so deranged that it seeks to destroy anything it can't control. And it fears your having contact with Dee. It's afraid that you'll find out what's happening to your daughter and find a way to end it."

"Wait a minute. Hold it. What about Carol? How come Renee doesn't take her over, or whatever you say happens."

"You forget, Carol was adopted into the Feld family. There is no blood relationship between her and Renee."

Braemer shook his head. "I don't know. This is . . . Look, I don't even know what you're talking about. You've got this explanation all built up, and you know all this stuff about what's happened. Maybe it's true,

153

maybe not. But even if I believe it—and I don't, I don't even know what I'm doing here—what am I supposed to do about it?"

"Her power grows stronger," said Pedersen. The anger inside him seemed even more tightly gripped, to keep his words from lashing across Braemer's face. "Every day a little more. First inside Kathy, now also inside Dee, out of her own body—then back again when her strength fades. But stronger the next time, and the time after that. Until she won't have to leave your daughter's body. A sort of immortality, the corpse inside the living child. From a ruined body to a young one, a child's—your child, Braemer." Pedersen pushed his chair back from the desk and pulled open the center drawer. He took out something wrapped in a white cloth and held it out.

As Braemer took it, he could tell, from the weight of the object and coldness of the metal though the cloth, what it was. The only weapon he'd ever held before had been a rust-specked .22 rifle which he and a cousin had plinked at cans and bottles with, years and years ago, when he'd been not much older than Dee was now. He set the weight on the desk and unfolded the cloth. On a bed of white lay blue-black metal gleaming with a skin of oil. An emblem of a dancing horse stamped in the metal above the crosshatched grip. He'd seen that emblem before but didn't know what it meant, what manufacturer it identified.

A bright yellow box, the sound of small metal rattling inside, fell beside the gun. "Those are hollow-points," said Pedersen. "They'll do the job. You should aim for the head."

Braemer touched the gun with one finger and felt the warmth of his blood drain away, as if the steel chill had bitten through his skin. A moment ago he'd been sitting in a room with no gun in it. Now everything revolved, transformed, around the object swallowing the room's space and light into itself. He looked up at Pedersen. "What are you talking about?" Part of him already knew.

"Renee's soul is still rooted in her body. She can reach out to your daughter's and take it over for a time, but she hasn't yet completed the process of transferring herself totally into Dee. I don't know how long that will take, but it will happen soon. Perhaps even within a few days' time. When that happens, your daughter's own personality will disappear, devoured by that of her mother. There will be only Renee looking out through Dee's eyes."

The gun sitting on the desk had taken everything up a notch. Braemer looked at the light glinting off the cylinder. Everything was serious now. You could play *what if* up until then: what if all this crazy talk were true, wouldn't that be wild? Sure is fun listening to lunatics talk—takes your mind right off all those boring psychiatrists and lawyers, all that stuff. You can sit in a room drinking coffee in the middle of the night and just be entertained. Then the gun drops in front of you, and the fun is over.

He brought his gaze up to Pedersen again. "You really believe all this stuff, don't you?"

Pedersen sat without moving. "You believe it, too, Braemer," he said quietly.

"That's where you're wrong." He gripped the chair's arms and started to stand up.

"Take the gun, Braemer. You know what you have to do."

"You bet. That's a hot idea, all right." He stood glaring down at Pedersen. "You want me to go plug my ex-wife, and then I'd get carted off to prison for it. Or

155

the hatch, more likely. That's just great. Even if I bought all this crap, and went and did it, who'd look after my kid while I'm locked up?"

"There's people who'd care for her. You know that. Carol would. And having her father in prison would be better than what will happen if you don't do it." He shrugged his wide shoulders. "Beyond that, the gun couldn't be traced to you. There's a chance, if you're clever enough, that nothing could be proved."

"Look, you're so hot on shooting women in comas, go do it yourself."

"The fate of your child is your responsibility, Braemer. Mine is guiding the people who depend upon me for that. I can't risk abandoning them by becoming involved in what the law would call a murder. This evil was brought about by Jess and Renee going beyond the limits where I could advise them. More evil might follow if I let that happen again."

"That's very convenient for you."

"I've done what I can," said Pedersen. "Take the gun."

Braemer picked it up, balancing the weight on his palm. If the things that Pedersen told him were true, then this was the answer. As simple as that. He could picture himself in the upstairs bedroom where Renee lay, the Feld house quiet all around them. Standing by the bed, looking down at the emaciated body, the short-cropped hair above the bone-and-skin face.

Raising the gun, both hands folded over the grip to aim. . . .

Then the trigger inching back under his finger, the cylinder rotating, bringing the bullet into the gun's precise mechanism.

Silence all around, outside the house silence, in the empty streets silence, and in the skeletal houses.

Then the nonsilence breaking, echoing from his fists

156

locked together, brief fire streaming down into the face on the pillow.

Yes. His whispered thought was salt in his mouth. Do it, you know it's true. Do it. Take the gun and—

His eyes were squeezed shut. He opened them and for a moment saw around himself, not Pedersen's office, but another room, one that he'd left behind him in the past, though it had never left from inside him. A room with a drafting table thrown over on its side and broken pens scattered across the floor. In the middle of the fragmented drawing tools lay an emaciated woman's body, Renee staring upward through a spatter of blood across her face. The gun trembled in his hands, still aimed at her.

Then that room faded into the one in which he held the gun pointed across the desk at Pedersen's chest.

Pedersen sat looking at him. "You don't have much time," he said.

The weight lowered Braemer's arms. He cradled the gun at his stomach for a moment, then slipped it into his jacket pocket. His hand reached to the desk, picked up the yellow box and the cloth, and stuffed them alongside the gun.

In the night air, walking to his car, he felt the weight of the metal brushing through cloth against his hip. It drew him downward, into the currents he could feel running unseen in the earth. The madness had been outside him before. Now he knew it was inside him as well. He had bought into it, swallowed it whole.

Now I know how Dee feels. To see your hands doing something you don't even want them to, and you just watch.

Pedersen gripped the chrome sill and leaned in the car window as Braemer fumbled the key into the ignition. "I'm sorry," he said. "Some things have to be done, is all. I wouldn't put this on you if it was otherwise."

The engine coughed into life. "I guess not," said Braemer. Automatically, he wondered how he could get back to the freeway, and to home. He couldn't see the unlit end of the street in front of him. He watched Pedersen circle in front of the car and head back to the building behind the chain-link gates.

Then he drove.

Sarah was waiting up for him when he got back to the apartment. Lights on, the TV murmuring ignored in the corner. When she heard Dave's key in the lock, she ran to the door and hugged him as he came in, the loose sleeves of her terrycloth robe gathering in folds behind him.

"I was so worried about you." She lifted her face from his chest and looked up at him. "What happened? Are you all right?"

His hands held her shoulders. "I'm fine. Tired, is all."

That was easy to see. The lids of his eyes were dark, hooded as if the fatigue were accumulating in the blood there. She could feel the tremor in his hands, through the robe and into her arms. "You don't want any coffee, do you? I mean, there's a pot on, but if you've been drinking it all night—"

"A little," he said. "While we talk."

They sat in the kitchen, Dave hunched over his folded arms and looking down into the cup as he spoke. She listened, pulling the robe tighter around herself.

There wasn't much for him to tell—just the drive down there and getting roughed up by Jess. "And then you just sat down there all this time?" Hours and hours of waiting, after he'd called from the coffee shop.

He nodded. "Drove around a little. Just thinking. I didn't want to come back here yet. It's . . . a little embarrassing, I guess. I go chasing down there, you know,

158

and get my ass handed to me. And after the way he pushed you around. . . ."

"It's okay." She touched his hand. "I mean, we'll get her back. We've got the lawyer and all, and we know where she is. It'll be all right."

"I suppose so."

"Did you think of anything else? About what to do?"

He looked to the window, where she couldn't see his eyes. "No," he said. "Not really."

"What do you want to do now?"

"Get some sleep."

In bed, she watched him as he lay on his back. With just the streetlight outside, she could see that his eyes were closed, but she knew that he wasn't asleep. She closed her own eyes and laid her head against his arm, waiting for the morning to bring light into the room.

She was waiting for him. She was always waiting for him, curled in the nest of fouled blankets and gray mattress on the cracked linoleum floor. The sound of the key in the door's lock brought her eyes wide in the darkness. Nerves not yet deadened to pain drew her muscles tighter, trying to contract into nothing and disappear.

Her body did that, its involuntary flight into itself, away from the sound of the door swinging open, then shut again. Her mind—her own, without her sister's voice crawling into it and then down into her arms and legs—kept her lying on the mattress, waiting and listening as the footsteps came closer and stopped beside her. The point of one of his shoes dug into her ribs.

"Hello, Kathy." The smile was in his voice. He could tell when it was her, and not Renee, that he was talking to.

She turned on her shoulder and looked up into her brother's face. No hallucination: she knew now that it was Jess, had always been Jess. His hands at her body, his voice in the room and all the other rooms he had taken her to, where other hands had waited to touch her. Even before the last haze of drugs had ebbed out of her bloodstream, a clearness beyond the post-toxic exhaustion had filled her, ordered her own thoughts. Then she'd known that what she'd hoped was delusion, part of the madness in which she sank, was true. The face and voice behind the mirror lenses were her brother's face and voice.

It comforted her to know that. No hallucination. This was true. Her only regret was that now there wasn't time to find Braemer again, to warn him about Jess. When she'd talked to him in the bar, she'd still been confused about what was real and what wasn't. Now she knew. If there was only time enough left, but that was also something she knew. Hardly any time left at all.

Jess started taking off his shirt. She watched, seeing things about him that had been lost in the darkness before. He was more muscular than she remembered him as a kid. The coiled masses were sharply defined under the pale skin. He looked pleased with himself as he drew the sleeves from his arms, as if something especially satisfying had happened this night.

He lay down beside her and took her in his arms, his breath against her face. This time there weren't any little rituals that ended with the point of the needle probing her scarred veins. She was grateful for that. Maybe he knows, she thought. It was so clear now. She wanted nothing to blur it.

His hands moved over the marked skin, the layer of flesh over the sharp-pointed bones. Where he pressed the fire echoed into her spine. His face was full into hers, smiling. His hand reached down and opened her, but before he was inside her, she said, "Why?"

The calmness of her voice seemed to startle him. He drew back a little, the hair on his chest springing where it had been pressed flat by his weight against her. "Why what?" he asked.

"I know what *she* wants. But what do you want?" She stroked his arm.

He looked at her, and for a moment he was the way she remembered him from a long time ago, when he'd just been her brother. "You almost understand," he said softly. "Don't you?"

She nodded. "Almost. Tell me before she comes back inside me."

The smile again. "Then you'd know more than she does. Wouldn't that be funny?"

"Tell me why. Hurry." She knew that if Renee's voice came into her now, there wouldn't be another time when Jess could tell her why he had done all that he had to her.

His hand was warm on her cheek, gentle. "How else could I have gone on loving her, after what happened to her, the coma and all—except through you?"

"I knew that," she murmured, closing her eyes. She'd known it from the beginning. "But the rest . . ."

"The rest? She has something that I want. That's all. She managed to do something that I haven't. Her soul is like . . . a crystal now. Hard, a diamond. She won't ever die now—her soul won't. But through you I can impose my will on hers. The pain you feel is hers, the breaking of your mind is my grip on hers. I can become her, become that thing that she's become. Then I won't die. You see? She's consumed your soul, but she doesn't know that I have my teeth in hers. Then she'll be gone, and there'll be just me, moving inside you, inside her daughter. There'll just be me—forever."

"Just you." She let herself fall back against the dirty mattress, muscles loose and without will. He could do anything now, everything he'd already done and more. Now that she knew why. All she wanted.

He held her as he had before, as though brother and sister were all they were, his warmth passing into her thin blood. At the same time he seemed miles away, falling into the expanding room. There wasn't much time left. The clearness that had come over everything, the room and her thoughts, was the clarity of ice. A spot of cold, which grew bigger with every breath, had centered beneath her ribs. She recognized it, even though she had never felt it before. All the small deaths of her flesh had been the forerunners.

This is something, she thought, feeling the warmth of his body, the cold of her own, that even he doesn't know yet.

DREAM HOUSE

The last hours of the night. She could tell by the thin gray light at the edge of the black. Dee lay in bed, awake now, face turned to one side on the pillow, watching each dark shape, black against black, grow clearer. The leaves on the tree branch crossing near her window brushed against the screen, a whisper against the rusting mesh. She listened, but that was all she could hear; the silence of the house was folded as deep as heavy cloth against the bedroom door.

Curled in the bed, hugging her own ball of warmth to herself. If she stuck her feet down farther into the covers, the cold would grip her bare ankles like a pair of hands (whose? but she knew) tightening skin against bone until the blood stopped and chilled to the same temperature. Better to stay small, knees up in the flannel nightgown, arms wrapped around, sheltering the heartbeat racing inside. If it would get light, become day, she could wait for her daddy somehow to come get her, the fear swallowed up in the sun's warmth and his arms.

Quiet, so quiet that if she did nothing, kept her breath warming the sheet drawn against her mouth, then nothing, no other voice would be able to find her and come inside her. She listened, and waited and watched in the dark.

Someone spoke her name.

She tensed, knees drawing tighter.

"Dee—" Not in the room with her, or in the hall outside the door. So quiet that she could hear the whisper downstairs in the kitchen.

Again, a tiny sound, like a leaf against the screen, the wind tugging the branch. But it was in the house, below her.

A knot uncoiled as she listened, her knees drawing away from her chest. Maybe it was him, her daddy, in the house. He could've sneaked in when Jess wasn't around and Carol was asleep, and now he wanted her to come downstairs. Downstairs, and then outside in the dark, then they would ride in his car, anywhere at all, away from here.

(Go away, please go away, please—)

Her own voice inside of her, begging in silence, because she was afraid for him. Everything was silent now, but when the other voice came inside her . . .

(Don't go, come get me, don't let her—)

Because she was scared.

Dee slid her legs out from under the covers, bare feet touching the carpet. The nightgown's hem brushed the goose-pimply skin above her knees as she stood up. She knew her way in the dark to the room's door.

Light tinted the hallway, coming up from the bottom of the stairs. She passed by Carol's door and her mother's, with its bright edge seeping out from beneath, then stood holding the smooth wooden ball at the top of the rail.

The light came from the kitchen, spilling across the

bottom steps. She waited, hoping to hear her name spoken again, but all stayed silent. Holding on to the rail with both hands, she edged one bare foot down.

When she was all but the last couple of steps away from the kitchen door, she leaned forward as far as she could, but saw no one.

(Go away, don't go—)

The other wooden ball, the one at the bottom of the rail, filled her hands, and for a moment she couldn't let go of it. The silent darkness filled the rooms above her, flowed down the stairs, a wave against her back that tugged her hands free. She caught herself from falling, reached and grasped the edge of the kitchen door frame, pulled herself into the light.

It was so bright inside the kitchen that her eyes watered and she couldn't see.

"Daddy?" There was someone sitting at the table, hands folded next to something that glinted all shiny.

The light cleared from her eyes.

Across the table and the empty kitchen, Dee's mother smiled at her.

He was in the house, the gun in his hand. When Braemer had gone back to the apartment he'd left the gun, carefully wrapped in the white cloth, tucked under the spare tire in the Datsun's trunk, so Sarah wouldn't see it. And it would be ready when he went back down to San Aurelio and the Feld house.

Now he was here, standing in the middle of the living room, all the lights in the house off except for the one upstairs that was always on. By that trace he could make out the room's familiar contents, the fading couch and chairs, the framed photo on the mantel with the picture cut in half, the stairway slanting across the end of the room. He walked toward the stairs, threading his way through the furniture, the crocheted doilies on the arms

164

of the chairs like dim white growths on rain-softened logs. The gun's weight dragging in his hand brushed against the threadbare upholstery.

He couldn't remember driving down here. It was as if he'd stepped from his own bed, Sarah asleep on her half, into this room, all spaces running together in the quiet and dark.

His free hand gripped the rail as he peered upward. The light seeping from under the bedroom door outlined the top steps, shading the ones below it. He listened but could hear nothing, not even the slow, rasping of air past Renee's cracked lips, the small sound that had always whispered behind every word he'd spoken or heard in this house. It was as if she knew he was down here, the gun in his hand, and was holding her breath, trying to hide from him.

He mounted the first step, then the next, climbing toward the faint light. Each footstep slow and careful, silent so as not to wake the others in the house. The silence would end soon enough, and then there wouldn't be any more sleeping.

Carol knew she was dreaming. She opened her eyes, and in the darkness of her bedroom there was something leaning over her. It was her father, the one who'd adopted her. She knew it was him—knew she was dreaming, and didn't care.

She raised her head from the pillow, but before she could say anything he touched one of his fingers to her lips, shushing her. "We don't want any of the others to know," he whispered. "Do we?"

She shook her head. Too dark to see his face; there was just the outline of his head and broad shoulders against the moonlit window. Even as he bent over her, she could see he was a tall man. She'd always wondered how big he'd been. Now it looked as if he could lift her

165

easily out of bed in his arms like a child.

"Come on," he said. Voice low, conspiratorial. "You didn't look everywhere yet."

His words made her think of an Easter-egg hunt, one she could barely call from memory, when she'd been too small—three years old?—to find every egg that had been hidden. She could remember riding on someone's shoulder—his?—to look in the crook of a tree branch, and a large hand drawing back the shading leaves just enough to show the bright red egg nestled against the bark.

"For what?" Her whisper hung in the room's still air. "Look where?"

But he was already stepping back from the bed, holding his hand out to her. "Come on." Inviting her.

She was afraid that, if she slid out from under the blanket, the dream would end. She would wake up in the bed's narrow limits, in an empty room in a house with a half-dead sister down the hallway (he didn't come back for her, he came back for me; that thought turned warm inside her) and a stolen niece in another room. She didn't want to wake up back there. She wanted to stay here, leaning her head against her father's strong arm all the long night. (My real father, he's the one who wanted me.)

But he was already at the room's doorway, beckoning to her. The hallway beyond him was even darker. She still couldn't see his face.

The floor was cold under her bare feet as she flung the blankets away. She ran after him, the dream's rooms unwavering.

His hand caught hers, the big, coarse-skinned fingers folding over hers and pulling her through the unlit hallway. "Where are we going?" asked Carol, breathless.

"Shh. You'll wake everybody up."

Even in a dream, she didn't want that to happen. This was something private, for her only. She didn't want to share it with her sister or Dee or anyone. He'd come for her alone.

He led her down the stairs, her bare feet padding behind him on the steps, and into the kitchen. He pushed open the back door, and they stepped out into a starless night.

The wind fluttered her nightgown around her ankles. She pressed close to his side and looked up at his dark silhouette. "What's out here?"

Silently, he stepped over to the cellar doors slanting at the base of the house. The lock opened in his hand without a click. He pulled the doors open, carefully laying them down in the tall, dew-wet grass. "Come on."

She followed him down the open plank steps, the cellar's musty air rising to her nostrils. She could see just a little, enough to make out the water heater, the pipes beneath the house's flooring, stacked cardboard boxes crumpling from damp and their own weight, a bicycle with one wheel missing, a barbecue filled with gray ash beneath the stamped-metal dome. Her father's back threaded its way through the clutter.

She was disappointed when he stopped and knelt by the old trunk with its frayed leather straps. There were no secrets about what was inside it. Carol had packed it herself, after her mother—or at least the old lady who had years ago gone along with adopting her—had died. All the old woman's stuff—mostly clothes and a few odds and ends, sachets whose scent had faded a long time ago, a sewing kit missing needles and thimble— had been put away in this trunk and a couple of old suitcases. It had been easier to stow it all down here than sort through it, trying to decide what, if anything, had any value. In the cellar the old woman's stuff could fade from memory, and rust and mildew until it could all be thrown away someday, with no regrets from anyone.

Her heart sank even more when her father lifted out the old photo albums with the tarnished gilt lettering on front. She knew what he was looking for, knew that he wouldn't find anything there. Just the mutilated photographs, yellow and curling against the stiff black pages, with every trace of his existence torn or scissored out. Carol had gone through the albums so many times as a kid, looking for even one photo that had escaped somehow, that she'd overlooked before, and now could recognize: one photo that would show her father's face. Something to give a form to all the vague memories— touches of his hand, riding on his shoulder—that had been laid down before he'd died and taken his face into the dark where she'd never been able to see it.

"But I did look there," she said. "I looked and looked."

He turned toward her, face still hidden by the dark, holding the photo album up to her. One of his fingernails dug under the corner of the inside cover, peeling the lining away from the cardboard layer beneath.

She could see something there, white against black, shifting as the lining gave way with a small tearing noise. She knelt down beside her father, watching to see what was revealed.

Her mother's smile was the way she remembered it from a long time ago. Dee stood in the kitchen doorway, looking at the face more familiar to her than the one that had grown onto the sleeping corpse upstairs.

"Hello, Dee." Gentle voice, hinting at the little secrets between them, mother and daughter. "Come sit by me."

She felt her fingers letting go of the door frame. The house's darkness pressed at her back, pushing her into the circle of light in front of her. A few steps across the cold kitchen floor and then she was in the chair across the table's corner from her mother, her own legs tucked up under herself. The shiny thing, a knife with its glittering blade, lay on the table.

Her mother's hand reached out and smoothed the hair from Dee's brow. "It's not so bad, is it?" A whisper, leaning close. "To be with me? I've wanted to be with you for so long. But I couldn't."

"You're asleep," murmured Dee. "Upstairs. You're always asleep." The softness of her mother's fingertips on her brow lulled her, a white feather traced across the skin.

"But that's not me, honey. You know that. Don't you? That's someone else. And you know she's not really asleep—don't you?"

"But . . . they said it was you." Her brow furrowed in puzzlement, the skin tightening under her mother's light stroking. "And—and that voice inside and everything . . ."

"It's not me, honey. That's not me. I'm right here. Right now. And you're with me, aren't you?"

"Yes." Her eyelids felt like closing, her head nodding into sleep curled against a warm arm folding around her.

"Don't fall asleep, sweetheart. There's something you have to do, isn't there?"

"What?" Her eyelids tugged themselves open again, and she looked into the dark space at the centers of her mother's eyes.

"You know." Her mother glanced down at the knife, then back to Dee's face. The conspiracy between them grew deeper.

"Oh . . . But—"

"You have to, honey. It hurts too much. You have to."

Silent, Dee nodded and reached for the knife. Her hand found nothing on the table.

"Get one out of the drawer. You know where they are."

She knew, from all the nights she had slipped out of bed, padded down in the dark, and stolen one of Carol's kitchen knives to hide under her pillow. She went to the drawer, reached in, and took out the biggest knife. Its blade glittered like the one on the table had.

"Go on, honey. Then we can be together all the time, you daddy and me and you—just the way it was. And she won't be there."

From the light-filled kitchen to the dark staircase, she walked slowly, bearing the knife in front of herself. Then up step by step, to the room where her mother lay. The other one.

Braemer stood outside the bedroom door. The light spilled from under its edge onto his shoes. The house's deep quiet was in the room on the other side of the door as well, but he knew she was in there, waiting for him.

In his hand the gun dragged toward the floor, a still pendulum. It would take both hands to lift it and aim, both hands squeezing its fire into the open.

The door swung away under his free hand. With the light full upon him, he stepped into the center of the room and halted, a few feet from the bed and the figure upon it. The sheet was pulled up to the edge of the dark hair.

The gun rose; suddenly weightless in his hands. Between him and the bed, the glint of oil on dark metal blotted out everything.

Carol looked up from the old photo album in her father's hands and into the black silhouette of his face.

Around them the narrow spaces of the basement circled, like the coils of a protective maze.

"Thank you," she whispered. The darkness shimmered in the tears welling in her eyes. "Now I know."

Each of them the same, in the same night's quiet and dark, separated by the walls of their dreaming, the motions of ghosts who cannot see each other.

Everything went faster and faster, as though she were watching one of those old, funny movies with no sound. Dee pushed the door open and strode through the room, lifting the knife above her head as the bed seemed to rush toward her.

At the edge of the mattress, the sheet dangling against her legs, Dee stood for a second looking down at her mother's emaciated face, clenched from beneath, a bubble of saliva trembling on the dry lips, the feeding tube snaking under the strips of surgical tape and into the nose. Then she stretched on tiptoe to raise the knife even higher, her arms aching with the strength to plunge it downward.

Then everything stopped. It was as if she weren't holding the knife up but hanging from its grip, dangling, her feet barely touching the floor. Slowly the knife inched downward, the point of the blade turning away from the figure on the bed. Her hands followed without will as her elbows bent, bringing the shining metal toward her own chest.

The point touched Dee's nightgown, pressed harder, cutting through the fabric's threads. She stepped backward, looking down at the knife in her own hands, the cold dot against her skin growing larger, turning warm from the blood beneath.

She heard the laughing then.

Her sight jerked away from the knife to the bed. The figure on it stirred, the sheet falling away.

Laughing, her mother sat up. Not the one downstairs in the kitchen, the one she remembered from a long time ago. This was the other one, the fleshed skeleton that had become her mother.

It laughed without stopping. The laughing filled the room, the air beating against the walls like fists.

The mother leaned forward, kneeling on the mattress, hands gripping the mattress edge in excitement. Breastless, spider-leg ribs arching over the carved pit of the stomach. The feeding tube across the face tore loose as the mouth opened wide over the yellow teeth, laughing.

Her legs gave way beneath her and Dee fell backward. The knife in her hands followed, digging into the flesh below her throat.

The laughing swallowed her in its own dark, smelling of pine and forest wetness, as she fell and kept falling.

The gun rumbled in Braemer's fists, the sound and bullet pouring from it in time slowed to freezing.

He felt the air grow solid, filled with the gun's roar. For a moment, his heart surging in his chest, that was all. Then a red flower leaped into blossom in the midst of the white sheet on the bed.

He stepped toward the bed and the figure on it. Blood welled and pasted the sheet to its ribs. His hand reached for the edge of the spattered cloth and pulled it down.

The face, eyes widened at him, blood seeping through the clenched teeth, was Dee.

She woke up, eyes flying wide open in the darkness of her own bedroom. Dee's breath was a fist inside her throat, a scream too big to squeeze through.

Closer to dawn now. There was enough gray light filtering through the curtains for Dee to make out the stitched patterns of the crumpled bedcover, the little table beside her, the other things that belonged in the room. She reached out and switched on the lamp.

Her eyes scanned everything that the circle of light reached. Nothing was out of place. She was all alone behind the closed door.

Something bright glinted on the floor.

Dee pushed the blankets away, crawled to the foot of the bed, and looked.

A kitchen knife lay on the carpet.

Her hand dug under the collar of her nightgown, reached in, and touched. When she pulled her hand out, a tiny dot of blood was smeared across the tip of her finger.

He stared at the dark ceiling of the apartment's bedroom, heart racing in his chest. Relief filled him, that the dream was over. He wasn't in the Feld house, climbing stairs in the stifling quiet, aiming the gun in the room where his ex-wife was kept. He was right here, lying next to Sarah, a trace of the morning in the window outlining her in dull silver.

The gun was still out in the car where he'd left it. Braemer's hands ached from the straining grip he'd had on it in the dream. He flexed them under the blanket, working the blood back into the fingers.

He closed his eyes, but he knew that any more sleep would be a long time in coming. That one was over, but the one he'd woken into was still all around him.

Carol thought she was in her bed, shoulder up against the wall behind the pillow. She opened her eyes, awake now, the dream's warmth drained away from her.

She saw that she wasn't in her own room. For a few seconds she gazed, puzzled, at the dark shapes crowded around her. Then she looked up to the open cellar door and the dim light slanting toward her, and knew where she was. The cold seeping through the bare concrete, chilling her legs tucked beneath her, was the cold of the earth beneath the house.

Stiffly, she got up, her legs numb from lack of circulation. Something heavy fell from her lap, landing on the dusty cement with a thump.

She stooped down and picked up the old photo album. Swaying a little in the cellar's darkness, she hugged the flat bulk to herself, trying to hold in the images of the dream before they faded where they couldn't be seen, like the details of her father's silhouette.

The light grew. She turned and climbed up the wooden steps into the day.

TEN

The next time he woke he was alone, and the light was streaming in across the bed. Braemer turned onto his side, shielding his gum-lidded eyes from the window. The blankets were still rumpled from where Sarah had been.

He squinted at the alarm clock. Eleven-thirty. Sarah would be at work. Probably figured there wasn't much else she could do right now. He lay back, kneading the bridge of his nose, trying to draw the last clouds of sleep from his brain.

The dream was still sharp in his mind. Images of the gun flaring into life in his hands, the blood-spattered sheet, Dee's face clenched in her last pain, red bubbling over her lips—it seemed no different from all the rest that had happened through that long night. Part of the whole sequence, dream blurring into waking, the boundaries erased in the dark. Coming home to find Dee gone and the policemen in the apartment, driving down to the Feld house to get his daughter back, being tossed away from the house like a rag doll by Jess. . . .

The scenes rolled against the back of the hand pressed against his eyes.

Then there was that whole business with that lunatic Pedersen. Braemer rolled his head from side to side on the pillow, his hand rubbing his eyelids. Whether it had been a dream or not, that had been the moment when the barrier holding back the madness had been broken. That whole rap about souls crystallizing, Renee eating her blood relations from inside out. Punctuated, a big black period but to the spiraling words, by the gun dropping onto the desk between them. He could see it even now behind his eyelids, like a gun-shaped hole drilled to the earth's core, no reflection of light at the bottom.

And it'd be so easy. So easy. Braemer knew that. The gun's weight still lay in his chest like a stone, limiting his breath. The attraction of the madness was that it made things better rather than worse, from all the usual confused muddle to perfect clearness, cutting right through all the clinging indecisions over his eyes, tangling his arms.

You buy into it, thought Braemer, marveling at the precise machinery of it, and then you know just how things are. And what to do about it. Suddenly he felt like laughing. So this is what it's like—not so bad after all. Just like stepping through a door, from one side to another.

And he wouldn't be alone. Never alone again, less than he was now with Sarah. He would be in that new world with Dee, Kathy, Pedersen, even Renee—all who had been beckoning him for so long to follow them. Just that easy.

The weight vanished from his chest. For a moment he felt filled with light, floating upward from the bed. If he turned he would see himself below, that other Braemer he felt so sorry for, who'd plugged along in dull sanity for so long. When all along the answers could be handed to him, wrapped up in the clean white cloth with the gun.

He opened his eyes. The alarm clock read a couple minutes past eleven-thirty. He pushed the blanket away, swung his feet out to the floor, sitting up and arching his spine free of the knots twisted in during sleep.

It was time to get moving. There was a lot he had to do yet, to get ready.

Sarah listened to the phone ringing at the other end of the line. She counted a dozen times before she took the phone from her ear and laid it back in its cradle on her desk. Between each ring, it had seemed as if she could hear the empty apartment echoing the noise.

At the other desk, Linda, with whom she shared the cubbyhole office, pulled her purse from the bottom drawer. Voices in the hallway signaled the other secretaries leaving for lunch. "Something wrong?" she asked, glancing up.

"Hmm . . . no. Nothing." Sarah managed a smile. "Just trying to get hold of Dave, is all."

"Hey, the guy's gotta eat. He's probably standing in line down at Pink's." She set her purse on top of the typewriter and snapped it shut. "I think everybody's going downstairs—that place with the salads. You coming along?"

Sarah shook her head. "I got here late this morning. I'm going to work through so I can leave on time."

Alone, she gazed at the telephone for a moment before slipping the dictation headset back on and swiveling her chair around to the typewriter. She hadn't even known what she wanted to say to him. Maybe just hello, she thought, are you all right, are you still with us? . . .

That morning, dragging herself out of the few frayed-edge hours of sleep she'd managed to get after Dave had come home and they'd finished talking about what had happened, she'd debated with herself about whether to go in to work or not. She'd wanted to stay there with him, but he'd had that look when they were talking. Gazing over her head at the walls, vision fixed on some point beyond her, dragging a private world around with himself which she couldn't enter. He came out of there, back into the world where she stood, sooner if she left him alone—she knew that from all the times before when she'd been talking to him and realized that the words she got back were painted on a wall.

I wonder what it's like in there. Dee got the same look, too, sometimes, just for brief moments. Like father, like daughter: carrying their secret thoughts around in little dark sacks hanging near their hearts. Even when you could guess what was inside—losing Dee, all this mess with psychiatrists and lawyers, what to do, what had already been done that should never have been—you still didn't know everything in there. You just waited for it to be shut away again, with him on the same side of the wall as you. And hope that it never happened, that the wall would seal shut for good with him on the other side, so that you'd have to live with those eyes that didn't see you for the rest of your life.

She switched on the dictation machine and listened to the letter winding off the tape. The time would crawl by eventually, if she just worked and didn't think.

The parking lot of Rawling Graphics was empty when Braemer pulled into it. He glanced at his watch. Just after twelve, everyone out to lunch.

He let himself in and strode down the hallway to his own cubicle. In the top drawer of the desk beside his drafting table was the bankbook he'd kept here, where Sarah wouldn't find it. A savings account, left over from the days before they'd moved in together—he hadn't told her about it, with vague notions of building it up bit by bit, and surprising her with something nice and more expensive than she'd figure they could afford, some big gold bracelet like an ingot with a wrist hole drilled through. That had been the idea. Now he had other uses for the money.

Straightening up, he slid the drawer shut and riffled through the bankbook to the total. Six hundred and fifty dollars. Not very goddamn much, he thought, scraping the page edges under his thumb. It would go a little ways, but not very far. Plus there was a couple of hundred dollars he could take out of the checking account without leaving Sarah flat broke. It would have to do. He slipped the bankbook into his pocket and turned toward the door.

"Hello, David." Rawling was standing there, shoulder against the door frame, watching him. With his sleeves rolled, his arms were folded across his rumpled shirt front. "I was kind of hoping that you'd show up."

Braemer met the other's gaze. "Well, I really just came by to pick up a few things. I'm afraid I'm not going to be coming in . . . for quite a while. Sorry to spring it on you like that."

Rawling shrugged. "I kind of figured as much. Sarah called me this morning, to let me know that you might be late today. She told me about some of the stuff that's happened, what's-his-name taking Dee and all. She thought you'd want me to know about it."

"Yeah, well. . . . I'm going to be busy with the lawyer and everything, getting ready for the custody hearing, stuff like that. So I don't want you to be counting on me for anything, when I'm not going to have much time for working on stuff."

"You're gonna get ready for a custody hearing by

quitting your job? Come on, David. Don't bullshit me."

Braemer said nothing, fingering the bankbook in his pocket.

"We've been friends for a while," said Rawling. "I know a little bit of what goes on in your mind."

"Do you?" Braemer scanned the other's weary-looking face. "And just what is it you think I'm going to do, then?"

"Probably what I'd do if I were you. Maybe what I should have done a couple of times. Just get your kid and take off where they can't find you."

Braemer nodded. Even that solution was from the other world, where there weren't people you'd never seen before handing you big black guns with instructions on killing your ex-wife. He felt saddened by the distance that had fallen between him and Rawling. The center pin of their friendship had eroded away: they were no longer both brothers in that dreary troop, men and women alike, who shouldered the wreckage of their marriages, and went on paying the bills and taking care of the kids and doing every other sane, sensible thing expected of them. Looking at him, Braemer could see that Rawling wasn't far away from the usual door off the treadmill, the one you go through and then all bills are paid out of the estate and the life insurance you leave behind, if any.

He wished he could take Rawling out to the car, open the trunk, show him the gun, and invite him into this clean, thin-aired world that had come spiraling out of Pedersen's mad eyes for him. But he knew it was already too late.

Instead, Braemer glanced out the window, then back to Rawling. "Maybe so," he said. "It's probably not a good idea for me to tell you exactly what I'm planning on doing."

"No, I don't suppose so. I'm not very good at lying to people, especially the police, when they come around asking me things. Though I understand some stuff just isn't looked into very hard." Rawling nodded his head toward the other end of the hallway. "Why don't you come on back to my office. I've got something for you."

Behind his own desk, Rawling pulled out the company checkbook. "This is for your last week and a half here," he said, scrawling across one of the blanks. He tore it out and handed it across the desk to Braemer. "Plus a month's advance."

He looked at the check, then back up. "You don't have to do that."

"What the hell. You're going to need it, and I can afford it. I'll cut a few expenses by letting that jerk Stennis go—he hasn't been doing anything around here, anyway. Besides, you might be back."

"I might not. Not for a long time."

"Eh, so send it back to me when you can. Or don't. It doesn't matter." Rawling flipped the checkbook shut. "I'll call over to the bank to make sure you don't have any problem cashing it."

They shook hands at the building's door. "Going to need any help?" asked Rawling. "I mean, other than cash."

Braemer smiled. "No," he said. "I've pretty much got my plans made." The gun still waited, tucked in the car's trunk.

"Okay, then. See you around." He turned and went back inside.

For a few seconds Braemer watched the round-shouldered figure trudge through the lobby. Then he pushed open the door and headed for his car.

Carol heard the sound of an engine turning into the

driveway. With a relief that eased across her shoulders, she recognized it as Jess's pickup truck. She set the pan back down in the sink, then stepped out the back door as she wiped her hands on the dish towel.

Jess had parked the truck under the tree where he usually worked on it. As the engine rattled, cooling, he stood with one foot up on the sill, digging behind the seat for his toolbox. "Hi," he said, glancing over his shoulder. His pallid face shone with sweat, skin stretched tight over the bones beneath. "Where's Dee?"

"She's upstairs. Taking a nap, I think." The dish towel twisted into a knot in her hands. "Jesus Christ, I've been worried—where did you go?"

He unlatched the hood and lifted it open. "I had a few things to take care of." His glasses flashed sunlight across the engine.

"What if David had showed up again?"

"That chickenshit? Not likely," he said, snapping a socket onto a wrench.

"But what if he *had?* What would you have expected me to do?"

"Hit him. He'll fold." Jess turned away and leaned over the engine. "Come on, I can't hang around here all day and night like some kind of bodyguard."

"Great," snapped Carol. "I hope you're ready for it when you can manage to show up around here, and Dee's gone." She turned on her heel and headed back to the house.

"I could handle it. Just have to go and get her again," he called after her.

In the kitchen, she threw the wadded towel on the floor. "Shit," she muttered through clenched teeth. She was just one more wrong word away from bursting into tears.

She was also close to wishing that things had been allowed to go on the way they were—that Jess had never gone up to Los Angeles in the first place to get Dee, and that David had just been allowed to keep her until whatever decision had come out of a custody hearing. The fight last night between the two men, what little she had seen of it, had frightened her. A mask over the current of violence that had lain hidden for years, like a live electric cable a shovel's blade from the ground's surface, had been scraped away at last.

All the politeness, all the rationally worked-out schedule of weekend visits back and forth, the cups of coffee at the kitchen table, had just gone to disguise, and not change, the real nature of the saw-edged ropes that bound them all together—her, David, Jess, Dee, even Renee locked in her decaying sleep upstairs.

Carol slumped down into a chair at the table and laid her head on her folded arms. Even if Renee were to die at last—and how she prayed silently, while washing and feeding that ragged flesh with the barely recognizable face, for that mindless clinging of life to let go—the war between David and the memory of her still wouldn't be over. Dee was the child of a marriage that had ground out its own life in hate and disgust. It seemed like something of a miracle to Carol that a child as lovely as Dee —and she was lovely: Carol had never seen her in one of her ballet classes, but could imagine her intent face, small teeth biting her lower lip, reflected in the mirrored walls—that such a child could have come from two people already warping around their loathing for each other.

(But if it was a miracle, it was one she knew happened all the time. Whenever she picked Dee up from school, half the children she saw running in the playgrounds, all as lovely as Dee, were from homes that had come splintering apart as messily as Dee's had, this being Southern California in the late-twentieth century.)

All those Sunday evenings when David had brought

Dee back here after spending the weekend in Los Angeles, when he had then gone up to Renee's room and looked at her comatose body, Carol had had an idea of what was going on in his mind. It had been like catching a glimpse of some slow-moving animal at the bottom of a stagnant pond, barely visible through the mud-choked water. To see him from the hallway's darkness, as he stood inside the room's doorway, gazing with folded arms and lowered chin at the figure on the bed, was to see the coarse rope tangled about the two of them still drawing blood. She could almost believe that Renee was skewered to the bed by the point of his gaze, just as if what had happened to her had been the working-out of his sharp brooding.

So that's why it was always going to come to this, she thought. Sooner or later. To pretend that they could have gone on forever, shuttling Dee back and forth between them, from this house to her father's apartment in L.A., that was nonsense. A lie she had known all the time she was hoping that it was possible. And all the friendly talk and cups of coffee wouldn't make it true.

The day would come, had come, pushed forward by the point of the knife in a sleepwalking Dee's hands, when David would claim his child all for his own. To the victor the spoils. The marriage had come apart like a hot-air balloon catching fire, and Renee had not survived the fall, her skull cracking open, eggshell on a rock, her muddled brain running out into the dust. So why shouldn't he have his own kid? He was the father, wasn't he? And Mom's out to lunch for good, and not coming back? Wasn't that how it was supposed to go?

If Jess hadn't gone and brought Dee back here . . . And whose idea had that been? All Carol could remember was sitting with him at the table after she had talked to him on the phone, and Jess's face darkening while she had cried about David keeping Dee up in L.A., then trying to grab Jess's arm as he stood up, slamming his chair away. . . . If he hadn't done that, hadn't brought Dee back to the house where she could hold the child close to herself, her hands feeling the edges of Dee's shoulderblades through her T-shirt, then she might have been able to accept it all. Accept the fact that the temporary arrangements were just that, temporary and now over, changed for good. Accept that the lie they had all been operating under, that they had all agreed to, was now fanned away in the air like stale cigarette smoke. There wasn't any Mommy upstairs for Dee to come home to after visiting her daddy. Just a corpse that had inherited Renee's name and the last of her breaths wheezing through the yellow teeth.

She might have accepted all that, and not even have phoned her own lawyer, the one who had handled her mother's estate, and told him to start getting the custody suit ready for court, and just have let David have what was rightfully his, if she hadn't been able to see Dee, to hold her, and realize that *she* was Dee's mother now. This was the child she had taken care of, more than David, more than anyone else had. And she wasn't going to give up, not now, not ever.

Maybe that was what Jess had known, had seen straight through to, when he'd gotten up from the table, driven to Los Angeles, and fetched Dee back.

Carol closed her eyes, feeling her lashes brush against the skin of her forearm. Now she had become part of the war she had always watched from a distance. A stand-in for her sister. What Renee had given birth to, she had inherited—the child and everything that went with her.

The little plastic kitchen timer sitting on the stove went off, sending its tinny racket through the kitchen. Carol squeezed her eyelids tighter, as if that could shut out the sound for just a few seconds. If she didn't set the timer to remind herself, it was easy to forget about going upstairs and taking care of Renee, the twice-daily feedings that drained down the nasal tube taped to the idiot face, the bathing and turning and dressing of the inevitable bedsores, all the little duties that kept the body alive and breathing out its whispered secrets.

I wonder if she knew, thought Carol. The photo album she'd dug out of the trunk in the cellar was now tucked away in the chest of drawers in her own bedroom. I wonder if everybody knew but me.

She lifted her head when the timer finally ran down. The house was quiet again, except fo the slow, small sound from upstairs.

There was something he had to make sure of first.

Braemer stood at the rear of the Datsun, the cloth-wrapped gun in his hands. He had pulled the car off one of the narrow roads that wound through the hills above the city, onto a dust-covered turnout carved out of the slope's rock and loose gravel. On the other side of the road's asphalt strip, brown scrubby brush fell away to the gray-hazed city at the foot of the hills.

The turnout was far enough from the city traffic that the silence was broken only by the muted buzzing of insects in the dry brush. He would be able to hear anyone else coming in time enough to throw the gun back into the car. If someone were to hear a shot ringing out from the hillside, he would be more likely to blame it on a couple of kids farting around with a rifle than on a divorced father getting ready to visit his ex.

He pulled the cloth from the gun and let the bare metal rest on his palm. A few notions about guns, derived from television and the movies, tangled in his head. He had never fired one.

His thumb pushed a smooth protuberance above the

crosshatched grip, and the chambered cylinder swung out of the gun, showing the six empty holes.

From the yellow box he took one of the bullets, shiny brass with a dull gray tip like a stylized wasp, and slid it into the gun. It fit precisely, one machine part lining up with its mate.

The cylinder clicked back into place. For a few seconds he held the gun away from him, feeling the new potency in it traveling up his arm like an electric current.

He turned the gun over, looking for the other catch that he knew should be there. He found the small lever and pushed it with one finger. The safety release made no sound as it moved. A bright red dot that had been hidden under it leaped to Braemer's eyes like a spot of blood.

Now only a tiny motion was needed, a tightening of his hand around the cold metal, and the roaring voice he had heard in his dream would come rushing out of his fist.

He turned toward the hillside, braced himself, and raised the gun. With both hands wrapped around the grip, he locked his elbows rigid and inched the trigger back.

The gun twitched in his hands as the hammer snapped forward.

The sound of metal striking metal was lost in the noise, sharper and louder than he'd expected, as though the air itself had taken a steel-cut edge for a split second. It slapped against his ears and faded, ringing, as his shoulders caught the force of his outstretched arms pulsing back with the squat little engine in his hands.

A bird flew up out of the brush below the road, its wings a flutter of brown against the sky as it beat away from the echo trailing from the side of the hill.

Everything silent once more, Braemer lowered the

gun. Somewhere past the gravel slope, the bullet was lodged in the dark rocks of the hill's interior, the heat of its firing leaking from the metal into the soil around it.

He turned the gun around in his hand to look at it. Quiet now, but the sharp echo was still in his ears. I guess that'll do, he thought. That'll do just fine. He picked the cloth up from the ground and wrapped it around the gun.

Dee stayed upstairs in her bedroom most of the day. She had told her aunt that she wasn't feeling well, and Carol had brought her up a grilled-cheese sandwich and milk for lunch, then soup for dinner.

All through the afternoon she had sat at the window, with jeans pulled on below the top of her cotton pajamas, watching nothing happen out in the yard and the street beyond. Whenever she'd lift her head, one side of her face would be red from lying on her arm on the windowsill for so long.

The sandwich had been cold and leathery by the time she had gotten around to eating it, but she couldn't taste it anyway. Her mind was on the dream she'd had during the night.

Wasn't even a dream, she thought, nuzzling her cheek against the sleeve's soft fuzz. Even before she had woken up and found the kitchen knife on the floor and the pinpoint scratch on her chest, the smell of the forest had given it all away. Pine that arched the nostrils open, and damp decaying stuff at the trees' roots, like dust in a closet that hadn't been opened in years. The smells, all mixed together so that they tickled and cloyed her nose, always came along with her mother's voice inside her.

It was all her. Like a TV show she made me see, Dee thought. More than just seeing it, the images sliding under the lids of her eyes—she had been in it, walking through it, fetching the knife and bringing it up here to her own room, pressing the blade's point below her own throat. Like when she tried to make me do that with my daddy. Only this time she wasn't just inside me, she was all around me. I was inside her, seeing stuff the way she sees it. All dark and . . .

The memory of seeing her mother, her old mother, sitting at the kitchen table and smiling at her—that brought a salt sting inside the bridge of her nose, and she didn't know why. The world outside the window blurred until she wiped her eyes on her pajama sleeve.

Better this way, she knew. Part of her still wanted her daddy to come and get her, take her back to his apartment far from this house and her mother. The other part was still afraid, afraid of the smell of pine and damp rot coming into her nostrils when there wasn't any forest around her, afraid of her hands moving when she didn't want them to, afraid of the knife they would pick up and what it would do as it dragged her along behind it, into the darkened room where her daddy would be sleeping.

Better if she stayed here in the house. Forever, she thought, watching dead air fill every street she could see from the window. Just stay here with Carol for the rest of her life. The two of them would shuffle about in the dim light behind the drawn curtains, the house quiet all around them, the grass outside growing high against the walls until it dried brown, brushing away the cracked chips of paint. She would become as old as Carol, and Carol even older until she died, and then Dee would be the one to slowly climb the stairs, to feed and bathe the thing in the bed.

Because it would never die. She knew that now. That was what it wanted. It would go on, shrinking until it was nothing but a grinning skull and one clawed finger digging into the blanket from the withered spine, forever.

189

Forever, thought Dee. A cloudless sky. There wouldn't be any more apartment, any more city around it filled with honking, oil-smelling busses and light flashing off the mirrored sides of the buildings. No more going to dance classes with Sarah—she would miss that more than anything.

She raised her head and looked around the bedroom. The house beyond the closed door was all there was, all there was going to be from now on. If she listened, holding her own breath, she could hear through the door the sound of the other breathing, drawing slowly all the air in the house, bit by bit, into its throat.

He wasn't there when Sarah came home. She knew it as soon as she stepped inside. She could feel the emptiness of the rooms stretching away from her, each filled with silence.

She slung her purse onto the couch and walked into the kitchen. On the counter was a half-empty cup of coffee, hours cold. A slip of paper dangled from under one of the magnets stuck to the refrigerator door.

Some things to take care of—I'll give you a call tonight—Love, D. She sat down at the chair that had been left pulled out from the table, the note held loose in her hand.

The few scrawled words filled her with dread. I should've stayed here with him, she thought, letting the paper flutter to the table top. I shouldn't have left him by himself.

There was no telling what "Some things" meant, or what the taking care of them would involve. Worse, she had ideas, visions that ran away from her grasp: Dave getting hurt, or hurting someone else. The story he had brought home last night, of being thrown off the Feld house porch by that son-of-a-bitch Jess, had scared her. She had said nothing about it then, listening to him as they both leaned over untouched cups of coffee. She hadn't wanted him to feel any worse than he had already been making himself feel over this scrabbling little defeat in some dirty front yard down in San Aurelio.

What she'd wanted was for him to squeeze the last drop of poison from under his skin, then go to bed with her, where she could wrap her arms around him, just the two of them secure in the warmth under the blanket. But when she had lain with him in the dark, she'd realized that what was festering in him, and had been for a long time, wouldn't ever be drawn out until he had Dee with him for good.

And that's what scares me, she thought dismally. A dull ache came with admitting it. She was frightened of Dee. Not of anything a child might be capable of doing, but of what she had already brought into being, this wide-eyed craziness that had burst out of the apartment and was now racketing about in the streets. It was as if Dee hadn't carried a kitchen knife about in her sleep-walking, but a key. A key that had unlocked the door letting out everything that had happened, everything that Sarah felt in the hollow of her stomach was still going to happen.

She sat at the kitchen table, watching the window over the sink grow darker. This was what it was like to be afraid of, and for, someone you loved. Not just Dee, but Dave as well. The silence he had retreated into, the walls behind his eyes, had frightened her as much as anything. She didn't know what he was going to do.

Maybe nothing, she thought. Maybe nothing at all. He'll just come home in a little bit, after he phones to let me know he's on his way, errands taken care of, and that'll be it, For now.

She had no appetite, but she started to wonder what she could fix for him, something that would stay warm until he got home. If she made something, and it was waiting here for him, maybe that would mean he really was coming back.

Braemer sat drinking, an empty beer glass and a half-full one on the booth's table before him. Not to get drunk, but just to kill time until it would be late enough to start driving down to San Aurelio. The alcohol had no effect on him, anyway. It just fell inside and burned away. If anything, he was more coldly sober with each sip.

He was in a different bar, not the one over by Rawling Graphics, though the space inside was just the same. Close, dark, an electric beer sign with a waterfall effect rippling over and over on the wall, the television's stark colors glinting off the stemmed glasses racked above the bar. He didn't want anybody from work to recognize him, to talk with him. He just wanted to pull these hours into his mouth, squeeze them between his tongue and palate, then swallow them, until it was time to go.

The gun was wrapped up in its white cloth and sitting tucked in the car's trunk, waiting for him.

Another swallow, sliding cold down his throat, the circle of foam in the glass brushing his lip. Everything in his life should have been this clear, this logical. This was what it was like to know just what to do.

ELEVEN

The driveway from the street to the Feld house sloped enough that Braemer could cut the engine and steer, headlights out, down to within several yards of the front porch. The tires crunched on the driveway's gravel, then were silent as the car halted. It was well past midnight. All the lights in the house were off, except for the one upstairs.

For a moment Braemer looked out at the darkened house, his breath and heartbeat the only sounds. He reached down to the gun lying on the car's floor. His hand hesitated, fingertips grazing the cold metal, then he pushed it underneath the passenger seat.

If he had been here, in front of the house, that afternoon, he would have picked up the gun and gone on inside with it. But the long drive down from Los Angeles, his thoughts rolling ceaselessly against each other, had drained—thankfully; like waking from a nightmare—Pedersen's words and their madness from him. In their place Rawling's advice—just get your kid and take off—had lodged.

He left the car door open, not wanting the latch's sharp metal click to sound. Stepping up onto the porch, he sorted through the keys on his ring, looking for one in particular. He found it, a spare key to the front door, one that Renee had given him before the marriage had gone bust. Back then, while her mother had still been alive, there had been some worry about the old lady having a heart attack or any other medical emergency while Carol wasn't around. So Braemer had added the house key to his ring in case he'd been the only one available to take her to the hospital. It had stayed on his ring, unused until now.

The key turned in the lock, the teeth meshing with the tumblers inside. He pushed the door open and stepped into the dark front room. Listening, he heard nothing but the slight noise of breathing from upstairs. His dream from the night before lay over the room for a moment, details matching, except that now there was no gun in his hand. Carefully, he threaded his way among the dim shapes of furniture toward the staircase.

At the foot of the stairs he looked up. The edge of the top step was outlined in the faint light from under the one door above. The silence held, none of the stairs creaking under his weight as he mounted.

In the hallway, he stood, the sound of ragged breathing from Renee's body closer to him. The door to her room, thread of light at the bottom, was just a few strides away. If he'd brought the gun with him, he could have been at the side of her bed in a couple of seconds, his arm swinging the gun up to the line between his eye and the body's head.

The gun was down in the car. Right where he'd decided to leave it.

Everything so quiet, everyone sleeping. No one would hear him go back downstairs and out to the car, then come up here again. It would take a minute, maybe less.

He pushed the thought away. He'd already made up his mind—for the last time—about what he was going to do.

He turned away from Renee's door and walked quickly down to the other end of the hallway, passing by what he knew was Carol's room. The door at the end was Dee's. The knob turned in his hand, then swung away as he looked inside.

Her bed was by the window, with enough moonlight through the curtains for him to make out her form curled under the blanket. He stepped to the side of the bed and leaned down close to her.

"Dee," he whispered. "Wake up. It's me, it's your daddy."

Her eyelids fluttered, then she looked up at him, wide-eyed. "No—"

"Shh. Be real quiet, honey. Okay? You awake? I want you to get dressed."

"But you—" She pushed herself up on her elbows, frowning in puzzlement.

"I came to get you, sweetheart. You're going to come with me." He stroked the pillow-ruffled hair over her ear. "Okay?"

Suddenly something frightened her, and she shrank away from his hand, her eyes growing even wider, breath hissing in and holding. Then her face softened, from alarm to trembling relief. "It's not her, is it?" she said, searching his face. "You're really you."

His heart split in the vise of his chest, and he barely kept himself from sweeping her up out of the bed and crushing her to himself. "It's me," he whispered. "Come on, it's time to go."

Dee threw the covers aside and scrambled out of the bed. She scooped up the small pile of clothing by the bed.

A few moments later, she looked up from tying her sneakers. "Should I take some stuff?"

"We don't have time. We can buy whatever we need later."

Her gaze sharpened. "We're going back to the apartment, aren't we?"

"Shh. You ready to go?"

He led her down the stairs, her hand in his. Her foot slipped on the last step, and he caught her from falling. They stood together, listening for any other sound from upstairs. "I don't think she heard," whispered Dee, holding on to his arm. "Come on, let's go before Carol wakes up."

The chairs' upholstery brushed against their legs as they headed for the front door. He pulled it open and stepped with her onto the porch. The car, its door open, sat in the driveway a few strides away.

A silhouette separated from the shadowed post by the porch steps. The figure straightened from where it had been leaning, its arms unfolding and hands jamming onto its hips.

"All right," came Jess's voice. "Just hold it."

Braemer said nothing. Jess seemed to fill the space between the posts, blocking the steps that led off the porch.

"That wasn't a very smart idea," said Jess. "Not very smart at all. Why don't you just let go of Dee, and then I'll let you leave. Nice and simple. Otherwise, you're in a world of trouble."

Dee had pressed herself tight against his side. He took her shoulders in his hands. "Stay right here, sweetheart." She looked up at him, silent.

Jess leaned back against the post to let him pass. A line of segmented white marked the smile on Jess's face as Braemer crossed in front of him. "Fuckin' queer," came the whisper, smirking triumph. "I told you you wouldn't get your dirty hands on her anymore."

He walked to the car, feeling the weight of two pairs

of eyes on his back. In the dark, he reached in across the seats, then straighted back up. "Jess," he called out.

The other stepped to the front of the porch, out into the moonlight. Braemer could see Dee standing in the doorway behind him, watching.

Braemer walked back toward the house, stopping a couple of yards from the porch steps. The white cloth fluttered to the ground as he swung the gun up, his outstretched arms holding it straight at Jess's chest. A fierce joy welled up in him, drawing his lips back from his clenched teeth, as he saw Jess's head jerk back, eyes widened.

"What the fuck do you think—" Eyes narrowing into slits, Jess stepped down toward him.

"Don't move."

Jess froze, gauging the distance between him and the muzzle of the gun. "You can't do it," he said finally. "You're too chickenshit."

"Find out." Braemer kept the gun hanging on the invisible line running into the other's heart.

Jess's eyes flicked from the gun to Braemer's face. "What are you going to do?"

"Don't worry about it. Dee," he called. "Go get in the car, honey."

The small form moved away from the front door. "Daddy—"

"Just do as I say. Everything's going to be all right."

Slowly, Dee stepped around Jess, then broke into a run past Braemer. She scrambled into the car, watching the two of them from behind the windshield.

"Okay," said Braemer. The gun felt solid in his hand, as though it had merged with the bone beneath, one solid piece into his shoulder. He glanced away from Jess and spotted the pickup truck under the tree at the side of the house. "I want you to walk over to the truck."

Jess studied him for a few seconds, his arms tensing at his sides. "You really would, wouldn't you?"

"You think I would—that's all that matters. Now go on over to the truck."

He followed a few paces behind Jess, keeping the gun centered into his shoulderblades. "Now open the hood."

Jess glanced over his shoulder at him, then sighed and worked the latch.

"Pull off the distributor cap and throw it over here."

The cap landed in the dust and rolled against Braemer's shoe. He bent down and picked it up, keeping his eye and the gun trained on Jess. "Let's go get the other one," he said, ticking the gun toward Carol's Chevy.

When both distributor caps were in Braemer's free hand, Jess leaned back against the Chevy's fender. "You know," he said, "I'll just come on up to L.A. and break your ass anyway."

"Fine," said Braemer. "You do that. I'll be waiting there for you."

"Fuckin' gun won't help you then."

Braemer looked across the top of the gun at him. "Then maybe I should do something with it right now."

Jess said nothing, but the rim of his nostrils flared and whitened. His hands flattened against the fender.

"If I thought I had anything to worry about," said Braemer, "I'd go ahead. Asshole. Now I want you to just sit tight for a while. Don't move." He began to back away, keeping the gun raised.

"I'll be seeing you." Jess folded his arms.

Braemer slammed the car door shut and turned the key in the ignition. He laid the gun on the floor, grabbed the wheel, and swung the car around. In the rearview mirror, Jess was still leaning against the pickup truck, watching the car head out onto the street.

Dee curled up on the other seat, looking at him. "Is that a real gun?" she said.

He glanced away from the headlights sweeping across the empty streets. "Yes," he said. "I'm sorry."

"I'm glad you came and got me." Dee laid her head on his shoulder. "Are we going home now?"

"No, honey." The lights of the freeway were already visible beyond the curve of the hill. "Not yet. We've got a long way to go."

Braemer slid a dollar's worth of quarters into the coffee shop's pay phone. At the other end it rang once before it was picked up. "Hello?" came Sarah's voice, breathless.

"It's me."

"Where are you? What happened?" Her words rushed out, a night's worth of worry behind them.

He drew his breath, eyes closed. "I can't tell you where I am—not right now. I've got Dee with me, and we're going to be . . . traveling for a while."

Silence on the line. "You went and got Dee? But—but where are you going?"

"I don't know." He really didn't; he hadn't planned that far yet. All his alternatives were the lines on the map in the glove compartment. "Even if I knew, I couldn't tell you, honey—just in case the police come around and ask you if you know where I am."

"But what are you going to do?" Sarah's voice strained close to the breaking point where the tears began.

"I've got some money. Dee and I'll be all right for a while. Then I'll stop someplace where I can get a job of some kind. When we're settled, I'll call you and let you know where it is, and you can join us there. I don't know when that'll be." He stopped, hearing his own words dwindle into the hazy future.

"Why?" said Sarah's voice. "If you've got Dee, why don't you just come back here? We'll get custody of her."

"I can't." He leaned against the wall, feeling a tiredness from more than lack of sleep slide into his back. "I don't even want to risk them getting her. Whether the court gives her to them, or that fucker Jess snatches her again—I just can't. Jesus Christ, she's screwed up enough from being stuck in that damn house with them. You know that. I don't want those people to get near her again. You can see that, can't you?"

"I know. I know." The weariness was in her voice, too. "I don't know what you should do."

"What else can I do? This is it." They were silent together for a moment, the wires stretching between them.

"But you'll be all right, won't you?" said Sarah.

"Sure. What can happen? The hard part's over. Now there's just driving to do."

"And you'll call me? I mean, not to tell me where you are. But just . . . on the way."

"All the time," he said. "Whenever I can."

"And it won't be long? When I can—"

"Real soon. A month, maybe a little longer."

"All right." Her sigh came over the line. "I guess. Do you have to go now?"

"Yeah. Dee and I just stopped to get something to eat. And to call you. I want to get a bit farther before we stop for the day. There's something else I want to tell you, though. Now this is important. When I went down to get Dee, I had to screw around with Jess. He was there. You understand? He's pretty pissed off, and he might come up there, not just to try and get Dee back, but to look for me. So I want you to be real careful. If he shows up, maybe you should call the police. I mean, since you don't know where I am, anyway. Okay? Just be careful."

"I will. You be careful, too, all right?"

"Don't worry. I'll call you—tonight, probably."

They said they loved each other, and then there was no more to say. Braemer hung up the phone, it rang, and he fed in the rest of the coins that the operator asked for.

Dee was mopping up the syrup in her plate with the last spongy wedge of pancake when he sat back down. "Where we going to now?" she said.

"Oh—Tucson." It was just something to tell her. He still had no idea of a route, other than staying on the widest highway heading east. Outside the coffee shop's window, the windshields of all the cars in the parking lot shone red-gold with the rising sun. Since pulling away from the Feld house, he and Dee had driven all the rest of the night until they had stopped here.

The waitress appeared and refilled his cup. "You're up bright and early today," she said to Dee, smiling. "You and your dad on vacation?"

"We're going—" started Braemer.

Dee broke in. "We're going back east," she said happily. "To see my grandmother." She glanced at her father, her fellow conspirator.

"That's nice. Got a long ways to go?"

"Uh . . ."

"Cleveland," said Braemer. "She hasn't seen her grandmother before."

"Well, that's wonderful." The waitress tore their check from her pad and laid it on the table. "You have a real fine trip, honey, and you stop and see us on your way back, okay?"

"Okay," said Dee. She smiled back at the motherly face.

Braemer watched the small charade close. He wasn't sure what it meant. Maybe she was just acting out scenes she'd watched on television. Or maybe, he thought, maybe she really understands. Hard to say. When he'd been ten years old, he wouldn't have been able to figure out a situation like this. But at that age he hadn't been through all that she had. Even an average kid nowadays was a combination of video gloss, hip as some jaded talk-show veteran, and the remnants of whatever was left of being a child. He had seen their eyes reflected in the screens at the game arcades, old eyes in children's faces, boredom that was half studied pose and half cataracts layered on by the dazzling glare they had grown up in.

Perhaps because the things Dee had seen had been real—a horror show on a channel that couldn't be switched off—more of her had remained a real child. She could appreciate real life, hang on to it.

Braemer watched her wiping her mouth with her crumpled paper napkin, a yawning, catlike motion. He could never become so sad about all that had happened to her that he would stop marveling at her. It seemed like the proof of some evolutionary law that the mating of two losers like himself and his ex-wife could have produced such a creature.

I'm never giving her up, he thought. I can't.

She looked up at him. "All set," she announced.

Not a game, he thought. She knows. They were into something new and different. All those times, taking her home on Sunday evenings, that he'd wished they could go on driving forever. And now here it was, the ultimate father-child relationship, just the two of them on the road, running away from Mommy.

He picked up the check, figured out the tip, and laid it on the table. "Well, come on, then," he said. "Let's hit it."

202

The phone was dead in Sarah's hand. She set it back down in its cradle, folded her arms in the thick sleeves of her bathrobe around herself, and rocked back and forth on the edge of the couch. If she could have cried, she would have.

Now I don't have anything, she thought, stricken. The door that she had seen opening with the key in Dee's hand was now flung wide, and the world she had feared on the other side was all around her. There hadn't been any unknown things waiting for her here, but instead the absence of things, nothing filling the apartment, nothing in all the streets of the city. She'd lost them both now. Dave was on some highway unknown to her, and Dee was with him. She was stuck here in the hole left behind by them.

Nothing to do now but wait. She stood and picked up the mug from the coffee table, the last of a half-dozen cups of tea cold inside it. The night had been spent curled up at the end of the couch, falling into scattered moments of half-sleep, then waking again to the muted jabbering of the TV.

Morning light outside the windows. She could see Dave's hand pushing in the headlights switch, the other pairs of lights on the highway—whatever highway— flicking off as the residue of night drained away.

She was exhausted from the night's waiting, but the apartment was too empty now to stay in. Instead of calling in a sick-day to her job, she decided to go ahead and shower, eat, catch the bus, just as if there were any reason to.

"Let's hit it," said her daddy. Dee looked across the table at him. Another, inside of her, looked at him with the same eyes.

She wanted to shout something, to scream across the

coffee shop's murmuring voices, but instead she felt her face smiling. Her legs slid from the seat to the aisle.

As she stood with her father at the cash register, her hand slipped into the pocket of her jacket and felt the thin edge of metal there. Some guy in the booth across the aisle from theirs had been having steak and eggs for breakfast. He'd left while her father was away making a phone call—she knew it had been to Sarah—and when nobody was looking she had stepped across and taken the steak knife. The flat of the blade was still greasy under her thumb. It had slipped into her pocket before she herself had realized what had happened.

They walked out into the parking lot and toward the car. *Don't*, she tried to shout, but her father, sorting through his keys, couldn't hear her.

The other voice was silent, but she knew it was there, in her arm, in her hand. Standing with her father as he unlocked the door, she felt her fingers draw over the knife. It wasn't a big knife, but its teeth and point were as sharp as the scent of pine that blew across the bare asphalt parking lot.

I'm not one I'm two, I'm not one I'm two, I'm not one I'm two, I want out now, I want out now, I want out now now now now now now now now . . .

—"We Must Bleed," lyrics by Darby Crash (1958-80)

TWELVE

"Do you remember . . . when we were kids. There was that one Christmas. When Mom got mad at something—" It hurt her to talk, to draw the breath below her stiffened ribs and then put it out as words she could barely hear herself. "I know what it was. She got mad at me and Renee because we kept on teasing Carol. And then Carol started crying and wouldn't stop. Then Mom got so mad she started screaming at all of us. She kept on screaming. And she dragged the Christmas tree right out the front door to the yard, and she set fire to it. Jesus, that seems so funny now." Her laugh turned into a cough that brought a taste of salt into her mouth. The back of her head rubbed against the cracked linoleum floor as she gasped to catch her breath.

"All that screaming," Kathy went on, the words falling away into the room's darkness. "And the tree went on burning, and Mom threw all the presents on the fire. She was so crazy. I remember there was one box that burned up, and there was a doll inside. All its hair turned black. And its face split open right down the middle. You could smell it burning. You remember?"

There was no answer. The room was so dark, darker than it had ever been before, that she couldn't tell if she were alone in it or not.

"And that night, when all the screaming was over and the fire was out in the yard, you sneaked out of your bedroom and down to mine. It was real late. And you had a flashlight and that doll's head. It still smelled all burnt. You hid under the covers with me, and you made the doll's mouth go like it was Mom's on the end of your finger, screaming and saying all those things she'd say to us. We started giggling, and we couldn't stop, but we didn't want her to hear us, because she'd get mad again. But it was so funny, that little doll's head all black and cracked open, screaming and calling us little bastards, it was so funny, it was so funny, it was—"

She stopped, choking on something thick in her throat. Her breath couldn't squeeze past to her lungs. The outline of the window dimmed and blurred. She turned her head and managed to spit something out onto the blanket. A string of red saliva lay across her swollen lip. Her lungs burned with the room's stale air seeping back into her.

"That's when I knew," she whispered to the room. She wished she could see Jess one more time, before there would be no more seeing. "I knew you really loved me. All along. Not her. You loved me."

Underneath the blanket, her numb fingertips traced down the sides of her body, across each red scar where his love had eaten beneath her skin.

Braemer sat on the park bench, the remains of his and Dee's lunch spread out beside him—a McDonald's bag with a couple of French fries at the bottom, soaking grease through the white paper, small squares of ice melting in plastic cups with a clown on the sides. He wadded up the hamburger wrappers, waxed paper crackling in his fist, and dropped them into the empty bag.

Several yards away, on the broad stretch of grass ringed with trees, Dee kicked a brand-new soccer ball around. He'd bought it just a few hours ago, when they'd finished shopping for new clothes for her, in the shopping center in the middle of the town's business district.

He slouched against the back of the bench and watched her. A pretty good little athlete, shuffling the ball from the inside of one foot to the other, then taking aim at the space between two trees as though it were the goal. He supposed she learned it in school; kids hadn't played stuff like that when he had been her age, though it looked like it would be more fun than baseball had ever been.

The shade had moved away from the bench. He let the sun's warmth sink into the fatigue along the back of his shoulders. They had been driving all morning long since leaving the coffee shop, stopping only for gas and to use the rest rooms. Before that, when he'd been speeding the car away from the Feld house, he'd decided at the last minute to head up north rather than going east. He knew from experience, the couple of times he'd driven to San Francisco with Sarah, how fast you could rack up miles on the long, straight Interstate 5 through Bakersfield. Plus, all the routes east on his map, Highway 15 through Barstow and Highway 10 through Palm Springs, went through the desert. The Datsun had developed a tendency with age to overheat, and he didn't know how well it would handle those routes. Heading north, he could still put a lot of distance between Dee and her mother, then start east when he hit Sacramento, crossing above Lake Tahoe to Reno and points beyond.

That would be tomorrow's driving. This little town they'd pulled off in, with its lawns sprinklered against the Central Valley heat, and neat, WPA-era stonework flanking the paths, was the first stop. He had steered the car off Highway 5 and found a motel at the end of the street where all the town's fast-food franchises clustered. Though he was so tired that he could have thrown himself on one of the motel room's beds right then and fallen asleep, they had gone out and shopped: jeans and tops, underwear, and a red nylon jacket padded like a skier's for Dee, a cheap electric razor for himself. So much for planning: his clothes, at least, he'd piled into the car's trunk before leaving the apartment for the last time.

Then to the park—Dee had been getting fidgety from being cooped up in the car all morning.

The warm sun weighted Braemer's eyelids, making him drowsy. This is all right, he thought, watching his daughter's solitary soccer on the grass. He smiled to himself. Should have done this sooner. Tomorrow there would be more driving, coffee-shop meals, another motel room, the segments of the road repeating themselves like squares of a checkerboard.

The little game went on, Dee fielding the ball past unseen opponents.

She wished he would come soon. It was so cold in the empty room. Kathy wanted him to come and lift her from the gray mattress, with one arm around her shoulders, then tease the warming blood to the surface of her skin, the point of his knife tracing out the pattern of crusted scars.

"Who was the other one?" she whispered. She knew there was no one else in the room, but spoke anyway. The words came out with her shallow breathing. "That other one . . ." She remembered hazily that her own name was Kathy, and her sister's name was Renee. Sometimes one, sometimes the other. Kathy was stupid, and had taken a long time to know how much her brother Jess loved her. But Renee was clever. She'd known from the start.

There was the little girl, the one she'd never seen. Renee's daughter. What was her name? Dee. That was it. That was the other one. Now she realized why she had gone and warned David, told him all those precious little secrets. Because she'd known that Jess loved the other one best of all, better than her or Renee.

She wondered what that love would be like, when Jess had consummated the hunger of it. To be inside the other, look through the other's eyes as Renee had looked through hers, to study the white, unscarred child's flesh with the soft fingertips of the child herself. Then the sharp point of his love could begin. His hunger that ate another's pain could feed at the warm, yielding source.

"If only . . ." she whispered, but there wasn't breath enough to say the words. If only it could have been me, she thought. She had come to give him everything else, but the last thing he wanted wasn't hers to give.

After work, and after the bus ride home, Sarah trudged down the street to the apartment building, her bag's strap heavy on her shoulder. She had been exhausted when she had gone in to work that morning, and eight hours of trying to get her leaden fingers in sync with some lawyer's voice dribbling from the dictation machine's headset hadn't helped any. If the fatigue hadn't gotten to the point of her nodding off on the bus and almost missing her stop, she wouldn't have gone back to the apartment just yet. A movie or, better, shopping without buying anything would have put off returning to the empty rooms a couple of hours longer.

She wondered for a moment what Dave and Dee were doing right then, whether they were still on the highway driving or had decided to stop for the day. Either way, she thought, they aren't here. She had scanned the cars parked along the street as she walked from the bus stop, looking for Dave's faded-green Datsun, hoping that there had been a change in his plans. Nothing.

His warning about Jess coming around to look for him popped up in her memory. She looked back along the line of cars as she came to the building's door, searching for the pickup truck she remembered Jess pulling Dee into. No sign of it, either. She fumbled her keys from her bag's side pocket and quickly let herself in.

As she got her mail, bills and a department-store flyer, from the box in the lobby, she glanced both ways down the hall. A door opening as she was looking away startled her, the strap of her bag slipping off as her shoulders flinched upward. One of the building's resident old ladies peered down the hallway at her, smiled, and gave a little wave before shuffling back into her apartment and closing the door behind her.

Sarah pulled in a deep breath, waiting a moment for her heart to slow before picking up her bag. She hadn't realized until now that there was a thread of fear laced in with her other worrying. The memory of Jess snatching Dee away from her was still sharp in her mind, a clip from some urban terror movie that she had found herself blundered into. That had been the first time she'd ever seen him, she had only heard Dee talk about him before. Backyard barbecues, working on the truck, or fixing things around that house she lived in with Carol. Nothing Dee had ever said had prepared her for the man she'd seen then, a face set hard, but not hard enough to hide the violence inside, a boiler tensed against the scalding pressure. His eyes, what she had been able to see of them beneath the squinting lids, had been all red, as though the tiny veins had swollen and burst into each other.

She pushed the image of the face away and started up the stairwell, carrying her bag. There was a bottle of German white wine in the refrigerator—a glassful of that set beside a steaming bathtub was what she really needed.

On the third floor she glanced down the hallway from the top of the stairs, to see that no one was there, before she headed down to the apartment.

As she closed her own door behind her and turned the deadbolt, she felt a hand grip her elbow, squeezing tightly. She gasped and started to turn her head, but another's face was already pressed close to her ear.

"Go ahead and scream if you want," came Jess's voice. "I'm very good at making people be quiet."

She felt him against her stiffening spine, and fought down the breath rising to break in her throat. "How—how did you get in here?"

From the corner of her eye she could see a smile tugging at one corner of his mouth. "These apartment-door locks," he said, and pushed her, stumbling, into the living room. "Kids can pick 'em."

His hand let go of her elbow, and she nearly fell, catching herself against the arm of the couch. She turned and saw him standing, hands resting easily on his hips, between her and the door. A pair of mirror-lensed glasses covered his eyes now.

"Go on," he said, "have a seat. Make yourself at home, you know? And stop looking so scared, for Christ's sake. I just want to talk with you, is all."

Shrinking away from him onto the couch, she watched as he lowered himself into one of the armchairs. He picked up a can of beer, which he must have gotten out of the refrigerator, and took a sip. The can sloshed in his hand as he tilted it back and forth, studying the white flecks of foam that washed on top. "Where's your boyfriend?" he asked without looking up.

Another part of the movie she had wandered into, now metamorphosed into a grade B hoodlum flick. But still scary. The sunglasses looked like unsheathed metal. "Dave's not here," she said.

"No shit?" The glasses lifted toward her. "I didn't know that—I really hadn't got around to checking all the closets yet."

A few seconds of silence, while she watched him sipping the beer. The muscles of her legs tensed as she gauged the distance between herself and the door. Her fingers dug into the fabric of the couch, anchoring her. Even if she got by him, Jess would be up and at her back before she could manage to unlock the door.

"So where is he, then?" Jess dangled the can lazily between one thumb and forefinger.

"I don't know."

"Just took off, huh? And left you to hold the fort. Nice guy."

"What do you want?" Her eyes flicked toward the kitchen—that doorway was closer to her.

"Come on. The same thing I came up here for last time. Dee's got a home already. That's where she belongs. I mean, Carol loves that kid. She's been the one who's really taken care of her all this time. And then your boyfriend gets this hot notion up his ass—"

"Dave's her *father*." A portion of her fear had been replaced with anger.

"Christ, what does that matter?" Jess pulled at the beer again. "Look, I know you probably think I'm some kind of monster, just strong-arming my way through everybody, but all I'm really concerned about is getting Dee back home where she belongs. That's all. So why don't you just tell me where David's taken her, and then you won't have to worry about it anymore."

She studied him settled back into the chair, then shoved herself away from the couch and ran for the kitchen.

The drawer came all the way out when she jerked it open, falling with a crash of metal on the floor. She knelt down, scrabbling through the mess, and came up with both hands wrapped around the handle of a carving knife.

Jess was already leaning against the side of the doorway watching her.

"Get out of here," she said, holding the knife out in front of herself.

His smile widened, and she could see his tongue sliding across the edges of his teeth. "You know," he said slowly, "I could take that away from you. And then you'd be in a world of hurt."

"Get out."

"You really don't know, do you?" He straightened, rocking back on his heels with hands tucked in his back pockets. Her face, in the mirrors of his glasses, was drained white. "Tell you what," he said. "You better believe that when your boyfriend shows up again, I'll be right there behind him. And I'll let *you* watch. Won't that be fun?" He turned away.

She heard the apartment door open, then close again. The knife stayed trembling in her hands as she closed her eyes, listening to the sound of his footsteps in the hallway beyond.

They were watching Dan Rather on the evening news —Dee's choice; her father wondered if it was some kind of a crush—when she announced that she was hungry again. The motel room's TV set, mounted on a head-high shelf by the door, had a persistent slow roll in the picture that no amount of reaching up and fiddling with the tiny knobs in back would fix. Braemer was just as glad to have an excuse to get away from the bifurcated heads, mouths above eyes, on the screen.

"Shower time, then, Pelé," he said. "You're still all sweaty from chasing that ball around in the park. I'm not taking you out in civilized society smelling like a locker room."

Dee, sitting crosslegged in the middle of one of the beds, groaned dramatically and fell backward, legs still locked together. "But I'm *starving*." She raised herself on her elbows. "Where we going to go?"

"I don't know. Pizza sound all right?" There was a place just a couple of blocks down from the motel.

"Sure." The food was the aspect of this adventure that Dee liked the most. One long chain of coffee shops and junk food stretching out before her, thought Braemer. He'd have to remember to stop at a drugstore and buy some kind of vitamins for her. A list of things they needed, like supplies for a Himalayan expedition, was lengthening in his mind. Toothbrushes—how could he have forgotten those? The small details of life on the run were starting to pile up.

Dee leaned over the side of her bed and rummaged through the department-store bags, pulling out a new top and pair of jeans. She rolled them into a ball, slid them off the bed, and disappeared into the bathroom. A moment later, the sound of running water and a wisp of steam came from under the door.

Braemer stood up from the low-slung chair and turned off the flickering TV. The news shrank to a point of light and blinked off.

A cloud of steam escaped from the bathroom when Dee opened the door just far enough to stick her head out, her hair pasted in damp tendrils on her neck. "Hey, you know what they got here?" One bare, wet arm held out a small paper-wrapped square. "Little tiny soaps!"

"So use 'em already, woman of the world." The bathroom door shut again as Braemer gathered up the department-store bags from the floor. He stacked them on the shelf above the clothes hangers, then started to pick up the other things Dee had left stewn about. Only a few hours into the motel room, and it looked like a pack of girls, rather than just one, had moved in.

As he fit one of the wire hangers into the sleeves of Dee's old corduroy jacket, he felt something in its pocket. He reached in and pulled out a knife.

He stared at it for a long moment, the sound of the shower's forced rain pressing louder in his ears. The knife had a plastic handle and a thin, serrated blade, the metal mottled gray with cold grease. A cheap steak knife, one you could snatch from the table at any coffee shop in America, walk out with it in your pocket if you wanted it.

His thumb flicked across the edge of the blade, found it sharp enough to cut whatever flesh was brought to it. The point, even to the eye alone, was capable of piercing the skin and sinking through blood until the thin metal would strike bone and snap in two.

Plastic and metal. Braemer, eyes squeezed shut, leaned his shoulder against the wall. Flesh and bone. He could hear through the plaster the murmur of a TV playing in another room, a soft voice whispering words he couldn't make out.

I forgot, he thought, the words already shifting into an accusation. You forgot because you don't want to remember. Why you're here, why Dee's with you, where you're going, what's behind you. You don't want to remember.

A happy little father-and-daughter excursion. With his thumb and forefinger he kneaded the ridge of bone between his eyes, where a dark knot was growing. He could have convinced himself of it, just letting the unpleasant parts fade back into memory. Take a vacation. Just hop into the car with your family and drive. See the U.S.A.

He heard the shower shutting off in the bathroom. Dee would be out in a few minutes. He lifted the store bag on the shelf and slid the knife underneath.

Farther, he thought as he rubbed the grease from the blade off his fingers. We still have to go farther away from her mother. Not because of all that bullshit Pedersen had laid on him—he wasn't ready to start buying into that again—but because Dee hadn't started to forget yet. Not underneath. The knife filched from the coffee shop proved that. They still had to get to that place where the past, all those knife-edged memories echoing in her head, would start to fade away. Some place far from here, where the forgetting and the healing start.

Fine, thought Braemer, we'll get there if I have to drive that friggin' car to Bangkok. The real problem is, what about tonight, and all the other nights, when I'm asleep and she's supposed to be?

An image came to him of his daughter's eyes opening in the middle of the night, another segment of her mother's psycho programming unwinding in the brain behind, and himself sunk in a sleep a few steps away.

The world was full of sharp-edged things. It would take only one, and then there would be no more waking up. For either of them. His nightmares would be over, but Dee's would just be starting.

Have to do something, he thought. The sad notion of what it would be was already clear in his mind. Just for a while. Just until we get to where we're going.

"I missed you," whispered Kathy. The room was so filled with the muffling darkness, soft black velvet, that she hadn't been able to see him come into the room or even hear the door being opened. Yet she knew he was there with her, at last. "I was afraid . . . it would be too late."

"Plenty of time." Jess's voice was both near and distant. Yellow-tinged light seeped through her eyelashes, and she could see his blurred figure standing in the center of the room, hand dropping from the bare lightbulb's pull-chain. The light dazzled from his face in two stars as he slid the mirror-lensed glasses back on. "We've got all the time we need."

He knelt down and lifted her from the mattress, one arm around her shoulders. His other had brushed the tangled strands of hair from her face. For a moment her vision focused tighter, and she could see herself reflected in the two oval mirrors peering at her.

A woman's naked body, drained white against the blotched gray of the mattress. Ribs like curved matchsticks over the concave pit of her stomach. Her hips were a butterfly-shaped bone swathed in a few layers of skin. The inside of her thighs ran hollow to the cleft of tangled hair. A blue vein pulsed, thin and rapid, in her throat.

And over the pale white skin was the network of scar tissue, strings of still-angry red crusted into ancient black along her forearms. She could trace the passage of his sharp-pointed love along every inch of her own flesh, as though his fingertips had brushed, slow and gentle, the raised tattoo through her skin, her own blood the ink he'd washed away to reveal the new language carved so that it could only be read from inside the skin. It had taken a long time for her to learn it. Clusters of red flecks inside her elbows marked where the needle had sunk its point, to heat the blood to the level where it had trembled to be let out.

A whole history was written there, on the limbs and

trunk of the naked figure caught in the small curved mirrors above it. Centuries of an etching fire, which had blanked out everything that had happened before she'd come to this room.

The voice, her sister's voice, had brought her to the room and to him, but now she knew it was her own will, broken and reset, that kept her here. She could no longer tell if it was Renee's voice or her own that laughed and spoke to Jess. Her sister's voice didn't seem to come into her body now, sliding like a wind through the broken panes of the window, but was pulled into her by Jess's hands—as though her body were the end of a rope tied to Renee. The cutting edge in his hands invoked and held the other voice inside her.

He laid her back down on the mattress and the abused/loved flesh reflected in his glasses receded as he stood up. She watched him strip off his shirt, his own skin pale, almost translucent, under the glaring light. "Plenty of time," he said, looking down at her. "But we'll have to hurry."

She closed her eyes and, a moment later, felt the point of the needle probing the inside of her arm, seeking where the vein could still be entered. A small bite just below the skin, and she felt the heat blossom in her arm, then wash through the rest of her body. Her heart raced. When she opened her eyes, she could feel the other already inside her, looking up at Jess. The summoning had begun.

Sweat gleamed across his shoulders and haunches, the skin over the coiled muscles taut and shiny as a snake's belly. It was as if the heat of the chemical in her veins had burst into the room and set the mattress on fire. The air shimmered in waves along his form as he drew the needle out of the crook of his own arm, leaving a red dot on the glistening white skin. He was naked except for the mirrors that were his eyes.

"This is the last time," he said, kneeling down. "This is the end of it for you."

"What . . . what are you going to do?" Her voice was a weak exhaling of breath, almost lost in the rushing sound of blood in the ears. The other voice inside her stayed silent, but she could feel it coming closer to hear Jess's words.

"Everything I did," said Jess, "was to bring her inside you. Our sister. Inside you, where she could feed. She's consumed you from the inside out, made your flesh into hers, made your eyes hers—everything. She's inside you now. And I'm going to let her out." Another point of light flashed, bright as the mirrors, from the blade of the knife gripped in his hand.

The room expanded in the chemical heat, space elongating to carry the walls and ceiling farther and farther away from her. Even kneeling, he towered miles above her. She managed to whisper one word: "Why?"

He gripped her ankles and parted her legs. "Because now it's my turn to feed," he said. "On her."

She felt his fingers work into her, spreading her open. A different ritual than before—a piercing that didn't require the knife held in his other hand. Then the small pain as he entered the narrow, bruised flesh, his weight pressing against the thin layer of skin covering her pelvis.

His breath close to her ear. "This is the last," he whispered, a note almost of regret in his voice.

She knew it. Her own breath began to pant in sync with her heated pulse. This is it, she thought, the edges of her vision darkening, collapsing into a tunnel. Everything else had been just getting ready for this moment. Her knees raised to clasp his sides as the flesh at her center grew soft and moistened around him.

The other voice inside her swelled in her throat, pressing out to the lips gasping for air.

Just as the contractions began, her flesh pulsing against his, he reared away from her. Still inside her, he curved his back into a bow, one hand gripping tight into her shoulder, the arm trembling rigid.

She looked up and saw his teeth clenched, lips drawn back. Her belly was reflected in his glasses.

The other point of light, the knife, showed in the mirrors as his hand raised it to the pale skin.

The blade disappeared, sinking into a red line sliding up to her breastbone.

She felt the sharper penetrating, deep inside her. She watched her flesh part open to show his forearm, red surging over his elbow, looped with the gray coils of her intenstines breaking open.

The knife slid from his hand as his fingers clawed upward, reaching through the soft tissue of lungs for her heart. The wave of red splashed across his face, spattering the scene the glasses held.

In her throat, her scream choked in blood.

The last she heard was her sister's laughter.

Dan Rather wasn't on at eleven—nothing but the local newscasters giving the late wrapup—so Dee settled for an old "Saturday Night Live" rerun.

Braemer sat in the chair by the door, watching his daughter watch the TV. When they had come back from the pizza parlor, Dee had put on the new red-and-white striped pajamas he had bought her earlier that day. Now she lay sprawled on her bed, feet tucked under the pillow for warmth, her folded hands and chin resting on top of the new soccer ball, her eyes following a dead comedian on the screen as his black-and-white image waved a samurai sword about. Braemer had wanted to phone down to Los Angeles and Sarah tonight, but at last he had decided to let it go; he didn't want to do it

222

while Dee was with him, and he couldn't think of anything to say. Not while the problem of how to take care of Dee while they slept filled his thoughts.

From the clothes he had piled in the trunk of the car before leaving Los Angeles, he had taken his oldest shirt, the one whose cloth was softest from age and washing. A blue cotton dress shirt, one button missing and replaced with another just different in color, the fabric at the elbows grown thin. In another year it would be ready to be thrown away. Now he held it crumpled across his knees, the TV's gray light flickering over the backs of his hands. No new idea had come into his head to replace the one that had been lodged there for hours. That's it, then, he thought. No other way. He unfolded the shirt, grasped its bottom hem in his fists, and ripped downward the length of the cloth.

Dee looked away from the TV and toward the tearing noise. "What're you doing?" she asked, puzzled.

"I'll show you in a minute." Face set hard, Braemer went on tearing the shirt into strips. Dee went back to the television screen, her forehead wrinkling as she glanced over at him every few seconds.

He laid the strips one by one across his knee, until the shirt was nothing but two-inch-wide fragments. The collar, cuffs, and front section with buttons he wadded up and threw into the plastic trash basket by the door. He gathered up a couple of the strips, threads dangling from the frayed edges, and tested their strength by wrapping the ends around his knuckles and snapping the lengths taut between his fists.

It was close to midnight by his watch. Come on, he prodded himself. Only what you have to do. He closed his eyes, the strips of cloth dangling from one fist, forced his breath deep and slow. Then he stood, walked over to the TV, reached up, and switched it off.

From her bed, Dee looked up at him, waiting.

"We've got to talk about something, honey," he said.

She frowned, eyes studying him. "'Bout what?"

He stepped to the shelf above the hangers and pulled out the knife hidden under the bags. Sitting on the edge of her bed, he held it out on his palm toward her. "I found this," he said. "In your jacket."

Dee drew away from the outstretched hand, her eyes shifting from the steak knife to his face and back again.

"You took it from the coffee shop this morning, didn't you? When I wasn't looking." In the light from the room's lamp, the thin blade looked mottled with disease, the congealed grease smeared with handling. "Didn't you?"

Her lips parted, the tip of her tongue thrusting forward a denial, and failing. She nodded her head slowly, still looking at the knife.

He folded his hand around it and slid it into his pocket, out of sight. Dee's eyes remained fixed, staring down at nothing. He reached out and stroked her hair. "Why did you take it, honey?" He tried to keep his voice low, soothing.

"Don't know," murmured Dee, shaking her head. The curved, shining edge of a tear welled along her bottom lashes and stayed there.

Another knife, invisible, slid into his chest. He felt himself hanging from it, from this moment in time. It's come to this, he thought, appalled. Your own child, and this is what you've got to do. "Was it your mother?" he said gently.

Dee nodded, then looked up at him with an odd gratitude. "She made me take it."

Madness, he thought. But in a way it was true: the things Renee had done to their daughter were the ultimate cause of the grease-stained knife lying in his hand. You didn't need to believe any occult blather—just a little thumbnail Freud instead—to see the connection. "Sweetheart," he said, "we've got a problem here."

Looking miserable, Dee nodded her head. "I know."

"If your mother made you take the knife, then . . . she might make you do other things. Couldn't she?"

Another nod, Dee gazing at her feet.

"So . . ." Braemer pressed on. Nothing was going to make it any better. "So we have to do something about that. I mean, so she can't hurt you, or me. Like before."

Dee glanced at the strips of cloth dangling in his other hand. He could tell that she had already guessed what he was going to do.

"This is just for when I have to get some sleep, honey. You know, when I can't keep an eye on you. And just for a little while. Just until we get to someplace where your mother can't make you do these things." He cupped her chin in his hand and turned her face toward him. "Okay?"

She regarded him with grave, serious eyes, eyes that had seen too much to be a child's anymore. "Okay."

"You ready to go to sleep? It's getting pretty late."

"Sure."

She laid down on her side, facing away from him, and he brought her forearms together at the small of her back. Pushing up the red-striped sleeves of her pajama top, he could easily hold both her wrists in one hand. He had been thinking for hours on how he was going to do this, and still didn't know. The bizarreness of the situation held its own grim repulsion. He had never anticipated that he would ever have to tie someone up, especially his own ten-year-old child.

The trick was to make the knots tight enough to keep her from doing anything during the night, yet not hurt her. The skin of her wrists was pale, delicate, the veins beneath showing as through translucent paper. His heart would break at the faintest mark of a bruise there.

Carefully, he looped two of the soft cloth strips around one of her wrists, then drew a knot down snug enough that she wouldn't be able to pull her hand through. He did the same with the other wrist, leaving a slack of an inch between the two knots. They were tight enough that he felt sure she wouldn't be able to pick them loose. He'd probably have to cut them off in the morning.

He checked to see that the circulation to her hands wasn't cut off by the strips. "Are those too tight, honey?"

She shook her head, face moving against the pillow.

"You'll be able to sleep like that, won't you?"

She said nothing, only hunched her shoulders and turned farther away from him.

That did it. He stood away from her bed and dropped the rest of the strips onto the floor. The thought of tying one of her ankles to the bedframe, to keep her from getting up and walking around during the night, had crossed his mind, but now he pushed it away. This was all that he had the stomach for. The prospect of doing this every night—for how long?—churned nausea in him.

He pulled the blanket over his daughter, laying the edge across her shoulder. He looked down at her for a moment, then turned away to get the paper-bagged object he had stashed in the room's dresser.

While Dee had been in the pizzeria's rest room, he had gone to the liquor store next door and bought a fifth of Cutty Sark. In the bathroom, he watched his hands twist the cap off the bottle. He unwrapped the crackling paper from one of the glasses by the sink and poured a half-inch into it.

The Scotch burned against the block in his throat, then spread a slow warmth through his chest. Hands gripping the white porcelain, he leaned against the sink and raised his eyes to the mirror.

You look like shit, he told himself. Eyes red-rimmed, black stubble against dead-white skin. Not enough sleep, too much driving and thinking. He turned on the cold tap. He'd have to be careful to keep his act cleaned up, or someone along the line, maybe one of the motel-keepers, might suspect that a man traveling alone with a ten-year-old girl was actually—touch of grim humor—a kidnapper.

He bent low to the sink and splashed the cold water into his face. With one of the towels from the chrome rack thrown over his shoulders, he covered the bottom of the glass with more Scotch and switched off the bathroom light. In the dark, glass in hand, he walked out and sat down on the edge of the bed. He sipped and watched the huddled figure of his daughter. This moment had been there right from the start, from before Dee had even been born, just waiting for time to uncover it.

Some time later, he set the empty glass down on the floor and lay back in his clothes on top of the bed. Still sober, but with the edge of his thoughts blunted, he found sleep in his forearm brought over his eyes.

A room, empty except for the figure of a man sitting on the floor, his back against the wall. On the cracked linoleum a few feet away from him, a pair of glasses upside down. The mirror lenses glinted in the faint light from the streetlamps beyond the window.

He breathed, slow and deep, as though recovering from a great exertion. His bowed head leaned toward his arms, draped across his knees.

There was something else in the room with him—an

object that had the rough shape of a human being, but wasn't one. Not any longer. It lay sprawled on a mattress that was soaked in a fluid now turning thick and sticky.

The man, eyes closed, tilted his head back, rubbing it slowly against the wall's flaking paint. The eyes opened to slits as he got to his feet and stood up.

He walked to the window and looked out through the dust-clouded glass, his hands gripping the sill. The muscles of his shoulders flexed and gathered, feeling the strength within as the hooded eyes gazed out at the night-filled street.

He heard something in the darkness, and awoke. Braemer lay still, gazing up into the darkness. Then the sound came again, and he was scrambling across the bed, reaching for the lamp.

The light snapped across the room, throwing the shadow of his hand on the wall. He saw his daughter on the bed across from him.

Dee had kicked the blanket away from herself. It lay in a crumpled pile at the side of the bed. She lay twisted about on her side, a low, whining noise seeping from her clenched teeth as she struggled with the cloth strips binding her hands behind her back.

She saw him, and fell silent. With the side of her face and one shoulder pressed against the bed, her eyes widened, focusing on him. The nostrils flared white, bloodless, under the tangled hair falling across her face, as her breath came in a sharp, panting hiss. It wasn't his daughter's face anymore.

His heart slammed against the limit of his ribs as he pushed himself toward the foot of his bed. The thing in his daughter's body stared at him, following his movements as he stood up.

"Dee—" He stretched his hand out cautiously toward

her, the fingers trembling in air. A line of sweat began to gather under his collar, growing chill in the room's still air.

Her eyes darted from his face to the hand approaching her. She drew away, curling into a ball, hissing as her lips bared her teeth to her pink gums. A trail of saliva stretched from the point of her incisor to her tongue.

Braemer walked to the bathroom door, reached inside, and found the Scotch bottle. The empty glass was by his bed. He carried the bottle back with him, picked up the glass, and poured it half-full.

With his back against the wall, he sat on the bed and drank, watching his daughter coiled across from him. Her eyes glittered, locked on his with a feral intensity.

The Scotch passed from the trembling glass in his hand onto his tongue, bitter and ineffectual. No matter how long the night took in passing, there would be no sleep. Only the watching, and waiting for the light to come through the curtain.

THIRTEEN

No phone calls had come the night before. None this morning. Sarah sat at the kitchen table, her bathrobe pulled tight around herself, hands drawing warmth from the cup they held. The tea inside it was brackish and too strong, even though nearly white with milk—she had forgotten about the tea bag steeping in the hot water while she had gazed dully out the kitchen window, her mind slowly pulling out of the fog of the night's fitful sleep.

She raised the cup and took another sip. The one virtue the tea had, other than enough caffeine to start her sluggish blood pumping again, was that it cut the stale film coating her teeth and tongue. Her mouth had been parched when the alarm clock had finally drilled her awake, as though she had been gasping for breath all night long in her sleep, or shouting out something in a dream that had mercifully faded out of memory.

Two slices of toast, stiff and cold as roofing shingles, covered the plate she had pushed away from herself.

Habit, rather than appetite, had made her drop the bread into the toaster's slots. Nausea, faint but tangible as a thumb pressing at the base of her throat, rose in her at the sight of last night's dinner still on the table—greasy waxed paper crumpled into a ball, the charred stubs of a few French fries mired in a clotted smear of ketchup. When she had gotten off work—no call from Dave had come for her there, either; she had told the girl at the switchboard to be sure and let her know if there was one—she hadn't been able to face the prospect of going back to the empty apartment and cooking a dinner just for herself. She had stopped at the first hamburger place she spotted along Santa Monica Boulevard. There, she had found herself, in her secretaries' uniform of panty hose and heels, giving her order while surrounded by chattering Thai and Salvadorean families at the graffiti-carved benches, and sullen, shaved-head teenagers feeding quarters into the video games in a chain-link wire cage. Some punk with a sense of local history had spray-painted CHARLIE WAS RIGHT and CEASE TO EXIST on the burger stand's wall. From across the street a plain-faced young girl, head wrapped in a white turban—one of the Bhajan followers who ran the vegetarian restaurant down on Third and Fairfax—had gazed with faintly sad eyes at the whole scene.

There had been no place for Sarah to sit down in the usual mix of Los Angeles city life, so she had carried the white hamburger bag the rest of the bus ride to the apartment. And had proceeded to stuff herself, going on eating long after her small apppetite had been killed.

Great, she told herself. Self-disgust was written on the flattened-out hamburger bag in invisible letters. Go on like this and you'll be big as a tank when you see Dave again.

The prospect of that *when* turning into *if* was the knot growing tighter in her stomach. To be here by herself, with Dave on some unknown stretch of asphalt God knows where; to drag herself to work in the morning and then back to the apartment so empty that the television's glare and yammer fell into it like a faucet dripping wet rust into a dry sink—to do all that without the help of the voice on the phone, his voice, which would keep certainty from drifting to hope, and then decaying further to a dread that gnawed without ceasing. . . . This is what it's like to go crazy, she thought. The tea, now cold, slid down her throat toward her heart.

After the business of finding Jess waiting for her in the apartment, she had given the building manager a check to pay for having another lock installed, a deadbolt heavy as two fists of brass. The manager, alarmed at Sarah's talk of finding traces of an intruder in the apartment, had gotten it done the next day. The memory of Jess's face, with its thin smile and hokey but still scary mirror sunglasses, had eased enough that she wasn't jumping upright, muscles snapped taut, every time the refrigerator's motor switched on. That had been Wednesday; the last time she had spoken to Dave was Tuesday, the morning he had called and said he had Dee with him, and that he was taking her away.

No other call that day, or the next. And now this was Friday morning, and Sarah felt her nerves being pulled taut in the silence that had enveloped her. She could literally feel it, not a figure of speech any longer, but a knotted cord running through her spine. Another couple of days without word, and the breaking point would be reached.

The clock above the stove showed ten minutes past the time she should have been getting dressed and ready to work. She pushed her chair away from the table and got to her feet, her body like a dead weight hanging from her shoulders.

There was nothing else to do but go to work. She

didn't know where he was, what was happening to him and Dee. (Did they have an accident did Jess find them oh God what if—) At work, the pressure of other people's eyes on her kept the tears bottled tightly inside her. Only once yesterday had she been forced to make her way, teeth biting her lower lip, to the ladies' room, to crouch behind the latched door of one of the stalls and squeeze a fist of wet tissue paper against her face.

It would be harder today. Loosening the robe's belt, she felt sick with knowing somehow that the phone still wouldn't ring today.

"Want anything else?"

Dee shook her head. Half of a stack of pancakes, sodden with dark syrup, lay untouched on the plate in front of her, along with an over-easy egg more messed about than eaten. She looked tired: smile gone, a dark trace beginning to circle under her eyes. A tired little girl. The nights in the motel rooms were being as tough on her as they were on him.

So you try sleeping with your hands tied behind you, Braemer told himself. See how bright-eyed you'd feel in the morning. He wiped his mouth with a paper napkin. "You ready to go?" he asked.

"Yeah, I guess so." She lifted her head from where she had propped her chin in her hand, cheek pushed up and nearly shutting one eye.

He felt mired in the same fatigue. At the cash register, paying the check, his thick fingers could barely fumble through the cash in his wallet. In his mouth, the sour taste of the alcohol necessary for the couple of hours of sleep he managed to get at night collected on his tongue in thick spittle.

The days were starting to run together.

They had reached Sacramento and, after spending one night in a motel there, had finally gotten off Interstate 5 and its endless straight miles north. Now they were heading east at last. Braemer didn't even know the number of the highway, only that he had to lower the windshield visor against the sun glaring in his eyes in the mornings.

Across the state border and into Nevada. Then another motel, just past Reno in the little town of Sparks. He knew they weren't making very good time, that with steady driving, just sticking to the highway, he could have been putting a lot more miles between his daughter and his ex-wife. But the fatigue had begun to set in so early now, a couple of hours after the nights finally ended and whatever fast-food coffee was sitting in his stomach like cooling lead. A couple of hours on the highway, and the cars in the lane ahead of him would wave and split in two, merging together again only when he took one hand from the steering wheel and dug his fingernails into his other forearm, the pain sharp enough to clear the highway of its fog for a few more minutes. Sometimes that wasn't enough, and his eyes would snap open at the rapid spatter of noise his front tire made as it drifted over the raised plastic dots separating the lanes. Once it had been the sharp blast of a truck's air horn, and he had jerked out of his rolling daze to see the truck's massive wheel, black rubber and blurring chrome bolts, inches away from his side window. He'd had to cut the steering wheel sharp out of the curve into which they both had been heading.

Keep that up, he told himself—again, and you'll get both yourself and Dee killed. That'd be a quick fix to your problems. Walking across the pancake house's parking lot with her, he dug his key ring out of his pants pocket. He unlocked the car door on her side, and she climbed in.

Going around to the other side, he started to fit the key into the door lock when he felt something wet on his

234

hands. He looked down and saw that the skin at the ball of his thumb, where he had run it across the key's serrated edge, had been cut open, as though the little piece of metal were a razor-sharp saw blade.

Amazed, he stared at the red line welling up from the torn skin. It grew nearly as wide as his thumb and trembled for a moment, a shining red oval, before it broke and streamed down the palm of his hand.

For a moment he couldn't move, could only watch his pulse beating at the source of the blood. His shirt cuff was soaked red before the current snapped in place inside him, and he wrapped his other hand around his thumb to squeeze the tiny wound shut.

The blood didn't stop. For a second it was hidden under the knuckles pressed white. Then the red seeped between his fingers, as though each space between them were another wound, spilling out more blood than he had ever seen before.

Dizzy, he lifted his hands clenched together, and the blood soaked through his sleeves to the elbows, dripping from there to the parking lot's asphalt.

The dizziness grew, his vision darkening with each surge from his heart to the wound. "Stop . . . stop it," he whispered into his fists. His legs gave way and he fell against the car.

His hands were too weak against the blood, and they opened from each other. He felt the warmth between one outstretched palm and the car's window. It smeared across the glass as he scrabbled at the door, his knees buckling.

Through the red-stained glass he could see, faintly, his daughter leaning forward and staring intently at something through the windshield. "Dee—"

She turned her head and looked at him. Another's eyes, not hers, and another's smile slowly lifting the corner of her mouth. Coming closer as he felt his face press against the glass, sliding across the smeared blood.

Then it was gone.

Dee, eyes wide with fright, crouched in her seat and stared at him through the perfectly clear window. He pushed himself away from the car door, standing upright on wobbly legs. Slowly, he turned his hands, palms and backs and then palms again. They were gray with dust from the unwashed car. No blood anywhere, except in his heart slowing from a racing pitch.

"Daddy—" Dee had crawled across the seats, unlocked the door, and pushed it open. "Are you okay?"

Braemer moved his tongue, stiff in his mouth, wetting his dry lips. "I . . . I'm fine," he said at last.

"What's *wrong?*" Dee's voice trembled with fear.

He caught a glimpse of his own drained-white face, reflected in the window. It was no wonder she was scared. "Nothing," he said. "Everything's okay, don't worry about it. Just got a little . . . dizzy, is all." He wiped his hands on his pants, sweat cutting the dust, trying to swallow the thick wad that had collected in his throat. Between his shoes he saw his key ring splayed out where he had dropped it.

In the car, with Dee watching him in silence, he managed to get the ignition key into its slot. His unmarked hand still looked like a fragile miracle to him. Jesus Christ, he thought, that was a rough one. Whatever it was. The engine chugged into life.

He had read somewhere of people who, for research or a half-assed desire to get their names in *The Guinness Book of World Records,* had gone without sleep for days at a stretch. What had struck him as the worst effect those people had suffered, was the way that their dreams, unable to come out during sleep, had begun to filter into their waking world. And not dreams, but nightmares—as if everyone had a source of self-brewed bad acid inside himself. And if it couldn't be drained off safely while one slept, then it would seep across the brain's tissues and into reality, a thin membrane over his face, with the worst night fears projected onto it.

Maybe that's what had happened. Braemer stroked his damp palms along the curve of the steering wheel. He certainly hadn't been getting more than a couple of hours of sleep each night of this grim little trek, and most of that was a cross between alcohol stupor and the dull blanking-out from fatigue that gave no rest, only a sudden jerk of the muscles and the sight of the hands on his watch having crawled a few more spaces around the dial.

The worse part of having your nightmares come while you're awake—a grim realization—was that there might not be any waking up from them.

Wonderful, he thought. That's all we need right now. The nights, and the days, had already turned into nightmare enough, without something even worse underneath breaking through. If pieces of the night were going to start coming out in the daylight, then the two of them were really going to be in deep shit.

"Daddy—" Dee's voice broke into his dark thoughts. "Are you okay?"

He didn't know how many minutes he had been sitting there, the engine running, while he gazed through the windshield at nothing. He forced his lips into a smile. "I'm fine," he said, dropping one hand to the gearshift. "Ready to hit the road?"

For a moment her eyes searched his face. "Sure," she said softly.

From outside the building he could smell it. Faint but unmistakable, curling in one's nostrils like mold from something he left forgotten too long in a closed cupboard. Something rotting in the warm, unstirring air of Los Angeles.

Pedersen stood on the sidewalk, gazing up at the rows of shattered or boarded-over windows. Strands of weeds as high as his knees, the stalks now dried into brittle yellow and brown, sprouted from the edges and cracks of the sidewalk. The gutters were filled with trash, cans with lettering faded from the sun, wadded newspapers baked to the same color as the weeds and crumbling to fragments with words that no one could speak on them. He had parked his panel truck blocks away; this street was empty except for the remains of some unidentifiable sedan with windows broken out and charred black upholstery, sitting low on its wheels with tires decayed into ragged gray strips around them.

Anywhere but in a section of abandoned buildings like this one, caught between the receding of money and the coming of the wrecking crews, someone would have caught the odor by now. In another day or two they might even have called the police. But this little pocket was too isolated for even the stray vagrant or bag lady to have crawled to, looking for a hidden corner to build a nest of warm, urine-smelling rags. Here the odor could have run its course, growing stronger and more nauseating until one's tongue would draw back into a ball at the base of the throat at the first trace of it. Then as more days passed, the smell would slowly fade into something dried and leathery.

Pedersen stepped across the littered sidewalk to the building's door. The whole place had the look of a warehouse that had been converted to some other use, maybe a clothing sweatshop, before the owners had shut it up without even torching it for the insurance, if any. A plain wooden door, the unpainted planks weathered to gray, hinges and a metal hasp pitted red with rust—

the only bright object was a new chrome padlock dangling near the door frame.

He tugged at the lock, then went back to the truck and came back with a short pry-bar. The hasp's screws pulled out of the dry wood with a sharp screech. He carried the bar with him as he pushed open the door and stepped into the darkness inside.

The smell was stronger in the unlit corridor. Light slanting in from the door showed more trash heaped against a sagging set of stairs. The guardrail, hammered together out of bare two-by-fours, swayed in his hand as the steps creaked under his weight.

The door at the top was unlocked. The smell came from behind it, seeping through and into the wood. Pedersen stood outside for a moment, listening. He heard nothing. His broad hand lifted and swung the door aside.

In the room there was more light from the windows that the boards had been pulled from, revealing the broken panes of glass. The light spilled across the floor of cracked linoleum to the corners.

A utility sink against one wall, a smear of rust under the taps. Food scraps, greasy paper wadded into balls. A mattress with a corpse on it.

Pedersen crossed the room, then stood looking down at the woman's body. Naked, the skin gray under blood dried to a dull black. Beneath her, the mattress' dirty striped cloth could barely be seen through the blood that had soaked into it. The flies had found the torn-open edges of her viscera. Their shiny, green-metal backs and gauze wings could be seen scurrying in the tangled entrails. The smell boiled upward from the corpse. He stooped down and brushed the stiff hair away from her face. Her eyes, open but filmed over with dull white cataracts, stared up at the ceiling. The cheeks were sunken, the teeth below outlined through the skin drawing tight against bone. It was a face he had seen before, but not through his own eyes.

His own face was expressionless as he stood up. He had known even before he found the building that he was too late, that there would be only the corpse in the room when he pushed open the door that he had seen dozens of times before without ever having stood in front of it. The woman, when she still had been a thing with a name, had been called Kathy, though a voice inside her would speak her sister's name. That was all past now. The motion of the flies was the only life the flesh would hold.

Pedersen stepped to the side of the window where he couldn't be seen and looked down to the street. Another would be coming to this room. He knew that, could feel his approach through the vacant streets around the building. He leaned against the wall, watching and waiting for Jess to return.

Braemer saw the sign marking the California state border ahead at the side of the highway, and for a moment he couldn't understand what it meant. He held the steering wheel and gazed at the sign coming closer, a flat official statement of geography. The other traffic on the highway kept pace with the car, or pulled slowly ahead, gaining speed over the curve.

"Jesus Christ," he said. It had suddenly dawned on him: he was heading west again, instead of east. Somewhere he had gotten turned around, probably when pulling out of the pancake house parking lot that morning, had taken the wrong on-ramp and driven all the way back to the California border without realizing it. Instead of stretching out the distance between his daughter and his ex-wife, he had started retracing the road back down to the house in San Aurelio and its half-dead ghost in the upstairs bedroom.

"Shit." Dee, curled up on her seat beside him, didn't hear. Her eyes were shut, and her mouth had fallen open. The last couple of mornings she had gone to sleep in the car right after they had started driving. That seemed to be more of a rest for her than the nights spent with her hands tied behind her.

An off-ramp for a truck weighing station peeled away from the highway just past the border sign. Braemer started slowing the car, edging into the right lane. He could turn around in the station, get back on the highway, and go back over the whole morning's mileage, just to get back to where they had started.

Shows how screwed up I've gotten, he thought wearily. He was tired already, tired of driving and tired of the motel rooms even narrower than the lanes on the freeway. If he hadn't caught the California border sign—more like it had caught him—he could have kept rolling on in his semialert daze, hands turning the wheel and feet moving from brake to gas automatically, until he had either plowed them into the back of a truck or woken up in the middle of downtown Sacramento. The only thing all the coffee he poured into himself every morning did to keep him awake was to fill his bladder to the splitting point. He swung the car down the off-ramp, hoping that the weigh station had public restrooms.

He glanced over to his daughter, still sleeping, her face pressed against the back of the seat. It's rougher on her, he thought. She was so small, and paler now. There was a limit to how many days they could go on driving, to get to that place where the child would be out of the reach of her own mother. Since that morning when he had awakened in the dark motel room, switched on the light, and seen that other face pulling the muscles of her face from beneath the skin, into a mask of bared teeth, and eyes hard and bright as an animal's in an uncovered hole—since then, Pedersen's talk about Renee's soul creeping into Dee's mind had taken on more weight. He still didn't know if he believed it, or believed anything other than just going on driving, racking up the miles away from that ragged-breathing death's-head at the highway's other end.

Don't take too long here, he told himself as he pulled into the weigh station, you got a long ways to go. He parked away from the trucks, the diesels murmuring softly as they sat or chuffing black smoke as they rumbled from under the tall shelters over the scales and back onto the highway.

A small rest area, complete with picnic benches, had been set up in a cleared space behind the station. A red-wood-sided building with GENTLEMEN painted on one side and LADIES on the other was at the end of a gravel walkway.

Dee was still out; it took a lot to wake her from these naps. Braemer locked the car door and headed for the rest-room, his shoes crunching on the path's white stones.

A few minutes later, the rubber ball in his gut deflated again, he walked back toward the car. Over by the nearest truck, he could hear voices shouting.

"That fuckin' coil's gone out again!" The truck was a big refrigerator rig, long white sides with ARCTICOLD painted on in frost-blue letters. Chrome strips outlined the edges and doors of the freezer section behind the Kenworth cab. One of the drivers, stocky and pissed off, had just pulled his head and shoulders from an open hatch at the front of the trailer, and was wiping his blackened hands on a rag. The other driver, hands dug into his back pockets, lowered his head and spat on the asphalt.

"I'm gonna make that asshole at the lot eat that piece of junk!" The driver's face was red and darkening.

"We'll be hauling a goddamn maggot factory into Fresno at this rate." He jerked a thumb toward the building by the scales. "Go call dispatch and tell 'em we're gonna be here a couple of hours while I work on this thing."

"Think ya can fix it?"

"How the fuck should I know? Christ almighty."

The other driver peered into the dark space inside the hatch, spat again, and headed for the pay telephone, brushing past Braemer with his hands still jammed in the back of his grease-stained jeans.

Before Braemer got the key into the car's door lock, he heard the truck driver sliding open the tall side door of the freezer section, rattling on its metal track. He looked over his shoulder and saw the driver pull himself up into the freezer, then disappear into the front, presumably where the malfunction was.

With the truck's side door open, Braemer could see the cargo. Frozen beef carcasses, gutted and skinned, hanging from the pointed curves of hooks thrust through the thick lumps of what had been the cattle's necks. The truncated animal corpses dangled from rails running the length of the freezer section, one row behind another—dark red flesh marbled with yellow-white fat, stumps where the legs had been sawn off, deep hollows where the ribs could be seen bending back to the spines. On the carcasses closest to the door, the thin layer of frost steamed with contact from the warmer air outside.

A truck full of dead meat. Braemer felt nothing looking inside it, not even a twinge of distaste. With the beef frozen, there wasn't even an odor drifting across to him, like the sharp smell of blood and sawn bone that hit one stepping into a butcher shop. In the freezer section, they seemed cleaner, more hygienic, a factory product.

Tough luck for the cows, is all, thought Braemer. He

had enough problems already without contemplating vegetarianism. And if you ate a hamburger, you had to figure that brown disk of gristle and grease inside the bun had come from somewhere, that somebody in red-stained overalls and a hard hat had brought the hammer down right between the pair of big eyes fringed with lashes delicate as your own. Happens all the time. Right on the . . . what was it called? The killing floor; that was it.

He shook his head to clear away the bleak reverie into which his thoughts had drifted. Something about the sight of the frozen carcasses, hanging silent in the freezer's dark interior, had tripped him up for a moment. In his present fatigued condition, he felt a certain kinship with a stiff side of beef. He started to turn away, back to fumbling with the key, when he glimpsed the small carcass hanging just inside the freezer door.

The icy interior of the truck reached out and envelop-ed him, drawing his skin tight, as he saw the thing clearer. Another carcass, gutted and skinned like the others, but much smaller and shaped differently, lacking the huge swelling chests and thick loins of the beef carcasses. Another difference—the head was still attached, lolling forward against the point of the hook thrust through the slender neck.

The head had a face on it. Frost steam drifted away from the slack cheeks, the mouth stretched open, the eyes turned upward to show dead, blank white.

Thick, dark hair, as fine as a baby's, fell across the exposed flesh and tendons of the body's shoulders.

His daughter's dark hair. Dee's face.

He felt the nausea well up through his fatigue. His heart raced with fear, not fear of anything hanging from a hook in the truck's chill space, but the fear of seeing things that weren't really there. The fear of losing it, of losing the grip of one's senses upon the world, so that another world tacked together of frozen corpses and blood came bubbling up in one's head. And then what use were you? It would be hard to rack up much mileage on the highway while your horror-show flashes were busy turning the other cars into things filled with gristle and raw flesh with no skin. Driving like that would be some fun all right, for as long as it would take for him to spook himself into a guardrail at a nice safe and sane, ha-ha, fifty-five miles per hour.

It's not there, he told himself; there's nothing there. He leaned back against the car and squeezed his eyes shut. But the vision remained. Behind his eyelids he could still see the small body hanging, head twisted to one side to make room for the hook protruding through the throat like a new steel tongue. The limbs had been sawn away—he could see the white bones at the center of the stumps remaining, the skin of the small, naked thighs peeled away to reveal flesh even more naked. Inside the gutted body cavity, the delicate fingers of her ribs arched.

It's not there, it's all in your mind, this is just fatigue toxins, dream residue seeping into the real world. She's really inside the car right behind you, right where you left her, sleeping all curled up on the seat, nothing wrong. If you open your eyes that other thing will be gone, there won't be any little corpse hanging from a hook. Open your eyes and it's just a truck full of frozen beef.

He couldn't force them open. His eyes stayed shut, the lids trembling over the sockets. Come on—thoughts pleading with themselves—it's not really there. Come on, come on, I suppose this truck makes deliveries to some obscure restaurant that has Prime Rib of Little Girl on the menu—when available—and while you were in the rest room they spotted Dee in the car, popped her

245

out, whack-whack with the cleavers, and hung her up in the truck? Jesus Christ, you brain's not just tired, it's sick.

The vision stayed, clear in the dark field behind his eyelids, and still he couldn't open them. He was afraid to. If he opened his eyes and a gutted body in the truck still had Dee's face attached to it, it would mean that the madness had sunk deeper into him, to some level where it couldn't be rooted out. Go away, make it go away, his thoughts ran on. In his mind's eye he saw the little hanging body shift on its hook, as though the flesh was thawing, blood melting from red ice into thin rivulets inside the ribcage, drops pattering onto the floor. The face moved, he could see it and it wouldn't stop, the mouth opening wider and the tongue gagging forward, the moan of pain choking around the steel hook spearing the neck. . . . Then he heard the sound, not a moan but the edge of laughter cutting through the roaring of his own blood in his ears.

The truck's side door rattled, sliding along its metal track. It slammed shut, followed by the sound of the latch falling into place and the snap of a lock.

Braemer opened his eyes, to bright sunlight and the truck's closed door. Nothing showed but the white side and frost-blue letters. Whatever horrors were inside were now safely sealed away.

His shoulders relaxed with his breath in a gasp. Under his arms, his shirtsleeves felt clammy. Jesus, he thought. That had been a rough one, worse than the business with his bleeding hand that morning. He shook his head, running his shaking fingers through his hair. Much more of this, and he'd be ready to turn himself in to the hatch. That would be one way to get the nice long rest he needed.

He heard the door to the truck's cab swing open. Looking across to it, he saw the driver who had gone to the pay phone. With one foot up, ready to pull himself into the cab, the driver glanced over and smiled at Braemer.

For a moment, Braemer squinted, the sun blurring his vision. He could see the driver's thin face breaking into a grin—gaps in the yellow teeth, leering secret knowledge. . . . The face of the vagrant outside the apartment building in Los Angeles, with its constant manic grin and cracked Bible verses, winked at Braemer before disappearing into the truck's cab.

Hands trembling, Braemer turned around to unlock the car door and saw the two empty seats inside. Dee wasn't in the car.

He whirled around, hands flattened against the door, and scanned the parking lot. Rows of trucks, and nothing else. "Dee!" he shouted, his voice cracking on the sour taste that had surged up into his throat.

Gravel crunched under shoes nearby. He turned and saw Dee passing between the picnic benches. In a few strides he had her, kneeling down and grasping her arms, his face close to hers. He saw her eyes wince shut, and knew his grip on her was too tight. "Where did you go?" he said, letting his hands go looser but still holding on to her. "Where were you?"

"I had to go." She pulled one arm free and pointed to the rest-room. "Over there."

He stood up, his hand resting on her shoulder. "All right. But next time don't leave the car unless you've told me where you're going."

"Okay." She glanced from the car to the highway. "Daddy, are we going back home?" She had figured out the change in direction.

He shook his head. "No, sweetheart. I just . . . made a wrong turn, is all. We have to keep on going the way we were."

A slight tremor worked the back of his knees as they

walked to the car. Beyond his fatigue, which had reached spine-draining proportions, the solidity of the ground itself had been put into doubt. The earth kept gaping open, showing its razor teeth and the small creatures torn by them.

He opened the door for Dee and she climbed in. Wearily, he pulled himself in behind the steering wheel and turned the key in the ignition. Swinging around onto the highway, in the right direction—east—this time, he hunched his shoulders against the tension strapped into the muscles. Sunlight washed across the windshield, the air clean enough to see the edges of the mountains etched sharp against blue. He drove, leaving the refrigerator truck and everything it held behind him.

There was one part of what he had seen back at the weigh station that was still rattling against the sides of his skull. Everything else—the frozen little corpse, the mouth opening—was falling back into memory. But the laughter he'd heard while his eyes had been sealed with fright, the laughter went on echoing in his head. He hadn't recognized it then, and it had taken him several minutes to sort through the accumulated years to when he'd heard it last. Then he knew.

It had been Renee's laughter.

Pedersen heard the footsteps on the sidewalk below, then saw the shadow of the approaching figure fall across the dry weeds and cracked cement. He flattened himself against the wall by the window and watched Jess come up the street to the front of the building, walking with the wary, immediate grace of a predator, keeping itself hid from its prey.

The building's door was right below the window from which Pedersen watched. Jess's shoulders drew up, visibly startled, when he spotted the broken hasp. His hand, with the key to the padlock in it, flinched away from the metal dangling from the splintered wood—an animal's motion, spotting the trap just before the catch was sprung. He backed a few steps away, hands outstretched, turning slowly to bring all the rest of the street into view.

Sunlight darted off the mirrors of his glasses as his gaze flicked upward, from one dust-clouded window to the next. Above him, Pedersen stayed frozen in his position, hidden from view, the rise and fall of his chest stilled. Jess reached and pushed open the bare wooden door, then raised his glasses with one hand to squint painfully into the darkness of the corridor behind it. He stood for a long moment, turning his head a few degrees, as if the sharpness of his hearing could better penetrate the space inside. Finally, he lowered his glasses again and stepped cautiously through the doorway, out of view of the window above.

Pedersen pushed himself away from the wall. With a lightness inconsistent with his bulk, he stepped quickly across the floor, his feet making no sound on the cracked linoleum. He crouched down in the darkness by the side of the door.

On the stairway outside the room, Jess's footsteps could be heard, rising slowly from one wooden step to the next. When they halted on the landing outside the door, Pedersen balanced forward on the balls of his feet, his arms held loose and ready on his knees. His breath halted as he waited.

The silence on both sides of the door stretched, a chain of seconds passing one by one. The only sound came from the flies hovering over the object on the dark mattress against the wall. Then the door's thin wood cracked, the noise splitting the air, as the rusted catch pulled away from the frame. The door flew open and slapped against the wall. The flat of Jess's boot hung for a moment in air, where he had kicked the door.

Pedersen leaped, uncoiling. He caught hold of Jess's foot, pulling him off balance. The landing's wooden guardrail cracked, almost breaking through, as the ridge of Jess's spine hit against it.

One hand clawed across Pedersen's face, digging for his eyes, as Pedersen pressed his weight to his forearm across Jess's throat. A hissing intake of breath bared Jess's teeth as he jammed his knees up into Pedersen's ribs.

Pedersen got to his feet, pulling Jess upright with him, the front of his jacket wadded in the huge hands. Jess's arms flew wide as the other lifted him clear of the landing, turning and then throwing him through the open doorway into the room.

Jess rolled on his side as he landed, scrambling onto his feet in one fluid motion. The mirror-lensed glasses, torn loose from his face, spun glittering into the mounded trash in one corner. He stood crouching, knees bent as though ready to spring at the throat of his opponent, his own face reddened with blood as his chest labored for the breath that had been choked out of him.

Pedersen stepped into the room from the landing, closing the door, its lower panel split in two, behind himself. He rested his hands on his hips, waiting and watching the figure trapped in the room.

His breath slowing, Jess straightened. His eyes were knife-slits focused on Pedersen. "What are you doing here?" he said, voice flattened to a cold edge.

For a fraction of a second, Pedersen closed his eyes. They were sadder when he looked again at the other. "You knew I'd be here someday," he said quietly. "You knew the time would come."

A smile thin as his slitted eyes creased Jess's face. "How did you find this place? I didn't think there was anybody who could tell you where my little . . . retreat was."

"I've been looking a long time," said Pedersen. "Through my eyes, and yours. You were very clever about that, but then you knew, didn't you, that I was there to catch whatever scraps I could pick up of your seeing. So you would slink here like an animal in the dark, from gutter to gutter, keeping your thoughts blank so there would be no clue as to where your feet were carrying you. And then when you were safely hidden in your little hole, you would focus your awareness again, letting me see everything that went on in this room. All so clever, Jess. It took my piecing together every glimpse of sidewalk, every trace of moonlight across a building front, to find this place. But I did find it."

"I'm glad you found it." Jess's smile edged wider. "I was hoping to see you again. That's why I came back here. And you've come just in time, haven't you?"

Pedersen folded his arms across his chest. "I'm too late for all I wanted to do. To save her." He nodded toward the form on the mattress. The corpse was hidden under one of the thin blankets he had found wadded in a pile on the floor—he had brushed the flies away before drawing it across the torn belly and staring face. "But there's time for the rest that has to be done."

Jess's laughter battered the walls. The space between him and Pedersen formed a line from which he hung suspended, his back arched against the loop of an invisible rope. Veins and tendons stood out against his throat, as his howling face turned up to the cobwebbed ceiling.

"You . . . stupid . . . shit." His face drew back into a ridged mask from the grin pressing his lips bloodless against his wet teeth. He rose up, elbows jammed into his ribs, the insides of his wrists turned out, fists trembling in ecstasy. "You fool, you burnt-out old fool! You don't have time! You're too late for everything!"

Pedersen stood silent, the storm of laughter breaking against him, waves on rock. "I'm sorry," he said at last. "What's happened is my fault. But it is too late for you, Jess. All sins can be forgiven, but some paths can't be retraced."

Jess gazed at him, his breath panting through his jagged smile. "Save that for your little flock of sheep," he said. "You keep them in line real well with that pious bullshit. Do your deep-breathing exercises, children, and Daddy will lead you all to the promised land, where your scrubbed-clean little souls can just sparkle in the sun forever. They really lap that shit up, don't they? But you knew I didn't buy it, and that's why you bounced me out—because you knew I was on to it, me and Renee and the couple of others that went with us, you knew we'd found the real way to do what we wanted. And we weren't afraid to take it, either. That's why you had to get rid of us—so your little flock of sheep wouldn't find out that we could do what their windbag teacher couldn't!" With each of his last words, his finger jabbed the air between them.

"There was a time," said Pedersen, "when I could have helped you. But no more. What you've done to your soul can't be undone. The blackened rock inside you won't be washed away even by death. When your body dies and rots in this world, in the other one that stone will still lie buried from the light."

"You're the one who's afraid of death, not me." Jess stepped quickly to the mattress and yanked the blanket away. He knelt down and lifted the corpse, his hands cupped in the hollows of the dangling arms. The slack, naked limbs flopped against him as he spun about with it to the center of the room.

"I've eaten death up," said Jess, laying his face against the blood-crusted head with its clouded eyes and mouth open in an unheard scream. He swayed, eyes closed, a man dancing in parody with a string-jointed doll. The gray skin broke and pulled away from the angle of the jaw beneath as its head lolled forward on a twisted neck. "Everybody can rot," Jess's voice a crooning whisper, "and I'll still be with the living, going from one sweet little child to the next, eating each one from inside, one after another. . . ."

The dance ended, the corpse torn from Jess's grasp and crumpling to the floor. Pedersen gripped Jess's shoulders, lifting him clear off the floor.

Their eyes locked and held, one face snarling, the other set like a fist.

Pedersen pulled a few inches away from the thing he had seen at the depths of the other's eyes. "It's not Jess," he said softly. "It's not Jess, is it. He went too near the fire. He came to eat, and was . . . eaten. You were stronger than he was."

The snarl broke into words, Jess's throat and tongue twisting into another's voice. "Fuck you," said Renee, mocking laughter curled beneath.

Jess's forearm lashed across the side of Pedersen's face as he tore free of the larger man's hands. The blow staggered Pedersen back a couple of paces.

In the fraction of a second before he regained his balance, Pedersen felt Jess—the thing inside Jess— claw past him. The door crashed against the wall, followed by rapid footsteps down the stairs. He didn't have to go to the window to hear the sound of running from the sidewalk below fading up the street.

He stood for a moment in the center of the room, the space filled with silence once again. He waited, then, head bowed and shoulders rounding into an old man's, bent slowly down to the corpse sprawled on the floor. Cradling it in his arms, he carried it to the mattress and laid it down. After crossing the arms across the gutted abdomen and smoothing the jaw closed with his hand, he stood up again.

For a while longer he stood over the body, until the room was drained of light, and the forms inside swallowed up by shadows.

The house was quiet now, empty except for Carol and her sister locked in sleep upstairs. She stood leaning against the kitchen doorway, a double handful of pieces of stiff paper clutched to her breast, and listened to the silence broken only by the sound of breathing from the bedroom above her.

There had been a child in the house once, whose laughter and talk had bounced against the walls like a bright-colored rubber ball. That had been nice; she remembered those days as all sunny. The little girl was gone now, and that had driven Carol to grief for a long time. But now she found it easy to wait. Her brother Jess had brought the child back here to her real home once before, and he would do it again. He was out there somewhere looking for her right now. In the meantime, there was a lot to do.

She switched on the kitchen light—evening had settled dark around the house—and carried the stack of old photographs to the table. Pulling one of the chairs back, she sat down and spread out the pictures.

Black and white and gray shades. Old snapshots, a few studio portraits, family faces in blurred vignettes. Old cars, the front of this house when it was new and fresh-painted, people squinting into the sun behind the camera. Time had been frozen into a gray block, then sliced into thin pieces.

None of the photographs was whole. Each had some part torn or scissored off, leaving a tattered or razor-straight edge running through the little family scenes. Half the pieces were yellowed and faded from the years of exposure in the frames out of which Carol had taken them a little while ago. The other pieces had been protected from light inside the cover of the album she had found in the cellar.

One by one, she began to search through them, matching each photograph with its missing piece, torn edge against another frayed segment, scissor-cut lined up with its mate. As she found each pair, she placed it carefully above the remaining jumble, as though putting together a jigsaw puzzle.

She tried not to look deep into each picture as she put the pieces together, but she already knew what they showed, what figure was held in the pieces that had been cut away and hidden. Her hands worked on, shuffling through the flat black-and-white fragments.

Although it was a different room, a different motel, the TV set seemed to be the same one. Late news murmured on, from the TV's angled perch across from the two beds: bombed-out rubble somewhere in the Middle East, and outside a church or mosque—Braemer couldn't tell which—a plain wooden coffin swaying above a shouting crowd, as though it were floating down a river of hands and faces.

Braemer sat on one of the beds, his back propped against the wall, his eyes seeing but making no sense of the images jumbling into one another on the black-and-white screen. A bathroom tumbler with a half-inch of warm Scotch filled the hand resting on his outstretched leg.

The coffin being carried by the TV mourners might as well have held the day's murdered remains, a crumpled-up calendar page. A complete waste. Braemer lifted his hand and took another sip, letting the liquid etch its warmth into his chest. On the screen a woman smiled at a carton of toothpaste.

The two of them, Dee and himself, were back in the town of Sparks, no farther east on the road leading away from San Aurelio and Renee than they had been the night before. After turning the car around at the weigh station, leaving behind the refrigerator truck with its load of frozen blood and meat—some real, some hallucinated—his shaking hands had steered them back along the highway and over the Nevada border for the second time. Even before they had gotten through Reno, he had realized he was burned out, holding the car on the road by clamping his teeth on his lower lip until the white dashes on the concrete would stop wavering and merge into a single line. The vision inside the truck, the child's body dangling from a steel hook, had drained him of what little strength the previous night's fragmented sleep had given him.

If he had gone on driving like that, his head snapping back from the heavy drag of his chin toward his chest, eyes wide to focus the slipping road back underneath the car, the last time he'd wake up would be to the sound of the car's metal ripping open to spill Dee and him out against a guardrail. As soon as they had hit Sparks, he had pulled off the highway and onto the row of fast-food shops and motels they had started out from that morning.

He wound up losing a half-block of distance in the whole round trip. Not wanting to pull into the same motel—Braemer figured that his fatigue-darkened face and trembling hands aroused enough suspicion already—he'd taken a room in one not even as far down the street as the last motel had been.

At this rate, he'd thought as he'd moved the car around to the side of the motel, we'd do better just staying right here. The idea was tempting. He could feel his bones like hinged iron rods dragging through his flesh to the ground.

A quarter-inch of Scotch remained in the glass, just enough to color the clear bottom. Braemer swallowed the heat, looking over at the other bed. In the bluish light from the TV, Dee was a huddled shape under the blanket, her face turned to the wall, only her hair showing tangled across the pillow. The blanket rose and fell with the slow rhythm of her breathing.

When they had gotten settled into the room, Dee had shaken her head when he'd asked if she wanted any lunch. He'd gotten the same response to a suggestion of taking her soccer ball to a nearby park and kicking it around. All she'd apparently felt like doing was flopping on her stomach on the motel bed and staring silently at the hectic gray shadows of daytime TV, without even bothering to switch channels, any program as good as another. She had looked pale, skin fading to porcelain, the circles around her eyes growing frighteningly darker and hollower—a small figure cropped from old photos of factory children in the nineteenth century, with only the dingy frock changed to jeans and a red T-shirt.

She'd picked up a dragging sniffle from somewhere, the start of a cold—Braemer hoped that was all it was. The sound of her breathing, just audible under the TV's noise, had a soft, liquid edge to it. What if she's really sick? he thought. The Scotch blurred the outlines of his worries but didn't take them away. Maybe all the driving, the escape up the highway, had exhausted her even more than it had done to him. There was only so much strength in a child, less in one that had gone through as much as Dee had. If he had come to the end of his rope, then maybe she had already let go of hers, falling away from him.

This is the real nightmare, he thought. The last smoky drops of Scotch seeped around his tongue to the saliva beneath. On top of the low chest of drawers under the TV stood the bottle, two-thirds of it air and the mingled ghosts of a week's motel rooms. A picked-at hamburger and bag of fries, the cold remains of Dee's supper, lay in the middle of a flattened paper bag. Braemer looked at the little domestic scene through half-closed eyes. Not the thumb gushing out more blood than it could possibly hold, or the rolling freezer with his daughter's body hung inside—this small room, space boxed inside four cinder-block walls, this was the nightmare to be feared. It held just the two of them, father and daughter, all the rest of the world left behind, milestones on a highway unraveling into distance, thread from the ragged edge of memory. A string of days had gone by without his phoning Sarah in Los Angeles. He knew she would be worried sick about him, wondering what had happened to them, what road had swallowed them up without a trace. But there was nothing he could do. The point at which he could have fed quarters into a pay phone, dialed, and exposed himself to her voice was long past, lost on the highway or in one of the sterilized motel rooms along the way.

You're too messed up to talk to her, you'll worry her more if she hears you talking like this, she could pick up the exhaustion and crazy stuff cracking behind your voice, you're too messed up . . . That had been what he'd told himself when he'd found himself unable to step outside the room and walk down to a phone booth outside the motel's office. He'd stayed lying frozen on top of the bed, his hands cradling the back of his head. Letting the noise of whatever program Dee had tuned in on the room's TV flow across him, or listening to her breath as she slept. That was what he'd told himself to begin with, but already he knew it wasn't the truth.

Lying on the bed, he knew it, a stone in a hollow space inside him. The truth was that the telephone, and any voice he could hear over the miles of wire, Sarah's included—all that belonged to that other world he and Dee had left behind. That other world was still going on somewhere out of his reach, the figures in it going about their business as they always had, always would. His memory of them was as remote as the people the TV held, phosphor dots coupling and uncoupling in patterns bounced by satellite from far away.

All that really mattered to him now was right in the motel room with him. A little three-person world: father, child, and the shifting presence of the mother. She's here, thought Braemer, balancing the empty glass on his stomach. Something else that he knew, had finally become convinced of. Pedersen was right. When one gets tired and scared enough, then the truth breaks through the walls one built against it.

He could feel Renee in the room, silent and waiting. His own exhaustion, and the Scotch on top of it, filtered out of his blood. The big world could go on forever, but this one in the motel room was being drawn to a close, a string pulled by a hand he couldn't see. The blood and death he had seen on his own hand and in the truck were what was underneath when the fabric wore thin, and now the whole thing was going to come apart like rotted cloth.

He set the glass on the floor, got up, and turned the sound on the TV all the way down, leaving the mottled black-and-white glow to dimly light the room. Outside, the noise of traffic on the street and the highway a little farther off—not much of it, just after midnight—faded in the dark. He sat back down on the edge of the bed to wait.

It didn't take long. A few teasing minutes, the warmth of the Scotch dying in his stomach, then something else moved under the shadows thrown by the TV screen.

The shape that was his daughter sleeping under the blanket on the other bed stirred, stretching out from where it had been curled. The back of the child's head moving against the hollowed pillow, the child's face turning away from the wall and toward him as he watched. Dee's eyes opened slowly, lazily hooded, a half-smile forming when she caught sight of him. "Dave," she said quietly.

It was Dee's voice, but different. He could recognize the other voice speaking in her throat and mouth. He said nothing, waiting for its next words.

"Take these off, Dave." Dee's shoulders hunched upward, drawing her bound hands against the blanket. "They're so tight, they're hurting me. Take them off, Dave. I won't do anything—I just want to talk with you."

"No," he said. His tongue was thick in his mouth.

"Are you scared?" The smile—Renee's smile—on Dee's face turned coquettish, the eyes watching him and turning bright with their own light. "There's nothing to be scared of."

"No," he said. "I'm not scared." It was the truth—he wasn't. He knew now that he had been waiting for this moment for a long time, almost from the beginning. Hoping for it, underneath the layers of all his other thoughts, since Pedersen had told him of Renee coming back inside Dee's body. Whatever words had gone unsaid when Renee had fallen inside the lock of her coma, those words could be said now. Not fear, but another emotion which trembled in his arms and the limit of his chest, had moved inside him.

"You're not?" In the dim light, the face against the pillow looked more like Renee than Dee. "I'm glad, Dave. Now we can talk. It's been years and years, and all this time I wanted to speak to you, say things to you, and I couldn't. That's why I came back, Dave. All for you."

Renee's voice was clearer now, the child's voice swallowed up in it. The smile and the light in her eyes was of self-pleased cleverness, crueler and filled with more avarice than any child's could be. Braemer felt the hair on the back of his neck grow erect, not with fright but like a dog standing its ground against two yellow eyes in a dark hole with the stink of an unsatisfied hunger around them. "What do you want?" he said.

" 'What do you want.' " Renee's voice mocked him. "You don't know, do you, Dave? I've got what I want. I wanted to be alive—and I am. I like it, Dave. It's nice being alive." The word *nice* lengthened into an overripe morsel between Dee's tongue and teeth. "I know what it's like not to be alive. Oh, I've been to that other place, and I'm not going back. I don't have to. I'm here, Dave —with you. Oh, no, Dave, the question isn't what I want. It's what *you* want."

This is a corpse talking. He closed his eyes, feeling the nausea well up inside him. *Dead words.* Inside his eyelids he could see a bedroom in a house in San Aurelio. The hospital smell of disinfectant masking decay traced inside his nostrils. *Corpse words.* The voice that spoke was the voice from inside the body curling around a withered skeleton's gut on that bed in that room. The smile was a skull's on a pillow, a feeding tube snaking into the dark hole above the yellowing mouth.

"There's nothing wrong, Dave." The voice soothed low at his ear. "Everything's fine now. You can have what you want now. We're together again. It'll be . . . nice."

He opened his eyes. Somewhere under the face returning his gaze was his daughter, but he couldn't see her. The TV's flickering light drew the shadows of

Renee's face onto the blanket. "Why aren't you dead?" he murmured.

The other voice turned sharper, almost breaking into laughter. "But you didn't want me to die," said Renee. "You never did. Maybe it was you who brought me back. You didn't want me to go the first time I left you, and you never stopped. You just went on. All those years, and you couldn't forget. I walked out on you, but you couldn't stop loving me. You poor thing. That was why you saw so much of Dee, went on taking her home on the weekends with you—because you could see me in her. You wanted to have that little piece of me with you all the time."

Her words caught him up, erased the time and events between this night and the last time he had spoken face-to-face with her, years ago. An old conversation, interrupted and now continued. A simmering anger that had never died out glowed a notch higher inside him. "I never loved you," he said. "That was just being sick and stupid on my part. And then I learned to hate you so much—when I heard what happened to you, when I saw you like that, I could taste it. It was like I had your blood in my mouth."

The smile didn't waver. "But I'm here now, aren't I? What you always wanted in your little girl, and now you can have it."

"Get out." His own face was drawn rigid, muscles pulled against bone. "There was never anything of you in Dee. She's not your child, she's mine."

"But you're wrong, Dave. You're always so wrong. There's everything of me inside her, inside this little body. And nothing left of Dee. Do you know what I mean, Dave? There's nothing left of her, there's only me now. Every time I came inside her, I ate a little more. A little more every time. And you didn't even know it. Sometimes you thought you were talking to her, your little girl, and it was really me looking up at you with her eyes, listening to you and smiling and saying, 'Yes, Daddy; no, Daddy; I love you, Daddy.' And then I would eat a little bit more of her. She'd be screaming inside, and you couldn't even hear her. Until she was all gone. And now there's just me. There's just me and you, Dave. All alone. And now you can do what you want."

"Shut up." His own blood was hot in his face. "Shut up."

The face's smile had become manic in its intensity, the eyes bright points of light against the TV's wash. "It's what you've always wanted, it's what you've wanted for so long. I know what you want, and it'll be nice, it'll be so nice. I want it too, now." The child's body twisted about on the bed, spilling the blanket to the floor. Lying on her stomach, face pressed against the pillow, the child lifted her hands from the small of her back, the thin wrists still bound together by the torn strips of cloth with which Braemer had tied them. "Take these off, Dave, they're so tight. Or do you like it better this way?" The smile on the child's face grew wider, filled with conspiratorial glee. "Is that the way you like it?"

Something hot beat against his temples from inside, trying to break through the shell of bone and drown the room. His breath filled the space, a few feet, between himself and the thing that moved inside his daughter's body.

"It'll be nice, it'll be so nice," it crooned, an idiot savor wet on the lips it spoke through. The rounded corner of a pale shoulder drew close to the neck, showing naked through the loose collar of the pajama top.

"Shut up." His vision had darkened, red to black. All he could hear was the voice, curling over the laughter beneath.

"You'll like it, it'll be me again, what you've wanted for so long, now you can do all you want to me, only now it'll be with this nice sweet little body, and you'll like that, too, won't you? Won't you? I like it, it's nice, it's mine now, and I do whatever I want with it, I touch it in there and it feels nice, it feels so nice—"

He felt the back of his head strike something hard, the wall behind the bed he sat on. For a moment, he saw above him the room's ceiling, smeared with the TV's light, turn and angle downward, pressing closer to his face. He ground the palms of his hands into his ears, but the voice seeped through, relentless.

"—we made her, we can do what we want with her now, I gave birth to her she's mine now she was a bad little girl she wouldn't do what I told her *and now she's mine—*"

"Shut up!" He was on his feet now, towering over the small body on the bed. His hands thrust down and gripped the child's shoulders, his knuckles straining white as though to crush the voice inside the fragile chest.

The voice was silent. The eyes burned up at him, drinking in their triumph.

He pushed himself away, stumbling backward and fighting to regain his breath, his mouth all hot salt.

"I'm inside her now," said Renee's voice, softer, less frenzied, but tauter with gloating. "For good. And there's nothing you can do about it."

The heat drained away from his blood, leaving metal in its place. The room steadied around him, gray light drawing the corners into focus. He looked down at the small figure on the bed, a corpse's face beneath a child's skin. "Yes, there is," he said slowly. The cold metal that stretched along the bones in his arms was dark as the metal wrapped in the white cloth and stored in the trunk of the car outside the room. They called to each other. Hands at his side, his fingers curled as though folding around the crosshatched grip, balancing the weight inside them. "There's something I can do about it."

What he had fled from in the house all the way down in San Aurelio had come up here to meet him. The thing inside a comatose woman's body on a bed was now inside a child's body on a bed, but it was the same thing. And the cure, which Pedersen had handed him, was the same.

"Really?" A sly cunning in Renee's voice. "Do you really think you can do it?"

As he watched, her eyes closed. Something ebbed from the face, the muscles strained with laughter now softening, and it was a child's face again. His daughter, Dee, sleeping, her breath coming slow and regular through her open mouth. A wisp of her dark hair traced lines across her pale cheek. Whatever had been just under her skin, like a hand inside a puppet, had sunk deep inside her now, away from his sight.

He sat down on the bed across from the sleeping child. For a time that passed by him without measuring, he leaned forward with his hands clasped between his knees. Just watching her sleep: the small motions of her breathing, the curve of eyelashes dark in gray light. He gazed at her as if to memorize every small detail, put life into an engraving cut somewhere inside him.

Time started around him again. The night outside the room wouldn't last more than a few hours longer. He stood up and untied Dee's hands. After folding the blanket in two, he bent down and wrapped it around his daughter. Dee didn't wake up as he lifted her. Her head, eyes still closed in sleep, pressed against his shoulder as he cradled her to himself. She seemed to weigh nothing at all to him.

Outside, in the stillness broken only by the low

rumble of trucks on the distant highway, he unlocked the car and laid Dee carefully on the passenger seat. Still asleep, the blanket wrapped around her against the cold, she drew her legs up and nuzzled her cheek against the seat back.

He walked around behind the car and unlocked the trunk. A white cloth wrapped over metal filled his hands when he straightened and stepped back. The coldness of the gun's weight seeped into his fingers.

Behind the wheel, he laid the gun, still shrouded, in the space between his seat and the one in which Dee was sleeping. Just enough light slid through the windshield to pick out the small fingers of one hand clutching the edge of the blanket.

He turned his face away, then watched his own hand turn the key in the ignition.

The old photographs were finally complete, each matched with its missing piece. Spread out, they covered the kitchen table. Carol stood up from the chair and leaned over the photographs to study them.

One of the pictures showed a woman in a dotted print dress, 1940's style, holding a baby in a lace-edged bonnet and wrapped in a knitted blanket. The woman didn't look happy, holding the baby stiffly, as though it were some weighty object that she waited for someone to take off her hands.

It was a picture that Carol knew well. It had sat in a little folding frame on the mantelpiece in the living room for as long as she could remember. The baby in the photograph was herself; the woman was the one who had adopted her.

Across the edge of the scissor-cut was the half of the picture that she had never seen until she had found it with the others in the album in the cellar. That half showed a tall, somber-faced man. When the two parts of the picture were put back together, it showed the man standing next to the woman, Mr. and Mrs. Feld, his arm reaching in back of her waist. The same man was in all the parts of the photographs that had been cut or torn off and hidden away.

Carol picked up the one picture, the piece with the woman and baby in one hand, the piece with the man in the other hand. She studied it for several minutes before setting it back down on the table.

From one of the kitchen drawers she took a roll of transparent tape. Carefully, lining up the edges of the photographs to a perfect match, she bent over the table and taped the picture together, running the tape on both sides. When she was done, the man, the woman, and the baby were reunited in their flat black-and-white world, looking at her from its depths.

Braemer drove until the town was behind them. The road was a thin strip of asphalt bordered by dirt and sagging wire fences by the time it wound into a flat stretch of land ringed by low hills. The greenish glow of the dashboard gave the only light.

He pulled the car off the road, bouncing onto loose gravel. He switched off the engine and the silence became complete, but for the distant scraping of a cricket in the dry brush. Dee was still asleep in the seat beside him. Slowly, his eyes adjusted to the faint starlight until he could see her face. Her skin seemed whiter now than he'd ever seen it before, as though all her blood had gathered around her heart. Her hair looked like a black ribbon against her cheek. The only sign of life was the slow breath coming from her open mouth.

Just a child, thought Braemer as he looked at her, his own breath slowing to match hers. Sleeping like that, no trace of anything but a little girl in the dreaming face. Only in his memory, a memory bound by the four walls of a motel room back in the town, could he see the other face that had come swimming up into this one, as though the pale skin were transparent as water over a dark pool with darker things in its depths. Just a mask —his thoughts had hardened and chilled into steel. There's no little girl, no Dee anymore. Just that other thing hiding inside her.

From the white cloth he took the gun and the yellow box. He inserted one bullet, then snapped the cylinder back into place.

He fitted his hand around the crosshatched grip, one finger curling inside the guard and onto the trigger.

With his other hand he reached out and wrapped his arm around Dee, lifting and pulling her closer to himself. Her head lolled against her shoulder.

The barrel of the gun was only a few inches away from her smooth forehead.

Inside him there was no catching of his breath, no speeding of his pulse. The space remained empty where his feelings had been hollowed away. He had come such a long way to do this, but now that he was here, it seemed like the fitting together of the gun and the bullet inside, precise and ordered.

All he could feel was the cold weight of metal in his hand. Beyond the gun's black shape he could see Dee's face, still far in sleep, cradled in the circle of his arm.

It's not Dee, he told himself again; it's her. The nightmare was already over for Dee. A small motion of one finger, a quarter-inch into his fist, and it would be over for everyone.

He looked at her over the gunsight. He knew it wasn't a child, his child, that he held. Another thing had taken her place.

His finger began to squeeze tighter upon the trigger. *Go on, go on!* Inside his head, a voice sang with an

268

impatient glee. *Go on and shoot her, I don't need her anymore, I've got you.*

His finger froze in place just as the trigger began to move back.

The excitement of the thought that had shouted inside him puzzled him. Then a coldness deeper than the gun's swelled into his chest.

It's her—it's Renee. His own thoughts now, not the high shriek of the other voice, the same one he had listened to back in the motel room. She's in me now. The realization grew, opening into the darkness around him.

Blood to blood, thought Braemer. That was what Pedersen said. She's become like a virus, moving into and infecting her blood relations—her sister and her child. But when those are infected, when she's inside them—then it can spread, she can infect their blood relations, too. Blood to blood. Renee's related by blood to Dee, and Dee's related by blood to me. First the child is infected, then the father of the child. A chain of blood . . .

He looked at the gun, still held between himself and Dee, as if waking up and seeing for the first time.

It's her, he thought. Not me. She wanted to kill Dee. She was inside me, she made me think that—

The gun dropped from his hand and fell to the car's floor. A sob broke out of him as he pulled Dee to himself, his arms crushing her to his chest.

She woke as he rocked back and forth with her. "Daddy?" She pushed herself a little away so that she could see his face. "Where—"

He grabbed her shoulders and held her, studying her face, searching the eyes blinking in confusion. "It's you," he said. "It's you, isn't it? It's not her, she lied, it's you. She lied."

"Daddy, what's wrong—"

"Oh, Jesus." He hugged her tight again, her head in the hollow of his shoulder. "Nothing's wrong, sweetheart. Nothing's wrong at all."

In the quiet darkness, he rocked his child, sheltering the warmth of the small body with his own.

She held the taped photograph to her breast as she climbed the stairs. Toward the sound of ragged breathing, her hand reaching for the knob of the bedroom door. She pushed it open, letting the light that never went off fall across her.

The figure in the bed slept on, withered face turned to the ceiling.

Carol stepped slowly across the room and sat down on the edge of the bed. She looked down at her sister. Now I know, she thought. All the family secrets had been opened to her—now she was on the inside with the rest of them. The photo rising and falling with her own breath had been the key that had let her in.

She sat gazing at her sister's face while the night worked toward morning.

Braemer fed the coins into the pay-phone slot, and heard the chiming in his ear as they fell through the machine's circuits. The operator thanked him. At the far end of the line, another telephone began to ring.

Through the glass of the booth he could see Dee waiting in the car, looking back at him. The bright morning sun glared off the windshields of the other cars in the parking lot.

"Pacific Auto Restorers," a voice spoke in his ear.

"I want to speak to Pedersen," he said.

"I've been waiting for you to call, Braemer."

He recognized the other's voice now. "I really screwed it up, didn't I?"

"Braemer, you fucked up in every way possible." Pedersen's voice was more sad than angry. "Where are you? Why didn't you take care of Renee like I told you to?"

"I didn't believe you. That's all. I just didn't believe you about her."

"And now you do. That's just great. Now what are you going to do?"

Braemer closed his eyes, smelling his own sweat trapped inside the phone booth. "Pedersen, please— you've got to help. It's gotten much worse."

"What did you expect?" The voice from the telephone was cold and harsh. "Did you really think you could run faster than an evil like that could follow? You never thought that, Braemer. You wanted to think that, but you knew what I told you was true. You always knew it, but you were afraid."

"Yes," whispered Braemer. "I knew it."

"And now what do you want me to do? There's nothing I can do to help you. There's only that which is necessary for you to do, Braemer. Do you still have the gun? You didn't get rid of the gun, did you?"

"I've still got it." The memory of last night, with the gun's dark shape blotting out Dee's sleeping face, made his hand ache as though it were squeezing the cross-hatched grip again.

"I told you what you have to do. That hasn't changed. You've wasted your time, but what you have to do is still the same."

"But it's gotten worse. She's inside me, Pedersen. Renee's inside *me* now. I felt her last night. Like she was inside my head. She made me see these things—like blood and . . . and dead things . . . And then there were thoughts that weren't my own. I almost killed my own daughter, because Renee made me think she was inside Dee, and that I could kill *her* that way. But then I

271

realized that was Renee inside me, that was her thought, not mine. She's inside me now—"

Pedersen cut off the rush of words. "That was nothing," his voice on the telephone spoke curtly. "I can tell that Renee's soul is still rooted in her own body. But she's gained more strength, more power. You don't have much time left. Soon she will be able to break away and take over a blood relation completely, such as your daughter. Then she would be immortal, a thing that would be able to pass from one blood relation to another. But at this time she can only touch your mind, Braemer. She can make you see things, whisper her thoughts into your head when your own thoughts are weak and confused—that's all that she can do to you now. And your being aware of it, being prepared for these visions, these thoughts that aren't your own, limits her power to touch you. For you, she can only suggest, not control. But if she leaves her body, then you will become her food. She will eat your daughter's soul, and then yours. Unless you do what I told you."

"All right." Braemer drew his breath, feeling his exhaustion as a weight wrapped around his arms, pinning him. "I'll do it."

Pedersen's dispassionate voice went on. "You'll have to be more careful now. Renee will be waiting for you this time. Her power has grown so much in this time you've wasted. She's infected Jess now; she can move inside him. You'll have to watch out for him. He'll be there waiting."

"All right. Whatever." Braemer massaged his forehead, trying to work blood into his cindered brain.

"I've done what I can, Braemer. But my task is to keep others from wandering into what Renee and Jess did. This is your responsibility, and I can't help you any more than I have. There is no help. And there is no time left to waste. There's just what you have to do, and it may already be too late."

"I know."

"Goodbye, then." Pedersen's voice was gone, terminated with a click from the telephone.

Braemer hung up the phone, pulled open the booth's door, and headed for the car with Dee waiting inside. The highway to the south outlined itself on a map inside his head. They had crossed back into California before the sun had come up: he had known already what Pedersen would tell him, what he had to do. From here it was back to Sacramento to catch Interstate 5, then a straight shot all the way down to San Aurelio and all that was waiting for him there. If he drove without letting up, just stopping for gas, they would be there by tonight.

"Are we going now?" Dee watched him as he slid behind the steering wheel.

He nodded. "Yes," he said. "We're going home now."

FOURTEEN

Another phone booth, this one at the end of the highway rather than the beginning. Braemer's hand trembled as he slid a dime into the slot. The hundreds of miles of concrete and asphalt, from above Sacramento all the way down to San Aurelio, had passed the vibration of the tires through the steering wheel and into his arms. His elbows felt stiff, as though still cocked into driving position. He dialed the number—there was no need to get this one from Directory Assistance; it was memorized in his heart—and heard the connection go through and then the drilling purr of the phone ringing in the Feld house.

He waited through several rings and the silence between them. It was going on toward midnight, and he figured it would take Carol a little while to get to the phone downstairs and answer it. That was all right: there was time enough, now that they had made it here. The phone booth stood at the edge of the parking lot for the gas station just off the freeway. The road that the off-ramp emptied onto ran in one direction into San

Aurelio, in the other direction to the tract of unfinished homes that surrounded the Feld house. The same road he had taken a hundred times before at the starts and ends of another life's weekends, ferrying his daughter from one home to another, like all the other twentieth-century fathers. That's over, he thought as he looked down the road running under the freeway overpass. This was the last time he'd be here, the last time he'd drive up into the hills above San Aurelio and through the skeleton houses. Just a little farther, and it's all over.

His free hand, resting on top of the phone box, looked pale and bloodless in the booth's jittering fluorescent light. The gas station's lights were all switched off, even the big UNION 76 sign on the two towering metal poles that lifted it high enough to be seen a half-mile away. The segmented gate was pulled shut and locked over the entrance to the unlit service bay. There was only enough light from the steetlamps for Braemer to see Dee sleeping in the back seat of the car parked alongside the telephone booth. He kept his eye on the small figure curled up inside the motel blanket as he went on listening to the sound of the unanswered telephone.

It broke off in the middle of a ring. "Hello?" came the voice after the click. It was Carol.

"It's David," he said. "I want to talk to you."

A little gasping intake of breath sounded on the line. "David? Where—where are you?" The blurred edges of sleep had drained out of her voice. "Is Dee with you?"

"I've got her. She's okay. There's nothing happened to her. But I want to talk to you. About her."

"What? What do you mean? Where are you?" Her words rushed into each other. "What's wrong?"

"There's nothing wrong," he said calmly. "I just want to talk to you, about you having Dee. I've had a lot of time to think, and I've decided it might be better that way. Better for Dee."

"Oh, David . . ." She sounded close to crying.

"I'm down here in San Aurelio. Me and Dee. But I don't want to come up there to the house to talk to you."

"Anywhere, David. Just tell me where to go."

"All right. I'm down at the gas station by the freeway. Just down the road from you. The Union station. You know the one?"

"No . . . yes; yes, I do. I know where it is. I'll be right there."

"Hold on, Carol. Listen to me. I want you to come by yourself. Just you, I just want to talk with you. Okay?"

"Sure . . . sure, anything you say."

Braemer turned away from the side of the narrow glassed-in space where he could see Dee in the car, and looked up the dark stretch of road past the freeway. "And I don't want Jess to know where you're going. Is he there in the house with you?"

"No. No, he's not. He's not here."

"Do you know where he is?"

"I haven't seen him in days. I don't know where he is. Honest to God, David, I don't know where he is." Panic drew her words tauter. It was obvious that she had guessed why Braemer had asked about Jess. The fear of losing the chance to get Dee back was in her voice.

"I don't want him to show up here, Carol. If I see him with you, or if I see him coming by himself . . . then there'll be trouble. You know what I mean. And I don't, and you don't, want that to happen in front of Dee. There's been enough of that. So just come by yourself, and everything will be fine."

"All right, David. I promise. Just wait for me there,

okay? I just have to throw on some clothes, and I'll be right down. Is that all right?''

"That's fine," he said. "I'll be waiting for you. Over by the phone booth. See you in a bit." He hung up the phone, leaned back against the glass panel, and let out a long pent-up breath. That went better than I figured it would, he thought. There had been a number of possible screw-ups that he had anticipated going wrong with the telephone call to Carol: all the way from Jess answering the phone to Carol hanging up and calling the police as soon as he told her where he was. From the frantic tone in her voice, the rush to comply with what- ever conditions he asked for, he felt sure that last possibility wasn't going to happen. He expected to see Carol's aged blue Chevy come speeding out of the hills and under the overpass in a matter of minutes.

He pulled open the folding door and stepped out into the cold night air, kneading the knotted muscle at the back of his neck. All across his shoulders and down into the base of his spine, the muscles were cramped with the tension that worked against the fatigue in them, keeping him upright and moving. Hours of solid driving lay behind him, broken only by pit stops for gas and brackish coffee from the vending machines in the 24-hour stations along Interstate 5. The combination of bone-tiredness and the constant feed of adrenalin into his blood dried the saliva in his mouth into cotton, and left the muscles of his arms and legs feeling almost weightless, as though his body had been replaced, sinew by sinew, with thin glass. His fingers wavered with a toxic excitement, until he crammed them in his jacket pockets to still their slight motion. The parking lot's asphalt seemed distant beneath his feet.

He pulled open the car door and slid behind the wheel, then closed the door quietly, not wanting to startle Dee awake. That had been a piece of luck, her drifting asleep as Interstate 5 passed through Los Angeles, and staying out all the rest of the way down here. He had wrapped her in the blanket and lain her in the car's back seat just before he had made the phone call to Carol. Negotiating with her aunt would have been more difficult if he'd had to keep more of an eye on Dee.

You have to watch out, he reminded himself. Renee's still inside her—somewhere. You can't turn your back on her, ever. She's still your child, but that other thing inside her—that's something else. Just watch her, is all.

With any more luck, she'd go on sleeping after Carol got there. He twisted around in his seat to look back at Dee. The blue light of the streetlamps made her skin seem even paler. A shaded hollow in her cheek, not yet as dark as the bruised-looking skin under her eyes—she didn't seem to be as much of a child as before, as though the thing that had been her mother had consumed the softer parts first, leaving the bones fleshed with just what was necessary for survival. Her breathing, thickened with a cold's mucus, dragged across her overlapped hands beneath the side of her face. The slight sound reminded Braemer of other ragged breathing he had heard, in a room where the light never went off.

Like mother, like daughter, he thought grimly. He had always thought, in the times before this, that Dee had taken after him in her appearance, that the lines of her face, the color of her eyes, were things that had passed from his blood to hers, an inheritance encoded in the genes and written out in her brow and forthright little jaw. But with the coming of the sickness, the cancer-like thing inside her, another face had been revealed, and the one he'd known eaten away from beneath the skin. Paler, weaker, the hold on the world outside her darkened eyelids grown faint, that world

278

gradually slipping out of her grasp as he watched. . . .
The image of her mother, the blind skeleton face on the
matchstick and stretched tissue-paper body, was rising
slowly in Dee's face. The weakness it showed frightened
him: the weakness of hunger, a creature whose blood
was too thin to nourish itself, who had to feed on
another's blood to keep its faint life going, without
regard for anything but its hunger, father and child and
everything else forgotten in that need.

Braemer straightened, drawing back from the small
form huddled on the back seat. He could still recognize
her as his daughter; that was enough. It wouldn't be
much longer before the cancer inside would be killed.
He turned away, resting his hands on the steering wheel
as he waited for Carol to show up.

A few minutes of watching the traffic on the freeway
passed before he saw the pair of headlights coming up
the road on the other side of the overpass. He waited
until the streetlamps revealed it to be Carol's old Chevy.
Then he reached down and pulled the gun out from
under the seat. He unfolded the white cloth and slipped
the heavy metal bulk into his jacket pocket. As the
Chevy pulled into the gas-station lot and headed toward
the Datsun, Braemer opened the door and stepped out,
closing the door gently behind himself.

Carol brought her car to a halt at an angle a few yards
away. She was out from behind the wheel even before
the engine finished rattling quiet. The hood of a faded
blue sweatshirt bounced at the back of her neck as she
ran up to him. "Where's Dee?" she said, panting for
breath. "You said you had her with you."

"Shh." He laid his hand on her shoulder. "Keep it
down. She's sleeping right now. I think it might be
better if we didn't wake her up until after we've talked.
Okay?" He led her to the side of the Datsun, the hidden
gun jogging against his hip. "You can see for yourself

279

that she's all right." Standing beside her, he watched as she leaned close to the window, gazing intently at the child lying on the back seat. For a moment he was reminded of some old nursery story—paradoxical outside a closed gas station in the middle of the night—of a princess under a spell being carried about in a glass coffin. Past Carol's shoulder he could see Dee's pale face, pressed sleeping against her hands.

He tugged Carol away from the car's window. "Come on," he said. "We've got to talk about some things."

"She doesn't look well." Carol turned an anxious face toward her. "Is she all right?"

Braemer shrugged. "She's got a little bit of a cold, that's all." He glanced over at the empty street running past the gas station, then back to her. "Why don't we go sit in your car and talk. It's cold out here."

Carol nodded. She took one more look at Dee in the back of the Datsun, then led Braemer over to the other car. She got in and reached across to unlock the door on the passenger's side.

He held his arm tucked against his side as he slid onto the seat, trying to keep the gun in his pocket from hitting anything. The door thudded shut, and the interior of the car was quiet and still, cut off from the murmur of the freeway traffic.

"Just what did you want to talk about?" asked Carol, leaning back against the door.

He'd had a long time to think, hours of studying the concrete lanes sliding under the car all the way down here. A long time to plan what to say and do, and now every bit of it was unreeling the same way the highway had, as though he'd pressed the start button on some giant machine that held them like cogs. He reached out and caught Carol's arm just above the elbow, drawing her, eyes widening, closer to himself. With his other hand he reached into his jacket and pulled out the gun. "Just this," he said, holding it a couple of inches away from her stomach so that she could look down and see what it was.

Through her arm he felt her spine jerk rigid, her breath sucked in a gasp. "David," she managed to whisper, her voice choked with fright. "What—what are you doing?"

"Don't worry," he said. He'd have to work to calm her down—she wasn't much use to him in this state. "I'm not going to hurt you. Just settle down. There's something that I have to do. And you're going to help me." He drew the gun away from her and rested it on his thigh, the dully shining barrel still pointed toward her. He kept his grip on her arm, relaxing it a bit. "That's all. I just need some help from you."

Puzzlement filtered into the fear in her eyes. "Help you? What are you talking about?" She tried to shrink away from him, drawing back into the corner of the seat and the door, but was stopped by his hand encircling her arm. "What is it you want to do?" Her gaze darted from the gun on his leg to his eyes.

"Don't worry about that. I'll tell you what I want you to do, you'll do it, and everything will be fine. Believe me, it's for Dee's sake. It's not something I want to do—it's something I've got to do for her. All right? You understand?"

Carol studied his face, searching for the key to his words. "What do you want me to do?" she said softly.

He kept the tone of his voice methodical, outlining the details for her. "I want you to drive me up to the house. In this car. I have to get into the house, but I know Jess is probably up there somewhere, waiting for me."

"How do you know that?" said Carol. "He could be anywhere."

He wanted to say, *Because the thing inside him is the same thing inside my daughter. Because it knows I finally saw for myself that it was inside her.* The voice stifled inside himself rose to a silent shout. *Because it knows that there's only one thing left that I can do, and that there's no place I could come except here, and it could just wait—inside Jess—for me to show up. Because I know what that thing wants.*

All the words remained unspoken. "I've got a feeling about it," he said simply. "I can't drive up there in my car. He'd spot it coming. He's going to know I'm there soon enough, but I just want a little time to do what I have to do."

"Why do you want me to drive you? Why don't you just take my car?"

He gave her a thin smile. "What would you do in the meantime? I can't really trust you—not when I'm this close."

She turned her head at an angle, her eyes narrowing as if to cut through what she heard him saying. "And why do you want to go up to the house? What's this . . . thing you've got to do?"

"I can't tell you. It doesn't concern you, anyway. Except that it's what's best for Dee." He raised the gun from where it rested on his leg, then set it back down: a small threat. "You just have to do what I tell you."

There was no longer any fear in the gaze that she leveled at him. "You're going up to the house to kill Renee. Aren't you?"

After a few seconds of silence he nodded and said, "Yes."

"Why?" Her gaze didn't waver.

"It doesn't matter," he said. "It's just something I have to do. If you want to think I'm crazy, that's okay. But I still have to do it. And you're going to help me, whether you want to or not."

"David," she said softly. "I know why."

He looked and saw a spark of shared knowledge in her sad eyes, one that he hadn't expected.

"It's because of what Renee's done to Dee, isn't it? Not what she did out there in the forest, in the past. That was bad enough. It's what she's done now. The way she's come . . . inside Dee. That's why you're going to kill her."

His hand sweated around the gun's grip. "What do you know about that?"

"Jesus Christ, David." She turned away from him, biting her trembling lower lip and staring out the windshield. "How could I not know? I'm not blind—not about Dee. She's more my child than anybody's, yours or Renee's. I've had her with me for five days out of every seven. Do you really think I couldn't see what was happening to her? Times when she was just a little girl, and then—those other times, when she'd change, change into something else. . . . Even without her saying anything, or doing anything, I could tell." She turned her face back toward him, tears trembling in her lashes. "You're the one who's been blind, David. You couldn't even see that there was anything wrong with Dee until you almost had a knife stuck in you. But I knew. I've known for a long time. There's something else inside Dee. Something sick, all twisted and . . . hungry. And it's her own mother."

"How do you know that? That it's Renee?"

Carol shook her head as she looked at him. "When you love people, you know what happens to them. Maybe you wouldn't know about something like that. You've had your life out in the world, doing things, going places . . . all the way to England, just leaving everyone who thought you loved them behind. No one told you how Dee cried about that, did they?—cried because she wasn't going to see you on the weekends like she always did." She stopped, as if hearing the bitterness that had crept into her voice. She closed her eyes and tilted her head back against the seat. "But they're all I ever had. For Christ's sake, David. Renee's my *sister*. I know, not my real one. But I grew up with her, I loved her. I could see her face inside Dee's, her eyes watching me, her voice inside Dee, talking to me. Nobody had to tell me it was Renee. I just knew. I knew that something had gone wrong with that stuff she and Jess were into, but that she was still alive somewhere inside her body. And then I could see her come creeping into Dee, taking her over, and I knew what had happened. I knew, that's all."

Braemer moved the tip of his dry tongue over his lips as his mind raced to digest what he'd heard. "You knew about Renee and Jess? About what they were trying to do? The Pedersen group, and—and the crystallizing of souls? All of that?"

She nodded. "Most of it. They tried to keep it from me. Little secrets. But even when she was a kid, Renee could never keep things hidden from me for very long. And this was so big, and doing it left her so screwed up—it was like there were pieces of it lying all around. If you could see them. Some books and pamphlets by that Pedersen guy—I found them in that camper Renee took Dee off to the forest in. They were all marked up, with crazy stuff scribbled over the pages, some of it by Jess. The really sick things I knew were by Renee. But there were things before that—stuff I overheard the two of them whispering about out on the porch, things she babbled when she was all messed up on that stuff they took, and she'd come crawling home and I'd have to put her to bed. When you have nothing else to do but watch the people you love, you can piece together a lot. When Renee disappeared with Dee, and then they found her and the doctors told me that she'd be in that coma until she died—I thought that was the end of it. Do you know what I mean? She'd been so unhappy, so hungry for that thing she wanted. I thought that maybe this would be a kind of peace for her. Maybe I was just hoping for that."

Braemer let go of her arm and wiped the sweat from his hand onto his pants by the gun. "I know what you mean," he said. "But you knew all this. And you didn't do anything about it."

"What could I do? I wanted to keep Dee with me, because I loved her the most, and I thought I could protect her somehow. I don't know. I thought maybe I could keep her alive, make her strong enough to keep her mother from eating her from the inside out. That's what I was trying to do."

"But you didn't do anything about Renee. It would have been easy for you to stop the whole thing. You were the one who was feeding her body, taking care of it so it went on living—so that she could go on feeding on Dee. You kept Renee alive all this time."

The tears broke and coursed down Carol's face. "What else could I do? Do you think I could have killed her? She was dying already. Do you suppose I could have watched her body starve?" She balled her hands into fists and struck the top of the steering wheel. "For God's sake, David, she's my sister! You don't know— you don't know what that means! *I loved her.*"

Pity had turned to ice inside him. "Your love is stupid," he said, one corner of his mouth curling with a sour taste. "It let sick things feed on children, and dead things walk around inside the living. There are some things that shouldn't be loved, things that people turn into. That's something you don't know. Your love's useless. You never learned the value of hating something. I know how to. That's why I can do what you couldn't."

She sank down in her seat, one hand hiding her eyes. The quiet inside the car held for several moments before she whispered, "I know. I know you're right, David. I knew it was wrong, but I couldn't do anything about it." She lifted her tear-wet face to him again. "You don't have to point that gun at me. I'll drive you up to the house. Then you can do whatever you have to do. I won't try to stop you."

"It'll be different," he said quietly, "when it's all over. I don't know what'll happen to me. For killing her. Technically it's murder. Other people won't know why. You'll probably have Dee for a long time. Maybe I won't ever have her again, not as a child, or . . . after." He pushed his knotted breath out and stared at the dark space beyond the windshield. Then he took the gun from where it rested on his leg and laid it down on the car's floor. "We'd better get going," he said. "We've wasted enough time."

Carol wiped her eyes with the sleeve of her sweatshirt. "What about Dee? We can't leave her here."

That was another thing he'd thought about during all the long hours of driving down to San Aurelio. He knew that the main threat was Renee moving inside of Jess— that was how she'd be waiting and watching for him. But if Dee was left unwatched, Renee could sour his plans through a child's body as well. A knife or anything sharp, picked up in Dee's hands and pressed against Dee's chest, would give the thing inside Dee the perfect hostage. He already knew the pleasure the thing that had been Dee's mother would get out of the child's death.

He had decided it would be necessary to bind Dee's wrists and ankles, but with Carol's cooperation now clear, he changed his mind. "We'll take her with us," he said. "You can watch her while I go inside the house."

The two of them got out of the Chevy and went to the

other car. Carol held the door open while he lifted Dee, still wrapped inside the blanket. She murmured something in her sleep, head against his chest. He laid her down in the back of the Chevy, folding the blanket under her chin.

"All right," he said as he slid into the passenger's seat. Carol was already turning the key in the ignition. "Let's go."

Silence in the house. A single rectangle of light fell from an upstairs window, slanting across the dust of the driveway, as it had through every night. The wooden steps led up to the porch, the shelter of the roof's overhang making it even darker than the night around it, cutting off the dim light from the stars. The shapes of the wicker furniture, sagging with age and the damp that had crept into their fibers, huddled on either side of the screen door. Something was waiting inside.

Past the front door, the empty rooms unfolded into each other. An empty photo frame set on the mantel in the living room. In the kitchen, the knives were racked neatly in their drawers, the cutting edges and points hidden under the counters like dead things entombed in the niches of a crypt. They were safe there.

Even though the house was empty of anything living —anything that lived as other creatures do—the air in the darkened rooms moved slightly with the sound of something breathing. A sound that had always been there, becoming part of the house's wood and paint, sinking in like grease spattered above the stove, yellowing the wallpaper in the hallways. The breathing, too soft to be heard under any other sound, had become the sound of the house itself. The sound of the house waiting, and watching.

It became louder up the stairs, and louder still toward the one bedroom where the light never went off. Inside the room, it mingled with the smell of disinfectant and the subtler, though more cloying, odor of flesh consuming itself. The thing on the bed, a rough sketch of a human form, seemed to be coalesced from the sound and the odor, as though the house had fleshed out a skeleton to be the soul at its core, a heart inside its empty rooms.

The house breathed and waited. In silence, with eyes not its own, the thing inside waited for the return of what it desired.

Somewhere on the highway, Braemer had passed through fatigue into another state he'd never known before. Sitting beside Carol as she drove, watching the road curve up into the hills, he felt his arms and legs to be like bags of sand knotted and tied together at the joints. He flexed his hand, watching the stiff fingers curl in on themselves. The toxins of all the sleepless nights, and nights when the sleep was more draining than any effort, had settled in his muscles like lead weights sewn under the skin. The heaviness dragged him back into the seat and toward the asphalt under the car.

Oddly, his brain felt quick, lucid, transparent as polished glass. Now I know, he thought, gazing out the side window at the dark landscape sliding by. *This is what it's like to be awake. Really awake.* It seemed like the first time it had ever happened to him. A small marvel, a gift, in the middle of the clotted blood and graying flesh that had been revealed beneath the world's skin. His body felt like some inert mass that had been shackled to his head. As if from a height miles above, he could see himself, and everything else: Dee, Renee, the thing Renee had become. This was where Pedersen looked at him from, he realized. From way up here.

The last of the adrenalin seeped out of his bloodstream, leaving him still alert, but calmer, the nerve endings in his heavy body quieting like sparking wires dying to the red glow of the current within. Everything was fine now, moving toward completion. The gun was on the car's floor by his feet, and he knew just what he was going to do.

The road leveled off and the car entered the empty tract, passing the first of the unfinished houses. Against the light from the freeway and the town farther in the distance, the bare wooden frameworks stood out, black skeletal lines etched in the night. Dead houses, stripped of everything living.

Of course, thought Braemer. He watched the outlined, unfinished houses glide by. They looked like sketches of houses, the black paper they were drawn on showing through the lines not yet filled in.

It had to be this place. It couldn't be anywhere else. This is what the world looks like when the flesh is peeled back to the bone. No illusions left.

The zone where no one was fooling anyone else any longer. Where you don't even lie to yourself anymore, he thought. The spaces between the stick houses looked vast, filled with a negative light, lucid air too thin to bear a scream. The battlefield stripped of camouflage at last, the bare landscape in which he and the thing he'd married, the thing that had given birth to his child, would move toward each other and couple for the last time.

He felt cold suddenly, as though the night air had penetrated the window glass and touched his blood, tapping off the warmth from his heart. To see things from that height—he knew it deep inside himself—was to court a final coldness, a vision that would freeze the world and everything in it to ashes.

Working his stiff shoulders inside his jacket, he glanced over at Carol. With her hands on the steering wheel, she stared ahead, her eyes following the sweep of the car's headlights over the road. Whatever thoughts she had were locked in her silence.

He turned in his seat and looked back at Dee. The blanket had fallen from her thin chest, half of it lying crumpled on the floor. He reached back and drew it up again to her chin. For a moment he felt her faint breath on the back of his hand. Her eyelids were so still, the fringe of eyelash so black against the pale cheek, that the trace of air stirring the fine hairs along his wrist seemed to be the only sign that she was alive.

As he let go of the blanket and turned back around in his seat, the car began to brake for the driveway leading down to the Feld house. Carol steered the car down the curving gravel drive, toward the dark silhouette with the one window full of light above the porch.

The car stopped several yards away from the wooden front steps, and Carol switched off the engine. It rattled on its own for a second, then died.

He glanced over at Carol. "Well," he said quietly. "This is it."

"That's right," she said. "This is it." Her hands left the steering wheel. She suddenly bent down, reaching toward the car's floor by his feet. Before he could react, she had straightened back up, the gun clasped in both her hands. She held the black vacant circle at the end of the barrel aimed straight into his chest.

"What the hell are you doing?" He reached for the gun.

"Don't," she said, level-voiced. The tone of the one word made him slowly draw his hand back.

"Carol." His heart sped up as he looked at the gun held motionless in her hands. He had left the safety switched off when he had laid the gun on the floor, and now he could see the edge of the exposed red dot, like a drop of blood on the black metal. "Why . . ." He couldn't think of any other words. "What are you doing—"

"There's been a change in plans, David." Her face was set as she watched him leaning back against the door. "You're not going in the house. I am."

He said nothing, letting the small space between him and the gun swallow her words.

"You're not family," Carol went on. "She's my sister. She's as much a sister as I'll ever have. This is something I should have done, and I'm going to do it."

"You don't have to, Carol. It's not your sister. Not anymore. It's . . . another thing. Give me the gun. And I'll take care of it."

She shook her head. "No. You did enough to her. When you were married. If you'd loved her, if she'd been happy, she'd never have become like this. But she came home to me. I'm the one who's taken care of her all along. I'll do this, too."

"You don't have to use the gun," said Braemer. "If there's some other way . . . a pillow or—"

"What's the difference?" The gun twitched upward in her hands. "This is the fastest way. And she's suffered enough. I just want it to be over for her." She lowered the gun away from him. "You understand, don't you?"

He gauged the distance between his hands and the gun. For a moment his muscles tensed, then he slumped back against the door. "All right," he said. "Go ahead."

She looked down for a few seconds at the gun filling her grasp, then one hand moved away from it and pushed open her door. He watched through the windshield as she mounted the steps to the porch, the gun a stilled pendulum at her side, and went inside the house. She left the front door open behind her. In the dark space of the living room he couldn't see her any longer.

Behind him in the car he could hear something moving. He turned to look in the back seat and saw Dee stirring, rolling her head from side to side as though fighting to come awake. A small moaning sound issued from her dry lips.

We must have woken her up, thought Braemer, talking like that. He leaned over the back of his seat toward Dee. "Shh," he whispered, stroking her forehead. "It's all right, honey. Go to sleep. Everything's okay." For a moment her eyelids gathered in a scowl, then her face relaxed again into sleep. Braemer turned away from her and went back to watching the house through the windshield.

Minutes passed. No other lights came on inside the house. His gaze moved up to the bright-lit window on the second floor. From this angle he could see only a section of a wallpapered corner and the ceiling meeting it. The thin curtains at the sides of the windows cut off anything else.

He took his eyes away from the house for a moment to search the darkness around the car. Jess had to be nearby, somewhere, watching. Maybe the business of coming to the house in Carol's old Chevy had fooled him completely. Braemer could see only the vague shapes of the trees and bushes in the yard. Maybe Jess was there, approaching the car, unseen. Or he was in the house, had been there all along. Maybe that's why he hadn't heard the shot yet.

A few more minutes, and then he knew it was too much time. The minute hand on his watch had crawled too far in silence. She couldn't do it, he thought; I'll have to go in there, after all. He looked back to make sure that Dee was still sleeping, then quickly scanned the unmoving silhouettes around the car before pushing open the door and loping in a few quick strides up the porch steps.

The light coming down the stairway was enough for him to make his way through the living room. He passed among the cluttered, musty-smelling furniture, his empty hands reaching ahead of him as though to fend off any surprise. When he reached the bottom of the stairs he grasped the rail and looked up at the light seeping from the bedroom above him. "Carol?" he called softly.

There was no answer. The house remained silent around him. He became aware of the low, whispering sound of air drawn, held, exhaled, repeating the cycle again and again. The sound of its breathing, the sound of the house's false life.

He mounted the first two steps, the rail sliding in his damp palm. The hallway and the bedroom at the end of it came closer to view. He stopped and called again. "Carol? Are you there?"

By now he expected no answer except Renee's breathing. He swallowed the salt that had gathered on his tongue and brought his foot down softly on the next step up.

The rail ended at the top in a carved wooden ball. He wrapped his hand around it and pulled himself from the last step into the hallway. The light from the half-opened bedroom door slanted down the narrow space, showing all the other doors closed tight.

The sound of the breathing was louder here. He felt its slow tempo dragging his own breath into sync with it, though his heart was racing faster in his chest. The hospital smell collected like wet cotton at the back of his throat.

He stepped toward the bedroom. When he was a couple of yards away, he could see the bed and the figure on it through the opening. The room seemed empty except for that. Then he saw the other thing, a small rectangle of stiff paper, mottled dark with a white border. A photograph. It was propped up on the doorknob, carefully balanced there.

Another step, and he was close enough to reach out and pick it up. A message left for him. Wary, with a puzzlement that gathered the skin of his shoulderblades toward his spine, he took the photograph between his thumb and forefinger. He had to tilt it toward the light from the doorway to make it out.

For a moment it didn't register, then he realized he had seen the picture before. Or part of it; he saw now that the photo was taped together, two halves lined up against each other, a straight scissor-cut running from top to bottom. An old photo, one side of it yellowed more than the other, as though it had been exposed to more years of light. Downstairs, thought Braemer; that's where I saw it before. That part of it. It was always in a frame on the mantelpiece.

It was the picture of Carol as a baby, being held by her mother, the woman who'd adopted her, face already settling into the meanness with which she'd treated Carol all her life. A sad little document, which Braemer had always wondered why Carol had left sitting out all these years.

The other part of the photograph—he had never seen that before. From its unyellowed appearance no one else had seen it for a long time either. Braemer, the moment of standing before the bedroom door expanding like a magic spell, brought the photograph up close to study it.

The other half showed a man, double-breasted suit, hat pushed back on his head, a half-smile breaking through his somber expression. He stood close to the woman, his hand behind her back to hold her by the waist. A loving couple, Mr. and Mrs. Feld. The man in the picture didn't know that he had only about three more years to live, just enough time to father three kids, one after another, on the woman by his side. The heart attack that would—no doubt gratefully—take him off, and the scissors that would afterward snip him out of the family history, were foretold in the face of the woman by his side.

His face, though—Braemer had never seen this piece of the photograph, but he had seen the man's face before. Not in the depths of a thin black-and-white slice of past time, but in present flesh. The strong jaw, the hinge of bone below the ear, the wide brow, eyes sad even when laughing. . . .A face handsome enough on a man, but not pretty in the usual sense on a woman. But that was where he had seen it before, realized Braemer as he tilted the photograph against the light. As a woman's face. Carol's face.

Like father, like daughter. If the baby held in the woman's arms was Carol, then the man standing next to them in the photograph was Carol's father—her real father. It had only taken the passing of years for the baby to grow up and into the only real legacy left to her by the father who had vanished into the cold ground before she was old enough to remember him. A coded message, written out in the angles of her face, a silent gift that said everything.

One thought began to connect with another inside Braemer, like a small hammer tapping at the edge of his skull.

A little domestic scandal could be read out of the photograph, the mistake that had led to Carol's father being excised from the family history as soon as he was dead. He must've screwed around and gotten some poor girl pregnant, thought Braemer, and then to get her to hush up and move out of the area, he agreed to adopt the result. If the kid hadn't looked so much like him, from earliest childhood, nobody would've ever known. So no wonder his widow clipped him out of the family photos—all the evidence is in his face, and Carol's.

He turned the photograph over. Someone, maybe whoever had left it propped on the bedroom's door-knob, had written something on the back. HAPPY BIRTHDAY, in a loose scrawl, the letters printed large in a thick red that smeared under his finger as he touched it, smeared like blood. . . .

The last circuit fell and sparked. Braemer stared at the red stain on his fingertip. Blood, he thought. If that's Carol's father in the photo, then she had the same father as the others. Her brother and her sisters—they're all related by blood. And if that's true, then—

He heard something moving behind him, a door opening. He whirled around, the photo still in his hand. Carol stood in the hallway, looking at him.

The family resemblance between her and the man in the photograph was perfect. But another face was rising in hers, a face he had seen distorting his daughter's features.

Carol's hand lifted the gun, leveling it at his chest. "Surprise," said Renee's voice.

For a second he stood motionless. He watched the smile widen on Carol's face, feeling the hollow under his stomach open. The thing inside her, the thing reaching into her from the coiled body in the room behind him, parted its wet teeth, holding its own laughter in its jaws.

"Renee," he said. The photograph fluttered down from his hand as he stepped slowly backward against the bedroom door.

"Why are you so stupid?" It was the same voice that had mocked him in the motel room, coming then from Dee's mouth, now from Carol's. "You're not much fun to play with. You're always so easy to fool." It stepped toward him, the gun riding the invisible line between its hand and his chest.

"You thought you were talking to Carol," it went on, smiling. "Out there in the car. And it was me all the time. It's always me, isn't it? It's always been me, it always will be me. You thought you were so smart." It crooned the words, cocking its head to one side. "That's why I let you come into the house. And find that picture. Now you know all the little family secrets, don't you?"

His hand found the doorknob behind him. If he could get into the room, behind the door before she fired— if he could move faster than the hungry eyes following him—

"Carol didn't even know." Renee's voice slid after him. "She didn't know until I showed her where to look, to find the other half of the picture. Then it was too late. She was stupid, like you are. But I like it inside her. I can kill you, and they'll think *she* did it. And then there won't be anyone to stop me from doing what I want. I'll have that sweet little girl, that bad girl who ran away from me, all to myself. That'll be nice."

As he watched, his spine pressing against the bedroom door, the smile on its face stretched into a grin of fierce delight. "You don't know what it's like to be dead. But I do." It raised the gun, eyes staring at him over the top of the black metal. "Now you'll know."

Its hands tightened around the gun's grip as his legs tensed to drop against the door, roll, make any motion away from the black dot focused on him.

He heard the gun roar into fire, the noise filling the hallway. Through his clenched eyelids he saw the tapering ball of orange flare for a second, as his legs gave way and his shoulder struck the door frame.

In the echoing silence that followed, he heard another

weight thud into the floor. He opened his eyes to a muffled scream, of anger breaking to fury.

A confused tangle of bodies thrashed on the floor. He saw a thin arm wrapped across a snarling face, a small hand clawing at the mouth that held Renee's voice. The hand with the gun in it reached back and clubbed against the child on the woman's back. Dee held on, scrabbling for her grip around the other's neck.

Braemer shook off his daze and grabbed for the flailing gun. He caught the fist clenched around it and pried the rigid fingers loose from the grip. As it came free, the hand's momentum spun it away from his grasp. The gun hit against the stairway wall and clattered into the dark living room below.

The thing on the hallway floor roared up on its knees, flinging Dee against the wall. It lunged at Braemer, its scream now rapid panting. He caught its face in his hands and toppled it backward, losing his balance and falling with it toward the stairs as its hands clawed into his shoulders.

He felt its teeth sink into the web between his thumb and forefinger as the force of his falling slammed his face close enough to suck its breath into his. Its mewing snarl licked at his ear as it rolled, scrambling up on top of him. The back of his head snapped against the edge of the top step.

Its fingernails tore across the flesh of his shoulder-blades as he drew his legs up, then pushed his knees against its breast. The shirt ripped into the warm sting of the blood beneath. She hung above him for a moment, then fell, still straining for him.

Gasping, he rolled onto his stomach and reached for the stairway post. He gripped it in both hands and pulled himself up onto his elbows. He looked down the stairs and saw the figure crumpled against the bottom steps. Carol's motionless body lay sprawled, broken of its own or any other life.

Braemer staggered up onto his feet, his pulse hammering in his ears. He stooped down and lifted Dee up into his arms. Her eyelids fluttered but didn't open as he held her against his chest.

A sound from outside the house jerked his spine into a crouch. Footsteps on gravel, heading for the front porch. Jess. The realization leaped through him: he's out there, and Renee's inside him now.

Cradling Dee, her heels striking his knees, he hurried down the stairs. Halfway, he snapped his head around, looking back at the bedroom doorway above him. It's there, kill it there! He remembered what he'd forgotten, but it was already too late. The sound outside became footsteps on wood, then the screech of the screen door being flung open.

He nearly fell across Carol's body as he carried Dee down the last steps. Turning, he saw Jess's silhouette filling the front doorway. It moved toward him, hands brushing aside the furniture.

Braemer struck the edge of the kitchen doorway with his shoulder, then he was through and across the short distance to the back door. Clasping Dee to him with one hand, he fumbled at the door's chain lock with his other. It rattled in its catch but didn't come free.

"David." The voice called from the other room as it approached, lower in pitch but still Renee's voice.

His fingers tugged the chain loose, and it swung rattling across the door. The night air rushed cold into his face as he ran outside with Dee.

She began to stir in his arms, twisting a pain-filled grimace against his chest and moaning. The child's weight ached in his arms. He gave a quick glance back at the door and the unlit space inside, then sprinted around the side of the house, toward the front.

Jess was already there, vaulting over the wooden porch rail and landing catlike, cutting Braemer off from the car.

"David—" Renee's voice shouted after him, teasing, as he turned and ran across the yard.

He fell with Dee in his arms and his shin caught a folding lawn chair unseen in the dark. Stumbling, he caught his balance and made his way to the straggling line of hedge that marked the yard's limit. Shoulder first, he pushed through the clawing branches, tucking Dee's face closer to himself to protect her.

Renee's laugh trailed after him in the darkness. "Daa-vid," it called in a singsong child's voice, filled with a cruel excitement. "I *seee* you." The hedge's tangled mesh rustled as the broad hands spread branches apart.

Braemer crouched down, watching as the black-outlined figure slowly scanned the landscape, searching as if to pick up the scent of fear in its nostrils. He could almost see the teeth of its smile. "David," it said. "Come on out. Let's play."

A stand of dried weeds screened him as Braemer crept, hunched over, a few yards closer to the curving street. Dee moved in his arms, and he pressed her closer to him to still any sound from her. If he could just get to the street, without the other spotting him, he could work his way from hiding place to hiding place in the unfinished houses. Just to there, he thought, staring ahead. An open space separated him from the gray concrete line of the street curb. If he could get to there, he had a chance of getting to the first skeleton house, then the next, all the way out of the tract and down the hillside, to the lights of the road and the town beyond.

He clenched his teeth against his own panting breath. The thing inside Jess came closer, turning from side to side with each slow step. Braemer drew his muscles tighter, ready to burst from his crouch behind the weeds and run for the road when its face swung the other way.

Its voiced sounded again, a sly whisper this time: "I know where you are."

For a moment Braemer was confused. The voice seemed closer than the silhouette of Jess in the weed-choked field. Then he looked down at the child in his arms, and saw the eyes staring up at him. "David," said Renee with manic glee, its smile contorting Dee's face. "Now I got you."

One small arm pulled free, swung and clubbed his face, catching him in the eye like a sharp-edged rock. The pain and flash of light jolted his head back as he heard its laughter, from the thing clutched to his chest and the other shape standing yards away in darkness.

He grabbed Dee's arm and penned it against himself as he stood up and ran for the street. A glance over his shoulder showed Jess walking after him, weeds brushing his thighs.

The thing inside Dee stretched its mouth close to Braemer's ear as his feet struck the road's asphalt. "I got you," it whispered fiercely. "Because I'm here, and I'm in Jess, too. You can't get away now."

His lungs were red sacks of fire when he reached the nearest house. He scraped his back against the bare two-by-four framework as he shouldered himself and Dee inside. He bent down, the child's body tucked close against his, and stared back along the road. Jess stood between the curbs, the thing inside turning its head until it faced directly at Braemer's hiding place. Then it broke into a doglike lope, heading straight for him.

"Here I come," said the laughing voice inside Dee.

Carol woke into pain, the taste of warm salt thick in her mouth. The shapes she could make out in the darkened living room were doubled into ghost images of themselves. She got her hands beneath herself and pushed against the steps she lay crossways on, then fell back, all breath jerked from her in a scream as an iron shaft twisted through her hip and into her spine.

The edges of the fractured bone grated against each other as she lay wedged in the corner between the stairs and the wall. The red pulse faded slowly from her eyes as she panted for breath.

She stayed where she was, letting the light from the bedroom at the top of the stairs fall across her as the jumble of her thoughts drew clearer.

She's not in me. The realization was like a boulder she managed to push away from her lungs. *Renee's not in me now.* It was the first time the thoughts inside her head were only her own since—she knew now—the night she had gone down into the cellar and found the old photo album. She had thought that night had been all dreams and sleepwalking, but now it was clear it had been the first edge of Renee's soul creeping inside her and taking control, bit by bit.

Everything that happened since then—the meeting with David in the car, the luring him inside the house to find the old photograph her hands had propped up on the bedroom's doorknob, the fight at the top of the stairs with Dee scrabbling at her neck—all that had played itself out as if on a screen just beyond the reach of her hands. She could only watch and listen to Renee's laughter inside herself. All during the lies and playacting of her sister—her real sister, the one true thing that had come out of the darkness—she had wanted to scream out a warning to David, shout at him to take Dee and run as far as he could. But Renee's words had gone on welling up in her mouth, masquerading as her own, her own face a mask to conceal the sharp-toothed grin of the thing that had slid up along her spine and into her skull.

Carol's breath slowed enough for her to listen to the house's quiet. In the stillness the other sound of breathing came, the slow movement of air in the bedroom above her.

She's still alive. Carol tilted her head to look up at the light. She's still up there. Alive.

David and Dee were gone. The house was empty except for her and the sound of the breathing from the bedroom. Two sisters, half-sisters, enough of the poisoned blood between them. She could see the coma-withered body twisting upon the bed, the unseen part reaching out to—*Jess*, thought Carol suddenly. She must be in him now. That's why David didn't go on and kill Renee. There wasn't time.

They were out there now, somewhere in the night. A man fleeing with a child, a thing with another's soul behind him.

There wasn't time. Not while the thing upstairs was still alive. It had been inside her, and she knew what it wanted. Its hunger had been like a tooth-lined pit, dark enough to swallow everything that fell into it, until it had fed enough to come free of the rotting body it was shackled into. Then it could go on feeding forever.

Carol rolled onto her hands again, trying to push herself upright, but the pain that surged up from her shattered hip blinded her and left her gasping for breath, face pressed against the ridge of the stairs.

Swallowing, she reached up and grasped the next higher step. She pulled herself toward it, trying to drag her unmoving legs behind herself. Her arms trembled with the effort before her hands gave way. She slid the rest of the distance to the floor, landing in another red wash that pulsed with her blood.

She opened her eyes as the pain faded. Above her, she could see the light shining from the open doorway. But I can't reach her, she thought, the daze ebbing from her mind. She's up there, but I can't get to her.

Slowly, as she gathered her breath into herself, a vision formed in her thoughts. A thing that could reach up into the bedroom and the body curled in its monstrous sleep there. A thing all heat and light in the darkness.

She lay on the floor next to the kitchen doorway. Twisting her neck, sharp fingers jabbing into the base of her skull, she could see the counter with the sink, the two doors beneath it, the square shape of the metal can visible through the gap at the bottom.

Again she looked up the stairs at the light from the bedroom. But it was Dee she thought of. Go ahead, she told herself, her own voice sounding old and broken inside. You've already lost her. Don't let—

She broke the thought off, leaving her sister's name unvoiced. There wasn't time. No time for anything but to begin crawling into the kitchen, her fingers digging into the floor, her legs dragging like steel hooks in her spine.

When she was finally close enough, she reached and pulled open the doors beneath the sink. She dragged the can of charcoal lighter fluid sloshing toward herself. With the red wash battering against her sight, she inched back toward the stairway beyond the door.

The sharp smell of the lighter fluid leaped into her face as she clawed the red plastic lid from the can. She tossed the opened can onto the stairs. It landed on its side a few steps up from her, gurgling as the fluid poured down the stairs and into a thin pool around her. The wet coldness seeped into her clothes, the vapor from it stinging her eyes.

A dish towel hung from the refrigerator handle just

inside the kitchen doorway. She tugged it free, then crawled the couple of yards back toward the stove. The lighter fluid smeared a trail behind her.

Clenching her teeth against the white fist tearing at the base of her spine, she reared up onto one elbow. With her other hand she clawed at the knobs on the front of the stove. One turned as her hand fell across it. A hiss of gas, then a blue rose flared up from the burner.

Holding one end of the dish towel, she threw it up and across the flame. It smoldered, then black crept through the white fabric, bursting into yellow fire.

She dragged the towel from the burner and flung it, sparks falling across her, through the doorway. It landed on the bottom step, a tangle of crawling red in the darkness. Then the stairway surged with light. The pulse of warm air brushed against her face as the flames licked across the circle of lighter fluid around the base of the stairs.

The wet trail burned across the floor toward her, then her damp clothes were fire against her skin.

Through the doorway she could see the stairway's old wood rippling with heat, the flames lapping up from one step to the next. The sofa near the rail's bottom post charred, then black smoke ribboned with red vomited upward. The wallpaper beyond began to darken, the printed flowers withering with sudden age until a furious life sprung from them.

Then she couldn't breathe the burning air into her throat, and it was too bright to see any more.

Inside the cage of the framework house, a pealing laugh sliced between the open rafters. The thing inside Dee rocked its head back, the tendons in the small neck working as the face strained back from its teeth. The eyes darted back to Braemer's face, inches away.

"You stupid shit," the face beneath the child's crooned, tasting its victory. The hands pinned against his chest clawed toward his throat. "You can't let go, you can't let go and run because you think you can save your little girl, but your little girl's dead. I eat bad little girls and she was bad, she ran away from me and now it's just me, it's always me, it'll always be me—" The last words rose to a shriek that beat against his ears.

In the middle of the house's empty concrete floor Braemer twisted about, Renee's voice tearing bloody into his head, the thing at his chest straining up to his face. "Shut up!" he shouted at it, clamping a hand over the child's mouth, the fingers pressing white into her cheeks. He felt its teeth rip and meet in his palm.

"David!" The voice cried from outside the wood framework. His head jerked around and he saw Jess clutching two of the wall uprights, leaning into the space between, his mouth moving as if tasting the blood drawling down Braemer's wrist.

Renee's eyes in Jess's face fastened on to his. She moved her brother's body, one shoulder at a time, through the gap between the two-by-fours. The same shout came from two throats as the thing inside Jess raised onto the balls of its feet, knotted its fists together, then clubbed them down and across Braemer's head.

He hit the concrete on the point of his elbow, a dull electric shock barely felt in the blank spreading over the side of his head. Dimly, he felt Dee's arms and legs scramble away from him as he rolled helpless onto his back.

A weight crushed into his chest. Through the darkness he could see Renee's face rising into Jess's above him. Its hands spread wide and grasped his head as if to squeeze it between them.

"Now," whispered Renee's voice. "Now you'll know."

It rocked Braemer's chin toward his chest, then cracked the back of his head against the concrete floor.

In the red burst that sang across his eyes, Braemer could see Renee's face twice, above him and in Dee's face just past the reach of his outflung hand. Crouching on the child's hands and knees like an animal, his blood running in lines down its chin, it stared eagerly as the hands slowly lifted his head again. . . .

The heat and gray layer of smoke seeped into the bedroom before the flames licked across the hallway floor. The thing on the bed didn't stir, but sucked the thickening air into its lungs, the sightless face turned toward the ceiling no longer visible.

Even before the line of black char crept through the bedroom's carpet, the heat from below burst the thin curtains into flame. They twisted brilliant in the rush of air from the window as it shattered, the heavy curtain rod twisting free from the burning frame and striking the glass.

The flames caught the edge of the bedsheet dangling to the burning floor. The thing on the bed didn't move, already caught in its frozen writhing.

Again bone against concrete, and Braemer felt the space around him expand on a sharp edge of black, then contract again to the face grinning above him. No more words came from its mouth, only a thin, excited mewing.

Suddenly, that noise broke into rapid panting. The eyes widened, the mouth stretching open as if trying to draw in more air.

Trembling, the hands let go of Braemer's head. Renee's face stared around wildly at the skeleton room, searching for something. Then its hands dug clawing at Jess's face, as though trying to rip it open and let out the thing beneath.

"Daddy!" He heard Dee's scream, and through the dark wave surging with his pulse, saw her face, drained white, looking with horror at the scene before her. She fell forward from where she knelt, rolling onto her shoulder and reaching for his hand.

The thing inside Jess reared back from Braemer's chest, dark blood seeping from between the fingers clutched to its face.

Its cry tore from its throat—

The bed burst into flames. Under the charring blanket, the body's muscles contracted, the heat drawing the last life from them.

The close-cropped hair above the fleshed skull singed, crackling against the scalp. From the dark nostrils, the plastic tube melted in a red line across the sunken cheek, a line swallowed by the blood breaking through the skin.

Bloodless lips drew back from the yellowed teeth. The face rising from beneath was a death's-head, white bone breaking through charring flesh.

—screamed and fell, its chest laboring for breath. No face, only the red hands shining wet.

Braemer rolled onto his side, closer to where Dee lay, her face now pressed blank and unconscious against the concrete floor.

The writhing thing arched its spine into a bow. Then its panting for breath was cut silent. The hands fell away from Jess's torn face, and he collapsed, crumbling like blood-soaked clothing.

Braemer crawled toward him. With one hand he turned Jess's face toward him. Dark red flowed from his mouth and nostrils, unstirred by any breath.

Then he saw the orange light flickering over the dead face and his own hand upon it. He turned and saw, through the black lines of the framework house, the fire in the distance, the flames leaping into the sky, curling around the gray funnel of smoke.

He could hear the fire roaring, louder than any sound of breathing but his own and that of the child close by him.

AFTER

In the morning light, the child walked down the road curving out of the low hills. A ten-year-old girl in a pair of jeans scraped and torn at the knees, her dark hair tangled and loose against her neck, striding purposefully.

She reached the crossroad at the bottom of the hill and turned toward the freeway overpass. The gas station was on the other side of the rumbling weekend traffic.

"Can you change this for me?" No cars at the pump yet—she had found the attendant in the office behind the cans of oil stacked into a pyramid in the window. She held out the crumpled $20 bill she had taken out of her father's wallet. It was damp from the sweat of her hand in her pocket.

The attendant was a straw-haired youth in a striped shirt, the company emblem on the pocket. "Sure," he said, after glancing from the money to the girl. He led her out to the cash box by the pumps, unlocked it, and began sorting out smaller bills.

"I need some quarters," said the little girl. "I gotta make a phone call."

"Here you go." He folded the bills and laid them in her palm, weighting them with a stack of coins.

She walked to the phone booth at the edge of the station's lot. The empty Datsun was still parked there beside it. She pulled the booth's door closed, reached up, and put the first of the quarters in, then more when the operator told her to.

The telephone at the other end rang only twice before it was picked up. "Hello?" came a woman's voice.

"Sarah?" The girl held the telephone close to her.

"Dee—" Sarah's voice broke in amazement. "Dee, where are you?"

"'S a gas station. Down by where I used to live."

Sarah's words rushed together. "Is Dave—is your daddy there with you?"

"He's hurt. You have to come get us."

"Jesus Christ. Okay. Okay, just tell me where you're at."

Carefully, Dee explained the mazelike course through the tract. "The one on the corner," she said finally. "We'll be in there."

"All right." Sarah's voice had fought itself calm. "Just stay where you told me. I'll have to take a cab to a rental place, and get a car to come down there. But I'll be there as soon as I can. Okay?"

"Okay," said Dee. "See ya." She put the phone back in its hook.

Plenty of quarters left. She went to the vending machine at the front of the station and got two cans of Coke, one for herself and one for her father.

The attendant was still watching her from the office doorway. Clutching the two damp cans to her stomach, she went into the LADIES room. In the white-tiled space,

312

she climbed up onto the sink, then dropped the cans through the window above before scrambling up and through it herself. She took a wide circle around the gas station before getting back to the road that went under the freeway. Then she ran.

Her father's face was crossed with bars of light from the open wooden framework around him. He lay curled up on the dusty concrete floor. His head, the back of it all dark and matted sticky, rested on his arm.

She flopped down beside him, tired from the long walk to and from the phone booth. Her T-shirt was wet from where she had carried the cans. She pulled one open and held it to her father's lips. Most of it ran from his mouth onto the floor, then his eyelids fluttered. He gagged and coughed, turning his face to the concrete.

A moment later, he turned his head to look at her. "Hi," he said, smiling weakly.

"Hi," she said, gazing down at him, holding the can in her lap.

He lifted his head, looking about at the framework of the unfinished house. It wasn't the same one where Jess's body lay. Dee had come to, cradled against his chest, as he had half carried, half dragged her farther away from the burning house, while the fire-engine sirens had cut through the night filling the tract's streets. Only when they had been safely hidden in this abandoned framework had her father finally collapsed. His eyes closed, as if he finally recognized where they were.

Then he looked at Dee again. "She's really dead," he said quietly. "Isn't she?"

Dee nodded. "Yes." She could feel it inside herself. The other thing was gone.

The sunlight, warm and bright, slanted through the framework walls. Her father saw how tired she was.

Wincing, he pushed against the concrete with his hands, until he was sitting with his back against one of the uprights. "Come here," he said.

She curled against his side, and he held his jacket over her, shading her from the sun. They waited for Sarah to come and take them home.

DO YOU KNOW:

- WHY *NOT* FEELING YOUR PAIN CAN INTENSIFY AND PERPETUATE IT?

- HOW TO FIND INNER CALMNESS AND SELF-CONTROL WHEN FACING TURMOIL?

- HOW TO CARE FOR YOUR FAMILY DURING A CRISIS?

- WHY MIXED FEELINGS ARE NORMAL . . . AND WHAT REALLY HELPS YOU DEAL WITH THEM?

- WHAT FOUR QUESTIONS MUST BE ANSWERED TO SPEED RECOVERY FROM EMOTIONAL TRAUMA?

- WHAT YOU CAN DO TO TURN STRESS INTO A POSITIVE FORCE IN YOUR LIFE?

- WHAT'S LEFT TO BELIEVE IN WHEN YOUR WHOLE WORLD HAS TURNED UPSIDE DOWN?

With words of wisdom you'll want to read over and over again, Dr. Paul Coleman brings you a gift of healing . . . in a very special book that keeps despair from your heart and brings meaning to your life.

LIFE'S PARACHUTES

Also by Dr. Paul Coleman

The Thirty Secrets of Happily Married Couples

The Forgiving Marriage

LIFE'S PARACHUTES

How to Land on Your Feet
During Trying Times

❖

DR. PAUL COLEMAN

A DELL BOOK

Published by
Dell Publishing
a division of
Bantam Doubleday Dell Publishing Group, Inc.
1540 Broadway
New York, New York 10036

Grateful acknowledgment is made to the following for permission to reprint previously published material:

from GUILT IS THE TEACHER, LOVE IS THE LESSON, copyright © 1990 by Joan Borysenko. Reprinted by permission of Warner Books, New York.

from FULL CATASTROPHE LIVING, copyright © 1990 by Jon Kabat-Zinn. Reprinted by permission of Delacorte Press, a division of Bantam Doubleday Dell Publishing Group, Inc., New York.

from THE DIFFERENT DRUM: COMMUNITY MAKING AND PEACE, copyright © 1987 by M. Scott Peck. Reprinted by permission of Simon & Schuster, New York.

from FURTHER ALONG THE ROAD LESS TRAVELED: M. SCOTT PECK SPEAKS ON TOGETHERNESS AND SEPARATENESS IN MARRIAGE AND FAMILY (Simon & Schuster Audioworks), copyright © 1988 by M. Scott Peck. Reprinted by permission of M. Scott Peck.

ISBN: 0-440-21102-6

Printed in the United States of America

Published simultaneously in Canada

June 1993

10 9 8 7 6 5 4 3 2 1

OPM

*To my littlest one, Julia
(the inspiration for this book)*

And in memory of

David I. Wangberg, my father-in-law

Don Gager, a family friend

*And Catherine Carabine,
my niece, who touched more hearts than she ever knew*

God love you all

Acknowledgments

To my wife, Jody, for her encouragement and sacrifice while I wrote this book;

To my literary agent, Mike Snell, for his enthusiasm and talent in helping me to develop this book idea;

To Jill Lamar at Dell Publishing, who possesses the two finest qualities of an editor: the ability to rework a manuscript until it shines, and to stay true to the author's style and intentions (even when the author doesn't);

To my mother-in-law, Beverly Wangberg, the best public relations person I have had east of the Mississippi;

To the many people who have shared with me their stories of hope;

To my kids, who've made my life and my work so much more meaningful;

To my mother and father;

I give you my warmest and most heartfelt thanks.

P.C.
1993

Contents

Chapter 1

❖

LIFE'S PARACHUTES

❖

❖

I<small>N</small> A WORLD where people are mortal, where sickness sometimes outraces medicine, where it can be a struggle to get by, let alone get ahead; in a world where accidents happen, soldiers go to war, and where promises, dreams, and hearts can break like pottery on an unforgiving surface, there is good news: Your trying times are temporary. No problem lasts forever. True, some problems can't be solved, but all problems can be *resolved* as you come to terms with all that has happened to you. Much pain passes eventually, but even those hurts that never seem to go away completely *don't have to get in your way.*

Skeptical? I don't blame you. Life's hardships and tragedies can overwhelm the hardiest among us. But being overwhelmed isn't the problem. Not really. The more insidious problem is a lack of faith: in yourself to cope with adversity, that recovery is possible, and that your life can still be meaningful when recovery—yours or a loved one's—isn't possible. No matter what the setback or misfortune, people who have a core belief that somehow, some way, they'll make it through the tough times often do just that.

WHAT ARE TRYING TIMES?

Everybody goes through trying times, often for weeks or months on end: suffering with chronic illness, grappling with a marriage that long ago lost its substance, coping with too many job demands, grieving the death of a loved one or the death of a romance or the death of a dream. Trying times occur when the money coming in barely exceeds expenses going out. Trying times need not be unexpected bolts out of the blue (though they often are). Simply confronting life on a daily basis forces us to face the ordinary burdens and transitions that can be trying: leaving home for the first time, getting married, raising children, changing careers, caring for one's aging parents, hugging dear friends good-bye, welcoming new ones, cradling the beloved family dog (who now has cataracts and can't control his bladder anymore) as he is about to be put to sleep. . . .

A normal part of life, you say? Yes, but not always easy.

Disease and illness are common enough. People expect to have their share of routine health problems. Steven Locke and Douglas Colligan, in their book *The Healer Within*, state categorically that stress is a contributing factor in well over forty diseases. Common stress-affected ailments include heart disease, headaches, diabetes, hypertension, gastrointestinal disorders, insomnia, asthma, hives and various allergies, and numerous other illnesses. The relatively new field of psychoneuroimmunology has demonstrated repeatedly in the past ten years how illness can be brought on in part by stressful life events. That is so because stress weakens the immune system. Stress can help bring on illness, but illness can create more stress (loss of income, worries about recovery, depression, etc.). When layers upon layers of stress build up, our coping resources can become rapidly depleted.

And what of the unexpected stressors? This year alone approximately 800,000 people will be told, "You have cancer." Despite a higher and higher cure rate, many cancer victims may not survive. And the many who will must undergo months and sometimes years of treatment, hoping they'll remain in remission. And for every cancer victim there are the secondary victims—the families and close friends who worry and cry and often feel helpless to do anything.

Nearly forty million people will be admitted to a hospital next year. The lives of many of them will change significantly and permanently as a result of their conditions.

The divorce rate shows signs of decline. Nevertheless about one million couples will divorce this year. (The chance that a child born today will experience a *second* parental divorce by the age of eighteen is an astounding 40 percent.) More than a million couples will separate. Still more will attempt to make an unfulfilling relationship satisfying—a worthwhile but sometimes taxing task. Janice Kiecolt-Glaser, a researcher at Ohio State University, established in 1987 that marital adjustment is connected to immune functioning. Comparing thirty-eight married women with thirty-eight recently separated or divorced women, Dr. Kiecolt-Glaser found that women who reported having a bad marriage also had weaker responses on three measures of immune functioning. Once again, stressors can build on each other as marital unhappiness leads to diminished immune responsivity, which can lead to poorer health, which leads to more adjustments and more stress.

Three percent of children born in America have some kind of birth defect. In 50 percent of such cases the deformity cannot be accounted for by maternal health, background, or life-style. Thankfully most birth defects are not catastrophic in nature. Nonetheless adjustments need to be made—sometimes life-styles need to be altered—in order for families to manage.

Approximately six million violent crimes occur in the United States each year. FBI statistics for 1990 showed a 10 percent increase over 1989 figures for the most serious crimes: assault, rape, and murder. In 1987 while at Purdue University, Dr. Charles Figley, a leading researcher on coping with trauma, reported that concerned family members of victims of violent crimes also displayed evidence of depression, social isolation, feelings of persecution, and disturbances in daily routines—even months after the crisis first occurred.

Six months ago Marie's daughter, Gina, was raped while on her way to an evening college class. Gina's school was over a thousand miles from home. After two weeks had passed and Gina was feeling a little better, she finally told her mother what had happened. Today, six months later, Marie still worries about Gina's safety and has suffered bouts of insomnia.

"It's an overwhelming sense of helplessness," Marie explained. "Gina is so far from home. How can I be there to help her if she needs me?" Concerned family members unable to be physically present during a loved one's crisis often develop symptoms of anxiety or depression.

No one is immune to stress. No one is spared pain. Yet day after day people not only endure hard times, they meet them head-on. Many not only "get through it," they recover and discover they've become better people for it. How do they do it? What exactly do people who cope effectively with pain, loss, or misfortune actually *do* that is different from those who falter? How can people, tumbling in free-fall from life's hardships, eventually land on their feet?

GRABBING HOLD OF LIFE'S PARACHUTES

What are life's parachutes? They are the *most helpful, fundamental, healing* attitudes and strategies people can use during trying times when they want to cope effectively. Will such strategies eliminate stress and suffering? No. While some pain can be considerably lessened, the ironic truth is this: *The tragedies of life are necessary if we are to learn how to fully live.* Where else do we learn about the meaning of deep love, compassion, hope, and forgiveness except from situations where love was lost, where compassion was shrouded in fear and selfishness, where hope was whittled down by despair, and forgiveness lost in a sea of bitterness? Ask anybody with a positive approach to living about their tough times and they will probably draw the same conclusion: "While I wouldn't wish what happened to me on my worst enemy, I'm grateful *in a way* that I went through it." Funny, but it seems that most of us spend a lot of our time *wanting,* whereas having what we want withheld usually helps make us better people.

However self-sufficient you think you are, whatever your strengths of character, the power of life's parachutes is enhanced by your willingness to seek help, to draw strength from others who've been there already or who care deeply about you. When you grab hold of one of life's parachutes, you are really taking hold of a gift given by others before you. *Determination* may be a gift instilled by a parent or childhood hero. *Creative problem-solving* may be a gift encouraged by a teacher, *forgiveness* by a friend or a loving God you've prayed to. *Hope* may have been inspired by some stranger, whose own story of overcoming adversity motivated you to persevere. All of life's parachutes are gifts. Whether or not those gifts are accepted, used, and developed is up to you.

WHAT TO EXPECT

Once you get a secure hold on life's parachutes, three things will happen: You'll *think* differently, you'll *feel* differently, and you'll ultimately *be different*.

• You'll change your thinking as you develop an entirely new perspective on your problems. In fact you'll discover that what you thought was the real problem probably wasn't the prime source of your suffering.

• You'll change your feelings too. Optimism and a sense of challenge will displace anxiety and helplessness. You will choose to capitalize on any anger you have left to promote growth and healing rather than allowing it to burn uncontrollably.

• And in the final analysis you will be different. You'll see the world in a new light. You'll appreciate what you previously took for granted. You'll have a sturdier self-esteem and a dignified, yet humbled, view of yourself and your place on this earth. Your life will have more meaning.

Through it all you will discover you have more say over what happens to you than you previously realized. You'll understand that in really trying times it's possible to reach down deep into the pockets of your soul and come up with an idea, a plan, some small change of hope, a firmness of faith, a willingness to struggle, and a purpose for being so that you can truly survive the tough times and come out better in the end.

WHY ARE LIFE'S PARACHUTES
SO EFFECTIVE?

Life's parachutes are opportunities for us to take some control in a situation that seems out of control. We begin by altering our view of the definition of stress. Stress is not a stimulus. It's our response. It does not originate from outside of us, but from within. We may be accustomed to identifying stress with such conditions as poor health, a demanding job, traffic jams, accumulating bills, an unhappy marriage, too many arguments, too little affection, too few moments of solitude, too much noise—all of these are potential stress*ors* but not necessarily stress*ful*. Our *reaction* to these and other stressors determines our level of stress. Anytime we overemphasize what is happening *to* us and underemphasize *what we can do* about it, we create stress. Sometimes we feel challenged by stress and make strides in overcoming obstacles to our recovery. But it's difficult to feel challenged when we place the responsibility for what happened outside our influence. And that is precisely what we do when most of our efforts at coping involve blaming others for our misfortune. Placing blame may help in understanding why some problems exist. But more often, blame-fixing leaves us with a too narrow view of the nature of the problem. Yes, Mother may have been the one to leave the marriage, but was she responsible for its failure? And whom do you blame when an accident happens? When disease strikes? When a company must lay you off among hundreds of workers? Is it management's fault? The union's? The politicians'? The solutions to these and other questions must involve a willingness to help ourselves. But there must also be a willingness to say, "I need help. . . . I'm doing all I can, but I still need help" when your own efforts fall short. Paradoxically we take more control over our fate when we place it in the hands of someone (such as

God or another person) who is much better equipped to handle our problems. Knowing what to do and when to do it, and when to leave it up to others—that's what life's parachutes offer us.

Life's parachutes not only help us cope with adversity, they help us understand and eventually come to terms with whatever hardships befall us. In the course of landing on our feet we learn about our strengths and weaknesses, reassess our values and goals, and make peace with our past. Life's parachutes help us *comprehend* what happened, *accept* reality rather than distort it, and *strengthen* our coping ability. Researcher Charles Figley, now at Florida State University, agrees that effective coping involves more than simply getting through the tough times. In his book *Helping Traumatized Families*, he states that four questions must be answered as people recover from emotional trauma:

• *What happened?* Answering this question requires openness and honesty, not denial or pretense. Minimizing what happened in an attempt to soothe emotional wounds prevents healing. Some people, caught up in a whirlwind of emotions as they try to cope with adversity, overlook the fact that other family members have been affected too. Asking the rest of the family "What happened?" is an important consideration that enables healing to occur.

• *Why did it happen?* Often this is a difficult, sometimes impossible, question to answer with certainty. But unraveling the sequence of events that led up to and possibly caused the current difficulty helps us to understand it better —and may help us to prevent it from happening again. But if we're not careful, we can get stuck at this question, doggedly asking, *Why? Why? Why?* when no answer would be adequate enough. Some people chalk it up to fate, bad luck, or God's mysterious ways. Sometimes those are the only answers left.

• *Why did I, and others, act as we did throughout this ordeal?* How we behave at the beginning of a traumatic event can be unusual behavior for us. It's easy to feel overwhelmed. Sometimes we say things we regret. Sometimes we withdraw, alienating those who require our comfort or reassurance. We may blame others unfairly or be unfairly blamed. And after the ordeal is over, we may be puzzled by some of our reactions to what happened. Some people routinely dredge up painful memories like muck from a lake. Others try hard to forget. Some become obsessed with guilt or bitterness (*Could I, or somebody else, have prevented it?*). Acceptance, tolerance, and understanding of your actions (and those of others) is important at this juncture.

• *If something like this happens again, could I handle it?* And could the family handle it too? Developing an overall faith in our ability to cope allows us to meet life head-on rather than meekly. Answering this question helps us to assess our resources and reveals areas that need improvement.

The chapters in this book will help you answer these questions.

SO, THERE IS HOPE AFTER ALL?

No question about it. But if you're in the middle of a crisis now, it may be hard to look past tomorrow with comfort and hope. This is so because when anyone feels threatened, the natural tendency is to focus on the threat and pay little attention to anything else. It bears repeating that all problems are temporary. And inner resources we've hardly tapped do exist.

What may be frustrating to a few of you right now is my insistence that matters will improve, that *you can feel better.* Perhaps you believe you've already done everything possible and nothing so far has helped—or could ever help. Perhaps you still feel hurt and angry that something unfair and unasked-for has befallen you. Possibly you've lost a loved one who should never have gone so soon. Or maybe a dream has died. When you don't deserve the bad things that happen to you, you can understandably resent having to pick up the pieces that fate, or somebody else, scattered. Painfully aware that just last year or last week all was well in your world, you may feel bitter about having to adjust to the awful turn of events.

And it's true that while your problems, as they exist now, are temporary, some degree of suffering can continue for a long time for many people. One quarter of widows interviewed by one researcher a year after the death of a spouse agreed with the statement "I would not care if I died tomorrow." Lynn Wikler and colleagues studied how parents of mentally retarded children coped. They found the parents' sorrow chronic, but not continuous. Periodically (usually as new developmental stages were reached by the child), these parents grieved. But they had happy times too. In a study of the long-term effects of losing a child or a spouse in an automobile accident, half of those interviewed reported that in the past month they relived the sequence of events that led to the accident. And this was now four to seven years after the tragedy had occurred. Fifty-two percent of those who lost a spouse and 62 percent of parents who lost a child sometimes thought, *If only I had done something different that day. . . .* These people adjusted somewhat to the tragedy, but suffering hadn't left them completely.

When Michelle finally conceived a child after years of infertility, she and her husband, Peter, were inconsolable after the miscarriage. Despite the fact that they believed their chances of conceiving again were good, the reassuring words from caring doctors and family stung like salt in an open wound.

"I guess it seemed to me that the underlying message from people was, 'Michelle, don't feel so bad. Don't feel the way you do.' They sort of understood my pain, but not really. They wanted me to be optimistic. What I wanted was my baby back."

Trying to move quickly away from pain with a manufactured burst of optimism isn't being kind to yourself. Yes, optimism must be nourished, but not at the expense of necessary grieving. When something precious has been taken from you, it is the most natural thing in the world to mourn. Take the time to embrace the extent of your loss fully. It's okay. In grief it's okay to feel angry, to feel unkindly toward hope. It's okay to feel cynical, to feel betrayed by faith. It's okay to feel like you don't give a damn about the future. It's okay. Really. When a light goes out in your soul, it's hard to behold a tomorrow full of promise. But there is a voice inside you that knows you must somehow adjust to the loss and let go of as much of the pain as possible. And you can. Maybe not today. But by giving yourself the time you need to grieve, you've already begun the healing process. And for so many it does get easier.

Chapter 2

THE UPS AND DOWNS
OF CRISIS AND CHANGE

The Gift of Determination

❖

TWO-YEAR-OLD SERENA woke up one morning and couldn't move. Panicky, Serena's parents brought her to the hospital in Taiwan, where she was diagnosed with polio. Death was a frightening possibility. But Serena didn't die, and with proper treatment she eventually regained the use of her upper body, though her legs withered. Unwilling to give up, Serena's family emigrated to the United States so that she could undergo further treatment at a Los Angeles hospital. After years of therapy she was finally able to walk again with the aid of a brace and crutches. But something inside her told her not to stop there. Eventually she even volunteered to help out at the orthopedic hospital where she had learned to walk. A young woman now, with deepening religious convictions, Serena wondered if a loving God could have allowed this tragedy to happen for a reason. Perhaps some good could still come out of her disability. In time she decided to enter medical school with the hope of helping people like herself. With support from her husband, and despite the concerns of many who didn't believe she could cope with the rigors of medical training, she succeeded. Today Dr. Serena Young, now an orthopedic surgeon, performs surgery while leaning on her crutches.*

PERSISTENCE PLUS

Serena Young persisted. But more than that, she was *determined*. Persistence pushes you forward. It keeps you trudging, stubbornly placing one foot in front of the other, again and again, through the blizzard that caught you unaware. But determination does that and more. Determination digs a shelter in your heart, a warm, replenishing place you can come to whenever discouragement has you wondering, *Why should I go on?* Determination is born out of knowing deep down *why you must* move forward. Persistence is the *how*. Determination is the *why*. Persistence is your hands and feet and legs and arms and head. Determination is your heart and soul.

I'd known Mark for some time when I'd heard his young daughter had been badly hurt in an auto accident. Brain damage, I later learned. How severe?

"They can't tell," Mark told me. "Marsha and I organize our days now around doctors' appointments and rehab therapies. I'm sure Katy will improve. But it may take ten or twenty years before she's fully functional. Then again it might take only one or two. We just don't know." Mark was understandably weary, and I wanted him to be sure to get some rest. He shook his head and smiled warmly.

"No time, Paul," he answered. "I've got to do all I can right now for my little girl. You know what I mean?"

I knew.

Mark's determination flowed from the wellspring of a

---

* Adapted from *Possibilities: The Magazine of Hope*, May–June 1990.

parent's love for his child. And it is that love which will nudge him farther along, even on those darker days when hope is but a mere speck of light, like some distant star; burning, but so insignificant in the spread of an infinite night sky.

Love provides purpose. And purpose rivets your resolve to make it through the trying times. Determination, then, is *persistence plus purpose*. Find that purpose and you'll persevere through trying times. But you won't discover it in vague dreams or fanciful wishes. The purpose you're searching for can only be found in the grit and bones of your existence. It may be rooted in those people who love you and who count on you to somehow make it through the tough times. Maybe your purpose will stem from a fundamental belief that God has better plans for you—if you can just see your way through. Maybe your purpose will be *you*. Sometimes you just have to say, "Damn it! I deserve better than this and I'm going to see to it that somehow I make it through." *Persistence plus purpose* will help you cope with the ups and downs of crisis and change.

WHAT YOU DON'T KNOW ABOUT CRISIS AND CHANGE . . .

. . . Probably has more bearing on your level of determination than you realize. As a psychologist I know a great deal about how to help people change. But ironically when people enter therapy they don't want change. They want stability. In fact by the time they've made their first appointment, changes have already begun. They've called me not to help them continue those changes but to halt them. "Things are getting out of hand," they tell me. The hardest work of therapy comes when people resist the changes that are inevitable. Which leads me to the nine points I think you should know about crisis, change, and determination.

1. *Once you adapt to inevitable changes, you'll get the stability you long for.* The concepts of change and stability are intertwined. One cannot be understood without the other. Stability precedes and follows change. And change precedes and follows stability. All people must change—that is, grow and adapt. The trick is to accomplish that while maintaining a sense of stability. Stability without change stunts growth. Change without stability is chaotic—and ultimately stunts growth too. We require both in order to grow. In a healthy family, self-esteem, faith, and love are the anchors the members hold on to when all else in their world is spinning. Eventually when the crises and changes pass, they'll reach a new level of stability as each family member in his or her own way adapts to the new developments.

2. *In the face of irrevocable loss, there is no "right way" to grieve.* Despite popular belief that healthy grief spends itself in predictable stages (denial, anger, depression, recovery), such a belief may well be a myth. Recent well-designed studies by Camille Wortman and colleagues at the State University of New York at Stony Brook reveal that the range of "normal" reactions to loss varies widely—more widely than previously believed. While sadness is very common, clinical depression (a more severe form of depression) is not. A mild grief reaction to a bereavement does not automatically signify stunted mourning. Nor is it necessarily a sign of poor adjustment to still be suffering greatly years after a loss or misfortune. In fact the more sudden and traumatic the loss, the more likely one's grief may persist long after conventional wisdom and well-meaning relatives say it should.

3. *When trying to change a long-standing problem, understand that you probably have more fears about improving things than you realize.* Don't be too hard on yourself. Tackling a problem head-on generates anxiety and frustration, maybe even sadness or anger, all of which are uncomfortable. Most people avoid as much as possible situations that bring on such feelings. Understandably you may have some mixed feelings about persevering. Many depressed people or people in unsatisfying marriages, while wanting desperately to feel better, are nevertheless reluctant to get a taste of hope—to see the possibility that matters can improve—because they fear those hopes will be dashed. Consequently just when it appears that their efforts to work things out may finally pay off, anxiety can prompt them to act in counterproductive ways.

4. *Despite dogged determination, setbacks will occur.* Even if you don't have mixed feelings about your desire to improve your life; even if you persevere; setbacks will inevitably occur. When trying to resolve long-standing and complicated problems, people prefer progress that is safe and predictable, something like a bank certificate of deposit. But in really trying times, progress is often volatile, like the stock market, and setbacks are normal. Keep in mind, though, that setbacks can't happen unless you've already made some progress.

5. *The hardest part about making changes is not the initial progress you make. It is sustaining those changes in the face of pressure from others to change back.* If you are trying to change a chronic condition (perhaps an illness rendered you too dependent and you now wish to become more independent, or maybe you want your marriage to improve), understand that the longer the condition has persisted, the more everyone involved has adapted to it. Which means others now have to change along with you—and they might resist. (The family bureaucracy is often harder to fight than city hall.) Many husbands want me to "fix" their depressed wives, but become far less supportive when their wives start asserting themselves. Many wives want me to "fix" their hard-drinking husbands, but balk at any efforts to help them understand their own influence on their husband's alcoholism. Such spouses aren't malicious, they're frightened. All change brings loss, and they're afraid of losing something—something they may not even understand. Staying determined in the face of others' nonsupport or criticism isn't easy, but it is necessary for lasting change to occur.

6. *You want some changes so badly, you may not trust them when they happen.* If you've been disappointed too often in the past, cynicism and doubt may cloud your vision. This is especially true in resolving interpersonal problems. Expecting others' efforts at improvement to be insincere or inadequate, you may not respond with encouragement and appreciation when they do make desired changes. Then they'll likely feel defeated and stop short of making all the changes you'd like. Be determined not to make a negative self-fulfilling prophecy unfold. Home in on the smaller goals that must be reached before the bigger goals can happen. Ask yourself, *What is the next thing that needs to happen for me to be sure matters are improving?* Focusing on the smaller steps, one at a time, helps sustain optimism and diminish fears, both of which will serve to strengthen your determination.

7. *Some changes are permanent, some aren't. But the negative effects don't have to be.* Death is permanent, so are some diseases. Divorces are usually permanent. Marriages used to be. We can't always control what happens to us, but we have a say over how we react to it. The sadness, the outrage, the fear, the desperate desire to curl up and die—all of

that feels awful but doesn't have to persist. When you can't change what happened, determine to change the negative effects. Norman Cousins, in his recent book, *Head First*, discussed people who angrily defied experts' opinions of their medical condition. When told they had multiple sclerosis, heart disease, or cancer, a special group of people decided not to accept their fate passively. They accepted their condition as real, but refused to go along with the prognosis. They were determined to foster a fighting spirit and defy the odds. And many succeeded. Their rallying cry, "Don't deny the diagnosis . . . defy the verdict!" brought a cavalry of desire, defiance, and determination to their rescue.

8. *During trying times, let those in the family who wish to help do so.* Don't always be the "strong one." Even if you think you can handle it all on your own, remember that your loved ones may feel more helpless if they can only stand by while you do all the coping. Letting them get involved may not only ease your burdens, it may ease theirs too.

9. *Commitment plus control plus a sense of challenge will improve your hardiness.* So says researcher Suzanne Kobasa, who has conducted studies on the stress-resistant personality. Hardy individuals are more *committed* to what they're doing (and to themselves as well). They are in touch with their feelings and have clear values and priorities. They also exert more *control* over what is happening to them. They are not, so to speak, inclined to recline—to sit back and passively accept whatever goes on around them. They view difficult times as *challenges*, not threats. When your determination falters, assess where you stand on the three Cs of commitment, control, and challenge. Making improvements in those areas can give you back the determination you need to plow ahead.

BUT SOMETIMES . . .
"I CAN'T" . . .

Yes, I know. Those hard times do exist. Determination is a furnace that doesn't burn forever. But you need to understand that the belief that you "can't" is often a desperate attempt to communicate something very different from utter helplessness. The person who says, "I can't," sometimes is really saying, "I'm afraid to . . . I don't want to . . . I'm lonely . . . I'm angry . . . I'm sad . . . I need help. . . ." *What is it you're saying when you tell yourself, "I can't"?*

Those times when you really, truly can't . . . well, there is still something you can do. You can tell other people precisely how they can help you. Give them direction, as much as you can muster. Offer encouragement when needed, and thanks when they're finished. Tell them what all they've done has meant to you. Or find somebody whom you can help. Really. You may not feel up to it, your energy might be low right now, but taking time to offer aid to someone who needs it can make a difference in how you feel. In that way you continue to help yourself even when you can't help yourself.

And of course you can pray. To some of you that advice is the stuff of which platitudes are made. But strong evidence exists of the power of prayer to soothe a troubled spirit.

One last thought. I remember a time in the not-too-distant past when I said, "I can't anymore . . ." and I gave up. In anguish I left a job, which in some ways I loved, because I could no longer tolerate a bureaucracy riddled with petty politics, back-stabbing, and mediocrity. I gave up the fight to remain on the job, but took up the fight to find satisfaction elsewhere. My determination didn't die, it shifted direction. I then realized that for two years I'd *per-*

sisted in my efforts to remain on that job (despite mounting unhappiness), but had lost my purpose for staying. However, I did have a purpose for leaving. I wanted more satisfaction from my daily occupation, more time with my new family, more time to write. So I resigned. It took me a few weeks to adjust to my decision, and the struggle ended there. No celebration, no fanfare, just the quiet realization that I'd made the right choice.

Persistence without purposefulness burns you out. Purposefulness without persistence leaves you hungry. But persistence *plus* purposefulness is the fire and the fuel that stokes your determination and keeps it burning.

Chapter 3

THE ONLY WORKABLE
PROBLEM IS A
R-E-A-L PROBLEM

The Gift of Creative Problem-Solving

❖

THE PROBLEMS IN YOUR LIFE are obvious, right? Not enough money, not enough time, not enough appreciation —or perhaps a family or health crisis has erupted. Regardless, the problems staring you in the face are all too apparent. Or are they? Actually, trying times are made more arduous when, in the throes of some misfortune, people misidentify the fundamental problems.

In very trying times you may not be upset for the reasons you think. Certainly there is pain from your loss or adversity, but a deeper anguish comes when you lose faith in yourself and your spirit closes up. When disappointment dims your hope, when the very fibers of your faith are worn thin from discouragement, when all seems dark and difficult and uncertain, it is your spirit that must be rekindled if you are to make it through the tough times.

Rekindling your spirit is a more immediate, and more important, problem to resolve than whatever misfortune has befallen you.

THE SPIRIT OF THE PROBLEM

When adversity strikes, it should be dealt with on two levels:

Level 1. Focus on the original problem. For a health problem, concentrate on finding proper medical treatment. For a relationship problem, perhaps you should take some quiet time to be alone and think, or try to improve communication with your partner. This is the commonsense level where people concentrate most of their efforts. Restricting your focus to this level helps best for short-term problems. *But when attempted solutions fail repeatedly, or when chronic problems exist (such as dealing with loss, a permanent injury, or lengthy illness), you should broaden your focus to include Level 2.*

Level 2. Address your *problem with having a problem.* At this level you contend with all of the possible emotional side effects—anger, frustration, anxiety, guilt, and depression—and how those feelings affect your overall coping abilities. For example, after a horrible auto accident resulted in the loss of Dave's lower left leg, the biggest problem he faced in his recovery was his own emotions. His anger at the unfairness of his loss (he'd been sitting patiently at a red light when his car was hit) and his resulting depression interfered with his participation in physical therapy. With his recovery time slowed even more, Dave became further depressed. In effect he was depressed about being depressed. Clearly the emotional side effects of his ordeal had to be addressed before he could begin healing physically.

Doug and Cindy's marriage had been unsatisfying for years. In a sincere effort to improve matters, they decided one evening to go out to dinner and talk positively about their life together—something they'd rarely done. Despite best intentions, their conversation over dinner was stilted and superficial, relieved only by long, awkward silences.

"We were so uncomfortable," Cindy explained unhappily.

"Most people would have felt that way under the circumstances," I said. "But being uncomfortable wasn't your problem. Your real problem was that you were *uncomfortable about being uncomfortable.* Next time you go out together, allow one another to feel nervous and self-conscious. If you can *learn to be comfortable about being uncomfortable,* spending time together while you're working on improving your relationship will be more satisfying."

At Level 2 you also assess your coping skills. Will you need more support from family or friends? In what specific ways can they show that support? What obstacles could potentially impede your ability to cope? What will you need the most to help you through this trying time? What is your overall degree of faith in your ability to cope?

Finally, with a Level-2 awareness you realize that the people closest to you are likely affected by the adversity too. They may need extra support, caring, and understanding.

When difficulties drag on, people often tell themselves that their negative feelings (anxiety, frustration, guilt, anger, depression—all Level-2 problems) will disappear as soon as the original (Level 1) problem gets resolved. In fact the reverse is usually true. During trying times, *unless you modify your negative feelings (at Level 2), you may not be able to fully cope with or resolve your difficulties (at Level 1).* That is the real problem—the real challenge—you must face.

CULTIVATING A LEVEL-2
AWARENESS

DISCOVERING THE R-E-A-L
PROBLEM

Once you've determined what the Level-2 problems are, you can begin correcting them. But how can you be sure you've accurately identified them? A clearly defined problem is already half solved. The first step is to realize that some time must pass before you can get a clear picture of what's really happened. During the first hours, days, or even months of hardship, you may be in too much shock to think clearly. And when your thinking finally becomes more realistic, the full impact of what happened to you and your loved ones may still not be immediately apparent. Many victims of natural disasters such as floods or earthquakes, once they get over the immediate shock or terror, experience a "honeymoon phase" of coping. According to researcher and physician Herbert Weiner, from one week to several months after a disaster, victims often feel hopeful and upbeat as they receive assistance from government and local agencies and experience a camaraderie with the other victims. But then disillusionment sets in. Cooperative efforts falter. Helping agencies fall short of their promised aid. Victims compare themselves to others and may feel hostile to those more fortunate. Communities can ultimately recover, but not before the disillusionment phase takes its toll on morale and cooperation.

Some people cope well during tough times, only to develop symptoms of anxiety and depression when the ordeal is finally over. It's hard to know ahead of time what additional difficulties will erupt. Nevertheless steps can be taken to improve the odds that if Level-2 problems exist, you won't overlook them.

THE R-E-A-L PROBLEM

When your efforts at coping have left you depleted and near despair, or when you can anticipate having to contend with adversity for many weeks to come, taking the following four steps can help reduce the Level-2 problems:

R REFRAME your negative beliefs and expectations into realistic but positive convictions. People who land on their feet during trying times emphasize their strengths, not their weaknesses, and ferret out the positive components in any difficulty.

E END the downward emotional spiral. Negative emotions build rapidly when coping efforts falter. People who cope well realize that their reaction to a problem will have more impact on their life than the problem itself.

A ACCEPT the reality of what's happened. And accept the reality that all problems are temporary.

L LOOK inward for answers, not outward to blame. In trying times, blaming (either yourself or someone else) does nothing to resolve problems and may prolong the agony.

Now let's examine each of these steps in more detail.

REFRAME YOUR BELIEFS

Reframing is not jargon for "look at the bright side." It more aptly means "look at the *right* side." When coping efforts falter, when misery or fear takes over, it often means you've misunderstood or deemphasized something that is important to understand. You can't do the right thing if you don't have a balanced view of the problem. Reframing corrects imbalances and distortions.

Two months ago Lauren underwent a radical mastectomy. She and her husband, Phil, hardly had time to adjust to the fact that she had cancer before the operation left her scarred physically and emotionally.

"And where has Phil been?" she asked rhetorically. "Oh, he's there for all the practical matters—doing the dishes, helping out with the kids—but for me, emotionally, he's been dead."

"What scares you about that?" I asked.

"I'm afraid he doesn't love me anymore," she answered swiftly and harshly. "I'm afraid he's repelled by the sight of . . ." Her words fell away quickly.

Phil was quiet during this, matching her description. But after some prodding he spoke.

"I've never been more frightened of losing anybody than I've been since this cancer thing began," he offered. "And I have no assurance the cancer won't come back. But the doctors told me to give her hope. How can I tell her my true feelings if it will only make her feel worse?"

For Lauren and Phil the emotional aftermath of the cancer operation sent them staggering. Some healing began, however, when each could *reframe* what they judged was happening with the other. Lauren had viewed Phil as insensitive to her feelings and emotionally aloof. However, a more accurate understanding of Phil revealed him to be not insensitive but scared. And he was coping with his fears in the way he knew best: bottling them up and pretending matters were not so bad. His reluctance to discuss his feelings was to *protect* Lauren, or so he believed. He didn't want to upset her. So he needed to reframe her upset feelings not as a bad sign but as a good one. She was doing some of the work of grieving, which was *necessary for her recovery*. Once Phil understood that, he made himself more emotionally available to Lauren. And once Lauren understood that Phil, like she, was mostly scared, she didn't take it so hard when he sometimes tucked his feelings away from her.

In order to successfully reframe, begin believing this: *Most of the time, people are doing the best they can with what they've got.* Also, *the more a person fouls up during difficult times, the more desperate he or she is feeling.* Intense fear and lack of information impede most people's efforts to cope.

Consider also that a person's weaknesses are really their strengths stretched to an extreme. While concern and compassion are strengths, overprotectiveness is a weakness. A perceptive person sometimes acts impulsively. The analytical person's weaknesses are indecisiveness and emotional restraint. An organized and responsible person can become compulsive and controlling. A thoughtful and considerate person sometimes takes the blame too often. During trying times, when other people's weaknesses begin to bother you, the task of *reframing* helps you discover their strengths of character that lie underneath the surface.

Perhaps the two most important attitudes to reframe are these:

• *"I am a victim"* must be reframed to *"I am a survivor."* A victim is helpless to do anything. A survivor pulls together all his or her resources and copes. Things happen *to* victims. Survivors *make* things happen.

• *"I am being threatened"* must be reframed to *"I am being challenged."* You can turn despair, unfairness, or crises around when you feel challenged. A threatened person either withdraws or uses scare tactics to get rid of the threat. A challenged person anticipates setbacks, explores alternatives, and perseveres with an attitude of "I can."

END THE DOWNWARD
EMOTIONAL SPIRAL

Fear builds on itself. The more frightened you are, the more you talk to yourself in a manner that fuels the fears. I often reframe a client's anxiety by telling him or her, "You don't have an anxiety problem (or an occupational problem, or a relationship problem), *you have a THINKING problem!*" What's called *catastrophic thinking* occurs when you start imagining the worst possible turn of events that could happen and believing the adversity will persist with dire consequences in most areas of your life. Catastrophic thinking typically begins with the phrase "What if . . ."

- "What if she leaves me for another man?"

- "What if he dies?"

- "What if the medication doesn't help?"

- "What if her condition doesn't improve and we have to go on living like this year after year?"

- "What if the business fails?"

- "What if the bank forecloses on the mortgage?"

These "what if" thoughts may not be irrational. In fact there may be some merit to them. The difficulty lies in the fact that people who catastrophize don't balance their catastrophic thoughts with more plausible ones. Consequently they become more afraid in a situation that probably requires calmness and rationality.

Research by Dr. Martin Seligman shows that *optimists*, people who tend not to blame themselves and who see bad events as time-limited and resolvable (noncatastrophic thinking), are at less risk for depression, illness, and even death during adversity than are *pessimists*. Pessimists tend to blame themselves when misfortune happens and believe the negative effects will last a long time and affect a vast part of their lives.

To correct catastrophic thinking, follow these guidelines:

1. Notice every time you think "What if . . . ?"

2. Remind yourself that under challenging circumstances certain hormones and chemicals are released into your bloodstream to help you to fight or flee—not to *think clearly*. Consequently your negative thinking *is a normal response to increased hormonal levels*. However, you can alter your negative thinking with some effort and practice.

3. Immediately begin thinking in terms of percentages: "Probably the odds of this happening are one in a hundred." Evaluating the odds helps you to assess the risks more realistically. Also, is there any evidence at all to support a more optimistic view?

4. If there is a reasonable likelihood that unwanted events may happen, focus on those aspects of the situation you'll have some control over. ("If the cancer comes back, I can join a support group to keep my spirits up.") This emphasis will decrease your sense of helplessness.

ACCEPT THE REALITY OF WHAT HAS HAPPENED

You don't have to believe that what happened was right, or fair, or inevitable. You certainly don't have to like what happened. But you need to accept that it did indeed take place. Utter disbelief is common when misfortune strikes. Denial helps dull the pain and buys you time. But sooner or later you must face what occurred. Arguing "This shouldn't have happened" may be legitimate, but it distracts you from grappling with the more relevant question, "Now what do I do about it?"

If you find yourself bogged down by repetitions of "This can't be!" it probably means you've lost something—or may lose something—so dear to your heart that surrendering to the truth is unthinkable. Perhaps you've lost love, or hope, or the faith in either yourself or some distant God to make everything whole again. It's better then to talk about what you've lost, or what you fear losing, and mention how scared you feel. Talking with someone who will listen (someone who won't simply try to cheer you up) will help you to gently embrace reality.

But also accept the reality that all problems are temporary and all pain can be lessened. Perhaps not now, but eventually.

LOOK INWARD FOR ANSWERS, NOT OUTWARD FOR BLAME

Your task at this step is to monitor your inner reactions to all that's happened and regularly assess how well you're coping. Is anxiety or depression getting to you? Have you been the "strong one," reluctant to express any fears of your own? Do you spend too much time blaming yourself or someone else? Finding a friend or objective third party to discuss your feelings may be useful. Blaming others for the misfortune may be accurate (although it often reflects a narrow, defensive view), but it can also intensify the emotions of everyone involved. Blaming generates defensiveness and hostility and prevents constructive coping and problem-solving. Blaming is not recommended. But if it must be done, save it for a time when the crisis is passed. Blaming keeps you *revolving*—running in circles but making no progress—and prevents you from *resolving* the problems at hand.

It's common to have disappointments and setbacks as you struggle through trying times. Setbacks may not be entirely in your control, but your reaction to a setback is. When setbacks happen, *look inward*. Assess your emotional reaction to the setback and determine what you could say, think, or do next that would halt pessimism and despair and rekindle your fighting spirit. That is your real problem —no, your real *challenge*—during tough times.

Chapter 4

❖

"DON'T TELL ME—
I DON'T WANT TO KNOW"

The Gift of Self-Awareness

❖

❖

IMAGINE A PERSON speeding on the expressway, hurrying to get to the airport before his plane takes off. He's frustrated, impatient, and worried he won't arrive on time. He hollers, "Can't you go faster?" to the car ahead of him. He thinks, *I can't believe this is happening to me—now of all times.* He clenches his jaw, stiffens his shoulders. He's doing all he can and worries it won't be enough. *God, how much longer?*

And as much as he wants to arrive on time, a part of him would like to know now what the outcome will be—even if he misses the plane—because he can't tolerate waiting anymore. He'd like it all to be over with just so that he'll know where he stands.

Isn't that how it is for you sometimes? When the anxiety is prolonged, when no certainty exists, you obsess about what could happen, focusing solely on the dreaded future, and wonder when it will end. It's an agonizing way to cope. And if I were to ask you then if you were aware of your feelings, you'd probably respond, "Absolutely! . . . What a silly question! I'm angry, I'm worried, I'm frightened! Isn't that obvious?" Well, yes, it is obvious. But your self-awareness may be more limited than you believe. The self-awareness I'm discussing has powers of healing. The awareness you possess might only inflame your wounds.

"SELF-AWARENESS? DON'T I FEEL ENOUGH PAIN ALREADY?"

Painful feelings wrench not just the soul but the body. Your stomach, muscles, chest, heart, and head can literally ache when your world turns upside down. You hurt so much sometimes, you'd do anything to get the pain to end, even for a little while. When the heartbreak is intense, don't you long for sleep, or something—anything—to distract you from the suffering? Well, distractions often help. Anything to get you back to your daily routine helps moderate the pain, although you may derive little enjoyment from those tasks at first. However, such an outward focus must ultimately be balanced by an inward one. When you're already hurting, full of anxiety, sadness, or longing, you may instinctively recoil from a self-awareness task, like when bright lights hit sleeping eyes. "Don't I feel enough pain?" you may ask.

You need to understand that although a *diminished* self-awareness may protect you at first by keeping you oblivious to your pain, it eventually intensifies and perpetuates pain. Why? Because you cannot fully work through a problem you've minimized or denied.

One form of biased thinking occurs when your *sense of time* is disturbed. During moments of heartbreak or adversity you will likely (and understandably) yearn for a happier future or past that seems cruelly out of reach, while you ignore the present. You'll obsess about what you once had or what you hope to have, but forget what you've got. Yet your wounds can only begin to heal when you *tune in to your thoughts and feelings while letting time stand still* for a while. Your urgency to push time ahead faster (or back to where it was) creates agony when there needn't be. When my five-year-old son runs to me crying after he's fallen and hit his head, I don't automatically tell him he'll feel better—even though I'm sure he will. First I hold him and say, "Oh, that hurts. I know it hurts when you fall like that." In such a moment time stands still. I'm not hurrying him along to stop crying; I'm telling him it's supposed to hurt and that it's okay for him to feel that way. When I do that, he's better able to accept what happened and to cope with it. It still hurts, but not like it might if I denied his right to be upset.

TWO FORMS OF SELF-AWARENESS

One form of self-awareness is to acknowledge whatever thoughts or feelings may be present and to observe them (at least for several minutes), tolerate them (don't try to change them), and ultimately accept them—while remaining a bit detached. It is an awareness that develops by your willingness (even for a brief time) to peacefully coexist with all that you are experiencing. It flows from your conscious decision to literally breathe easier in the face of your suffering. It is the awareness I described earlier, when you remain in the here and now and let time stand still for a while.

A second form of self-awareness builds on the first and involves asking questions of yourself and searching for the hidden, deeper aspects of all that is going on inside of you. Why do you feel the way you do? What is the nature of your hurts? What are your desires, goals, needs, longings? What is most meaningful to you in your life today? The better your ability to coexist with your answers to those questions, even when they unsettle you, the freer you will be to dig deeper and learn even more about yourself—to become more self-conscious. As such, each form of self-awareness—that which observes and accepts and that which probes—is the other's lifeblood.

AN EXERCISE IN
SELF-AWARENESS

Let's begin with the first form of self-awareness—that of identifying, observing, and accepting what you are thinking and feeling at this moment.

Right now while you're reading this, inhale deeply. Now exhale slowly and completely. Once again inhale . . . let your stomach expand as you breathe in . . . and slowly let it out. . . . Continue breathing in this manner, regular and more slowly. . . . Now gently turn your awareness to what you are feeling. Sadness? . . . loneliness? . . . fear? . . . helplessness? . . . a vague sense of longing? . . . You are not what you feel. You are not sadness or fear, you're simply someone who feels those emotions right now. They are of you but not you. You are not your suffering. After you've identified what your main feelings are, watch them. Take the time to sit with those feelings and observe them. Don't try to change them or make them go away. They may be very uncomfortable, but you can watch them. Be with them. Locate them in your body. Are they in your stomach? Your heart? See where they are. Notice how they may change locations. They whirl in and out and around. Continue breathing regularly, perhaps more slowly now as you observe your feelings. . . . When you notice a sense of calmness accompanying your feelings, continue what you've been doing for another two minutes or so.

Now that you know what to do, you may want to repeat this exercise again without reading the instructions. Don't worry, I'll wait.

* * *

As you watched your feelings you may not have noticed it at first, but your feelings weren't constant. They changed. They flowed in and out, up and down. In any given moment they may even have disappeared. That is the way of feelings when left to themselves. They're fluid, always in motion. *And they are not permanent.* It is the same with your thoughts. As you repeat the exercise, pay attention to your thoughts. They, too, will change in kind and intensity. They will come and go. Notice them as well.

This type of self-awareness is what stress researcher Jon Kabat-Zinn, author of *Full Catastrophe Living,* calls *emotion-focused coping.* Dealing with emotional pain requires coping with one's emotions as well as coping with the problem situation *(problem-focused coping).* People who don't land on their feet during trying times often fail to cope with one or both of those domains. Interestingly the self-awareness exercise described earlier, by helping you tolerate and accept your feelings, allows you to examine the problem situation with greater insight and clarity.

Remember, self-awareness begins the healing process if you remain focused on what you are feeling *now.* Pain intensifies when you project it to the future ("What if I can't make it on my own?") or to the past ("How could she have done such a thing?"). It lessens and *becomes what it is* when you *stay in the here and now.* And what it is, is rarely more than you can handle—despite how much it hurts. By detaching somewhat when you observe your feelings, you will no longer feel as victimized by them.

Try this for two minutes:
Instead of thinking Why me? *or* Why now? *or* How can this be? *simply note what it is you are feeling right now. For example, if you are feeling frightened and angry, repeat to yourself,* In this moment I am feeling angry . . . I am feeling

frightened. . . . I feel angry right now. . . . I feel frightened right now. . . . Isn't that interesting?

After just two minutes of simply reporting what you are
feeling, you'll discover that while the situation hasn't
changed, your reaction to it has. Maybe not a lot, but
enough to take the edge off, to give you a clearer perspective on matters. Author Jon Kabat-Zinn recommends, during your next period of suffering,

> try listening for a calm inner voice that might be saying,
> "Isn't this interesting, isn't it amazing what a human be-
> ing can go through, amazing how much pain and an-
> guish I can feel or create for myself or get bogged down
> in?" In listening for a calm voice within your own heart,
> within your own pain, you will be reminding yourself to
> observe the unfolding of your emotions with wise atten-
> tion, with a degree of non-attachment. You may find
> yourself wondering how things will finally be resolved,
> and knowing that you don't know, that you will just
> have to wait and see.

You may regard your suffering as an enemy. If you do,
you'll want to run from it or beat it back. But I'm sug-
gesting your suffering can be an invited companion. It can
be your teacher, but only if you take the time to understand
the lesson.

THE DEEPER FORM OF
SELF-AWARENESS

How am I handling this? Why am I behaving this way?
What are my deepest feelings? Those are just three of the
questions you need to ask yourself. But so often people
choose not to look too closely at themselves. Fearful of what
they might discover, they close off the inner voice that tries

to communicate what's really going on. They create what author Nathaniel Branden calls *the disowned self*, barely recognizable to its owner. If you don't know your strengths or weaknesses or motivations very well, you can't make sound judgments during trying times.

How can you become more self-aware? Your knee-jerk reaction to a crisis often reveals your instinctive coping defenses. Do you *deny* what is happening? Do you acknowledge it but *pretend* it is no big deal when perhaps it is? Do you *run*? Do you go *numb*? Do you try to *make peace*? Do you *blame* somebody? Think back for a minute on some crisis or trying time that occurred during your childhood. Maybe your parents received some bad news, perhaps your sister had to be rushed to the hospital. Maybe your best friend betrayed you. How did you react then? You might discover that the way you responded then is similar to the way you're reacting now, particularly if the incidents are similar.

Pay attention to your body's signals. Has your back been aching recently? Is your stomach tense? Has there been a change in your sleeping or eating habits? Have you been sicker lately? Are your dreams more upsetting and more frequent? All stress-related physical symptoms indicate not only that you are stressed but that the stress has gotten to you. It means you've been ignoring your innermost nature. You've been self-*un*conscious.

The lessons of self-awareness can be difficult reading. In fact it's a good rule of thumb that the more uncomfortable self-awareness makes you, the more you have opened to chapters about yourself that have long needed to be read. Reminding yourself that the most immediate purpose of self-awareness is simply that—awareness and understanding of yourself—doesn't always make it easier to get through.

Cynthia's new relationship had all the markings of disaster. She was still married to someone else; her boyfriend had just ended a long, painful romance. Neither of their families approved of their budding relationship. In fact his parents were about to disown him for shaming the family name. He was twenty-two and unemployed. She was forty-one. But she was "in love" and wanted to know what I thought about it.

"I'm happy that you're feeling so good, but it seems wise to reexamine your feelings for this man," I said.

"You sound like everyone else. No one believes this relationship can work," she argued.

"I must admit, Cynthia, this relationship has a lot going against it. But I'm not interested in talking you out of it. I'm interested in both of us *understanding* how it happened and learning how you can best handle it from now on. Does that sound reasonable?"

"No," she said.

I never heard from her again. What was Cynthia afraid of? She was afraid of learning truths about herself she didn't want to hear. She was afraid of herself. But when you try to run from yourself, there is no place to hide.

Last year a house burned down on the street where I live. It was struck by lightning during a ferocious rainstorm. As the fire trucks arrived, the neighbors gathered— some just to watch, some to offer help where possible. I heard one neighbor say, "It just couldn't have happened because of the lightning. There must have been some bad wiring too." I wondered why he needed to believe the wiring was bad. I didn't ask him, but I sensed that for him to believe the fire was a purely random event—something that could have happened to *his house*—was unacceptable. It frightened him to think that. It made him feel less in control of his own destiny. He needed to believe that all bad events were avoidable, and therefore faulty wiring was the culprit. Or maybe he, like so many, believed that life was fair and therefore if hardships befall you, well, perhaps in some way they were deserved. In your journey of self-awareness, excessive blaming or fault-finding may be due to your need to see life as fair and fully controllable. Altering that perception may free you from the bondage of excessive guilt or resentment and allow you to more adequately cope with your adversity.

SELF-AWARENESS: THE ''WRITE'' WAY

Taking the time to write out your thoughts and feelings helps you to understand them, to accept them, and to heal. Researcher James Pennebaker, in his book *Opening Up: The Healing Powers of Confiding in Others*, points out numerous benefits to writing out your feelings. Writing helps you to:

- Sort, clarify, and rethink your thoughts and feelings

- Dispose of built-up tension

- Detach yourself a bit from your inner experience

- Clear your mind of clutter and confusion

- Put obsessive thoughts to rest more readily

Writing about your heartbreak or trauma gives you an opportunity to reexperience it, in a cathartic way, but also in a manner more controlled by you. Such catharsis and control help lower your emotional reaction to the memory of the event. Also, the act of writing down your painful feelings and thoughts allows you to forget about them during the times when you'd rather focus on something else.

Many therapists advise writing with your *nondominant* hand. Theoretically that will help stimulate the nonverbal, unconscious part of your mind as you write. But doing *any-*

thing that emphasizes nonverbal activity, such as playing an instrument, listening to music, sketching, dancing, or doing any physical activity, may help stir and awaken hidden ideas and feelings—all of which can enhance your self-awareness.

During adversity you may not solve your problems in the manner you'd hoped. Your business may fail, your illness may recur, the love of your life may die. Fortunately healing does not depend on outcome. We can heal regardless of what happens. But we can only heal that which we are aware of. We can only soothe what we're willing to embrace. Healing begins when self-awareness happens.

Chapter 5

"IS IT OKAY
TO FORGIVE GOD?"

The Gift of
Spiritual Recommitment

"I'VE ALWAYS WISHED that Dad had protected me from my mother's drinking," Margaret said, "that he had comforted me during the worst times. Sometimes he did, but often he didn't." She was sad, her voice was scratched and ragged from rambling on about events she'd replayed in her head for months now, all to no avail. "First it was my parents, then my boyfriends, now my husband. I've never truly been able to count on any of them." She paused, measuring her next words. "I don't like admitting this," she revealed. "It disturbs me to think this, but I blame God most of all. He's let me down the most over the years. Where was He when I needed Him?" Her anger broke through a voice weakened by hurt and confusion. "More and more a part of me believes that God failed me, but part of me wants to think He is all-loving and wouldn't do that to me. Am I right to blame Him? Is it okay to forgive God?"

THE SEARCH FOR ANSWERS

Chronic marital dissatisfaction had whittled away Margaret's faith that life could be a joyous enterprise and unearthed long-buried feelings of hurt and resentment toward her family. In the past her religious beliefs pulled her through the worst times. Until the fog of disillusionment rolled in. Now, like a boat that had snapped its moorings, Margaret was adrift in misty, uncharted seas.

"I don't know what to believe anymore," Margaret continued. "Does God really care? Did He ever? I wonder if I've just been taken for a fool all this time—believing that God would be there for me."

She spoke at length and I listened. She was hurt and confused and needed an opportunity to express what had been preoccupying her for weeks, without being judged, challenged, or rushed. But she also needed more than emotional release. She needed help seeing her way through. When she asked, "Is it okay to forgive God?" I sensed she'd handed me a torch in hopes I'd keep it lit. So one day I held that torch aloft and reminded her of the question she'd asked.

"I'd like to say it's okay to forgive God, but I really don't know," I told her. "But for the first time you've asked me a question that implies a direction you can take. Until now," I said firmly, but gently, "all you've done is blame others." The strained expression on her face as I spoke made me question whether I was coming on too strong. "If I sound accusatory, I apologize," I said. "My intent is to tell you what I've observed, not to criticize you. For months I've listened to you blame your husband, your boyfriends, your parents, and now God. But never, until recently, have you spoken about what *you* might do to improve your life. Would you like to move ahead with this forgiving-God business?"

She nodded. Not a rousing affirmation of her intentions, but it was a start. Later I began to wonder less about her willingness to do something productive and more about her actual question. Is it okay to forgive God? My initial response was no. It doesn't make sense to forgive God when God does nothing wrong. But my intuition told me something else. When people feel bitter about life, they lash out at God. They blame Him for creating an unfair world. Telling them they are wrong in blaming Him misses something important. Whether or not they are correct in their thinking isn't always the most relevant issue, at least not at first. What matters is how they feel and their willingness to allow those feelings. You connect with someone at a deeper emotional level when you allow them to feel their feelings without insisting they shouldn't feel the way they do. Margaret didn't need an answer to her question. She needed an opportunity to experience her pain and confusion as understandable and okay—not as something to feel guilty about. And perhaps forgiving God could be a healing experience for her. I remembered the countless couples I've worked with who grew closer to each other not just because they ultimately found forgiveness but because *the process of working toward forgiveness strengthened their love and intimacy.* A sincere attempt to find forgiveness usually involves openness, honesty, dialogue, active listening, and an increased awareness and acceptance of both oneself and the other. Working toward forgiveness soothes the wounds and re-establishes a relationship. Finding forgiveness heals the wounds and reunites the estranged.

One thing I've learned as a psychologist: There is no true reconciliation without forgiveness. Margaret wanted to reconcile with God, but in her heart He was the guilty party needing forgiveness. But not only was she angry and blamed Him, but she also felt guilty about her anger. She felt trapped in a no-win situation whereby forgiving God

would have undermined her faith in Him (because to forgive Him would mean He isn't perfect) as much as holding
on to her resentment would. What could she do? I know
that when people suppress anger because they feel guilty
about it, the result is usually more pain. They either withdraw, feeling worse about themselves or more resentful of
others, or they eventually lash out. Regardless, the result is
only greater estrangement. But if they talk about their confused feelings with the one they blame, and do so in a respectful way, the healing process can begin. Sometimes
feeling guilty about one's anger is appropriate because the
anger is misplaced or overdone. But sorting through those
feelings with the other person helps to clarify that. Saying
"I'm angry, but I'm confused about my anger and I need
your help sorting all this out" is a fine way to begin.

That's where Margaret began. Her confusion about
whether to blame God for her suffering was made more
arduous and lonely by not including Him in the process of
trying to understand. Wouldn't God like to be part of the
sorting-through process? Doesn't He already understand
and care about our dilemma and wish to comfort and sustain us in our struggle? We are estranged from anyone to
the extent that we can't be ourselves in their presence. We
remain estranged from God to the extent that we hold back
our feelings from Him, even if the feelings frighten us. And
if we deny our feelings because we are afraid of them, we
become estranged from ourselves as well.

Margaret began her dialogue with God this way: "God, I
am angry with You for the way You've betrayed me. I
blame You for the way much of my life has gone, but I'm
also afraid to feel that way. I need to believe that You can
accept how I'm feeling right now, even if I am wrong."

What Margaret doubted and needed to rediscover was
that God loved her no matter what. By being herself in His
presence, with no pretense, she felt closer to Him. By be-

lieving that her feelings were acceptable, whether or not they were misplaced, she felt accepted in His eyes and had no reason to feel ashamed.

If we remain frightened of our anger at God, we may punish ourselves to alleviate our guilt. But such punishment only further diminishes our self-esteem, which keeps us frightened of our negative feelings and farther away from God.

If we remain frightened of our anger at God, we place limits on His love for us. We doubt His love. That doubt keeps us further separated.

If we remained frightened of our anger at God, our spirit closes to Him. But He has given us a gift of disclosure and spiritual openness, if we'd only accept it.

I'm sure it is true that those who feel closest to God struggle less with the concept of forgiving Him. Much of humanity does blame God from time to time. At such moments it is not our anger at Him that keeps us separated but our fear of being ourselves in His presence.

Is it okay to forgive God? I think so, not because God needs forgiving, but because the struggle and desire to forgive God can bring us closer to Him. And I suppose if it is not okay to forgive God, He will forgive our misconception.

Chapter 6

BUT ON THE
OTHER HAND . . .

The Gift of
Tolerating Ambivalence

❖

I HEAR IT ALL THE TIME:

"My feelings are mixed. Part of me wants to reconcile, or at least give it a try, but part of me says, 'Don't be a fool. She'll hurt you all over again.' It's all too confusing."

"I love my mother. I just don't know if I can take care of her anymore. I want to, but it's been so hard on me, my husband, and my kids. Sometimes I wish God would take her. Is that an awful thing to feel?"

"What's worse? What's ravaged me more, the cancer or the chemo? Don't try to answer because you'd be wrong no matter what you said. I can't figure out what to do, but my doctor told me I have two choices. 'Get up or give up,' he said. I wish life was that simple."

It's called *ambivalence*, and it has a public relations problem. Having strong mixed feelings about important people or situations makes many of us uncomfortable, even in the best of times. During tough times it can be agonizing. People with ambivalent feelings don't usually describe themselves as "uncertain." Rather they depict themselves as "torn," "pulled in two directions at once," or "at war with myself." Ambivalence hurts. And like most painful experiences, people seek to avoid it, numb it, or heal it as quickly as possible. And therein lies the problem. People can create unnecessary conflicts when they don't know how best to handle their ambivalence. Consequently bad situations get worse and distressing emotions intensify—all a direct result of failing to manage one's mixed feelings appropriately.

In hard times you want to be certain that what must get done will get done. You want to be able to read your feelings, assess the situation, and ultimately do what's best. But the best thing may not be the right thing, and the right thing may not be the easiest thing, and the easiest thing may not be the quickest thing, and the quickest thing may not be the moral thing, and the moral thing may not be the kindest thing. . . .

So what do you do? And how do you do it? And how can you get others to support you? And what if they don't? And what if your efforts don't work? You mean, you're not sure yet?

Ambivalence tugs at you, it wakes you from a sound sleep, it reminds you repeatedly that your situation is complex and that the decisions you make will have consequences. It makes you doubt yourself at crucial moments. It advises you that there are many sides to the issues confronting you. The hardest thing about ambivalence is that it keeps throwing reality in your face, at a time when you may not want reality to interfere with your decisions.

THE WAYS OF AMBIVALENCE

Most people have mixed feelings about most things most of the time. *Certainty* is rare in human emotional systems.

Your mixed feelings about a person or issue may not be divided evenly. They could be split ninety-ten or seventy-thirty, as well as fifty-fifty. And even those divisions can vary over time and contexts. If you regard your ambivalent feelings about people you love as a "bad sign," consider this: There can be no deep and abiding love without ambivalence. People we love and cherish will, from time to time, disappoint us, bore us, ignore us, hurt us, restrict us—and we will do the same to them. And while it's probably true (but so unromantic) to think that there is no "one" person whom you could be happy with in life, a deeper love can be had when you and your partner choose to grow and mature and find joy in your relationship with each other. It's nice to know that your partner remains with you not because you're perfect and irresistible but because you're imperfect and resistible and she still wants you anyway.

THE ORIGINS OF AMBIVALENCE

I believe the source of all ambivalence is our humanness. We are imperfect and therefore unable to completely erase doubt and uncertainty from our minds. We are the species that can believe in a glorious afterlife, an eternal place of joy, yet we fear death. We love, yet we hate. We strive for peace, yet we war with one another. At the root of our ambivalence is fear. No matter how healthy any of us is emotionally and spiritually, doubt drones deep within us, a primordial call to our souls asking, "Am I really loved?" And from there, "Do I have what it takes? . . . Can I succeed? . . . Will others forsake me? . . . Am I forgivable?"

As if that weren't enough to account for ambivalence, there are the rules and admonitions we learned growing up. Many were good and necessary, some less so.

- "If you can't say anything nice, don't say anything at all."

- "You should know better!"

- "Will you ever amount to anything?"

- "When in doubt, don't!"

- "If it wasn't for you . . . " (life would be so much happier).

- "Always expect the worst, that way you won't be disappointed."

- "It's selfish to put yourself first."

- "What's wrong with you?"

Then there were the unstated but keenly understood rules:

- "Don't rock the boat" (or you'll be sorry).

- "Don't express your truest feelings" (or people won't like you).

- "Don't grow up and lead your own life" (it's not fair to me, after all I've done for you).

- "Don't ever stop needing me" (or I'll die).

Each of the above statements reflects an attitude that can hurt you. But as a child you tended to believe that others were right and you were wrong. So you learned to doubt yourself, suppress your natural tendencies, and kindle a feeling of inner shame—a belief that something must be fundamentally wrong with you.

Anytime you feel repelled by the very thing that once attracted you to a person, ambivalence lurks. A man from a family that never experienced emotional closeness is attracted to a woman from a tight-knit family. But over time he feels smothered by her affections and annoyed at her family's "overinvolvement in my life." In truth he always had mixed feelings about attachment and togetherness. He wanted closeness, but not too much. He wanted distance, but not too far. It isn't the ambivalence that is the problem per se. It is how the ambivalence gets managed.

MISMANAGING YOUR AMBIVALENCE

People mismanage their ambivalence in one of three ways:

1. *They deny their ambivalence or pretend their feelings aren't so mixed.* Such people will plow ahead on a course of action without much forethought, unprepared for certain obstacles their feelings tried to warn them about. They may make snap decisions about important events, such as whether or not to have surgery, end a relationship, or seek professional help. If complications ensue, rather than saying, "Hold on. Matters are getting out of hand. Let me stop and consider other possibilities," they roll forward, like tanks through a grove of saplings, ignoring all indications to think twice. Such people are frightened of their ambivalence. They regard it as a sign of weakness. And *that* is their main difficulty.

2. *They obsess about what to do and paralyze their coping efforts, unwilling to take action until their feelings are one hundred percent resolved.* Eventually action must be taken in spite of uncertainties and mixed feelings. But just like the people described above, their anxiety about their ambivalence interferes with their decision-making. Their fear of making a mistake is so great, they'd rather risk defeat by procrastinating than by making an error of judgment.

3. *They separate their mixed feelings, claiming one side and ignoring the other.* This is most common. Rather than admitting to themselves things like, "I want control, but it's nice to be told what to do sometimes," "I want my space, but togetherness feels good too," "I love my father, but I don't like some of the ways he treats me," they admit only one half of how they truly feel. They can then project the other half onto someone else, typically a spouse. Consequently the woman raised by an alcoholic father resents her husband's contempt for him, while never admitting her own anger toward her father. Or the lenient parent resents his spouse's strict manner with the children, never admitting his own frustration with them.

Anytime you and someone close to you appear to have opposite traits or opinions (you're tidy, he's a slob; you're logical, she's too emotional; you like to plan ahead, he's spontaneous; etc.), it's possible you've each denied some unacceptable side to your personality and handed it to the other. One way to tell if this is the case is to stop opposing your spouse on one issue and agree with him (and act accordingly) for a week or so. So, if he's unemotional, you try to act that way too. If he shows signs of altering his usual stance in reaction to your change (that is, if he gets more emotional), then the two of you have probably been mishandling your own ambivalent feelings.

RESOLVING YOUR AMBIVALENCE

Ambivalence is not a problem, it's just a part of life. It is a reflection of you, of how you feel about things at the moment. Soul-searching helps modify your feelings and increases the odds that you're not distorting matters, but you'll still have some degree of mixed feelings when all is said and done. Esteemed family therapist Edwin Friedman says it's a mistake to try to resolve your ambivalence by seeking *certainty*. You can't be absolutely certain what's best to do when your feelings are mixed. The more you seek certainty, the more you'll deny some of what you really think and feel. What you want is *clarity*—full awareness of your thoughts and feelings, however contradictory they may appear.

Sandy and Carl were trying to repair a marriage torn apart six months ago when Sandy discovered Carl was having an affair. Carl repented and ended the affair, but Sandy was stung too intensely by betrayal and deceit to forgive him. Now, six months later, progress has been made. But when Carl surprised Sandy with tickets for a romantic weekend on a cruise ship, she was ambivalent. On the one hand she knew their weary marriage needed a boost. On the other hand she didn't want to give Carl the impression that all was well now in their relationship. She decided not to go and hoped Carl would understand. Then she changed her mind and told her husband they could start packing. When she changed her mind a third time, Carl got angry. And Sandy knew then that no matter what she decided, she wouldn't be happy.

Sandy's mistake in managing her ambivalence was her search for *certainty*. She wanted to feel strongly about her decision no matter what the decision was. But in seeking *clarity* she eventually realized that certainty was not possible. And she understood that no matter what she decided about the cruise, it would be important to express her mixed feelings to Carl so that he wouldn't misinterpret them. Eventually she told Carl, "I've decided to go on the cruise with you. But please understand that my feelings about our marriage aren't sorted out yet and I may not enjoy myself as much as we'd like. I'll do my best, but don't expect it all to be perfect." By simply expressing both sides of her ambivalence—by being *clear* about her feelings instead of *certain*—she avoided complicating an already difficult situation. Had she chosen not to go, she might have said, "Carl, I've decided not to go on the cruise. It matters to me that we do something positive for our relationship, but I'm just not ready for this kind of trip yet. I'm sure you're disappointed, but I hope you can understand."

Recognizing and expressing ambivalent feelings goes a long way toward neutralizing any negative effects. If there is an essential component to properly managing ambivalence, it is this: Learn to tolerate not knowing. Be patient with all the questions that weigh heavily in your heart. Don't push for answers that can't come yet. I'm not advocating fence-sitting. Decisions ultimately must get made and actions taken. But you must accept not knowing—or, more to the point, not knowing for sure—as a legitimate state of mind. In fact if you open yourself to receiving the right answers and trust that they will come in their own time—at the right time—then you can accept not knowing because now is evidently not the time to know. When you can tolerate not knowing, you'll eventually make decisions, perhaps *with* some fear, but not *out of* fear.

Mixed feelings are differences within your heart. Learning how to tolerate them is the key.

Chapter 7

HANDLING THE WAIT

The Gift of Patience

❖

I<small>T WAS A COLD</small> December rain. Holiday shoppers spilled out of the mall and scurried to their cars in a futile effort to keep themselves and their packages dry. The parking lot, nearly bursting with parked cars, traffic lines, and herds of wandering pedestrians, held its own against a biting wind that had lost all sense of the proper Christmas spirit.

It was late. And I was in a hurry to get home.

Standing under the shelter of the mall entrance, scanning the parking lot for my car, I became distracted by a woman in a wheelchair. She seemed oblivious to the rain as she steadily rolled herself about thirty yards to the area reserved for handicapped drivers. As she maneuvered herself around a curb, the side of her face came into view. She looked about sixty. I noticed for the first time a package, wet and windblown, but nestled snugly in her lap, a lap partly covered by a bright green coat, a lap that ended abruptly at the place where her legs should have been.

Alongside her car now, she fished for her keys, found them, attempted the lock, and dropped her keys on the pavement. She adjusted her chair slightly, calmly reached down and retrieved the keys, and tried again to unlock the door—this time successfully. The keys went back into her pocketbook, and she opened the door just a few inches. Then, still holding the door ajar with an extended arm, she backed up her chair until it no longer blocked the door. Steering her chair until it faced the inside of the open door, she rolled forward, pushing the door farther open at the same time.

The wet package was the first to go in.

Then, holding on to both the car seat and the steering wheel, she carefully hoisted herself out of her chair and into the car. Next she took less than a minute to expertly fold up her heavy chair and haul it inside, herself sliding back along the bench seat to allow room for the wheelchair. With both herself and the chair now occupying the front seat, she lifted the chair once again and let it topple into the rear seat. She slid back over to the driver's side, removed and shook out her rain hat, and finally closed the door.

That's patience! (And a whole lot more.) A minute later she backed out of the parking space and blended into the night. Her red brake lights, along with those of dozens of other cars meandering in the holiday traffic, blinked like Christmas tree ornaments in motion.

Somehow after watching her, it seemed so very unimportant to worry about getting home on time and dry.

THE MEANING OF PATIENCE

Patience is a noun, but an active one. Passivity breeds helplessness, not patience. Patience is not a grit-your-teeth test of endurance. It is not simply "tolerating the wait." *Patience is the peace of mind that comes from knowing you're on the right track.* When you're on the right track, you may be *eager* for the outcome, but not really impatient. When you're not sure if the path you're on is the right one, you will grow impatient, no matter how brief the wait. Patience comes from trusting; impatience, from not trusting. An impatient person wants everything to be over with so that he can see where he stands. A patient person knows that whatever the outcome, he'll eventually be in a place that is good. So he can wait.

AFTER WINTER COMES THE SPRING

In the acute stages of grief or misfortune patience has little meaning. When your world suddenly turns upside down, shock and disbelief take over. "My God! No! This can't be happening," you cry, echoing a sentiment as ancient, and as consuming, as fire. If your crisis passes quickly —if your loved one survives the accident, for example— you'll breathe a sigh of relief, give thanks, and begin to get on with your life. Again, patience will have little meaning.

Only when the loss or misfortune is permanent, or when the agony and the recovery are prolonged, does patience mean something.

Only in winter, when the pain has settled in like a late-December frost, does waiting patiently for spring's promise of warmth have any meaning at all.

Gloria's husband has a degenerative neurological disorder. With his capabilities deteriorating steadily over the past several years, Gloria has had to adjust, and readjust, to her husband's failing health. And she's had to cope with raising two teenagers who, while old enough to understand, were young enough to have predictable problems of their own.

She speaks of patience.

"I used to hate those moments when I would help Jim feed himself. I hated that the whole disease had to happen.

Now it's not so bad. In fact it's okay. And I've learned to be more patient with all that keeps happening. It comes, I think, from a kind of contentment, a belief that I've done all I could and that I'm doing all I can—without getting too crazy and compulsive about it. I've learned to spend less time being angry and more time accomplishing things. And it helps a lot. By the way, I've resumed my piano lessons and I even started a vegetable garden. Show me a gardener, someone who must wait for seeds to properly take root and grow, and I'll show you someone who understands patience."

Impatience is a form of pain. All pain, physical and emotional, intensifies when you feel helpless. It diminishes when you believe you have some say over what happens to you. Gloria did not stand idly by as a way of coping. She took action. And like any true gardener, she understood you can patiently await the harvest season when it has been preceded by hard work and optimism.

THE GIFT OF PATIENCE

Patience is a jewel with many facets.

P PREPARE—to ready yourself for whatever happens.

A ACCEPT—your situation as it currently is. And *AFFIRM* your strengths, blessings, and possibilities.

T TRUST—your faith in yourself to cope, faith that God is good.

I INTRIGUED—by the possibilities that lie ahead.

E ENDURE—while things pass in their own time.

N NEARER YOUR GOAL—remember, all problems are temporary.

C COMFORT—a time to be grateful, to know that you are not alone.

E EASIER—it does get easier.

Prepare: Patience allows you to better prepare for your future. It provides time for you to rebuild your inner reserves of strength. When you're patient, you can sleep more restfully and eat properly, thus meeting your basic needs. You can pace yourself.

Do what you need to do to help you prepare for whatever lies ahead. If you want time to be alone, take it. If you want companionship, friends to talk to, seek them out. Find some activity that brings pleasure and invest in it, even though true joy may seem out of reach right now. And yes, take a little time to imagine matters not working out the way you've hoped. Can you list two or three things that will help you cope if that were to happen? If the situation doesn't improve, will you have any regrets? Is there anything you can do now that would eliminate those regrets? With patience you can put into perspective all that has happened and prepare for all that might yet happen.

Accept and *Affirm:* Patience is nourished when you finally regard the current situation not necessarily as right, or fair, but acceptable. An acceptable situation is one you've committed yourself to coping with. When you've abandoned the futile cry "This shouldn't be!" and have come to accept what is, only then can you find the patience to deal with it squarely. To regard a difficult and unfair situation as acceptable is not to surrender your values. "What happened to me was *wrong*! How can I accept it?" Your values can only be put into action when you've accepted the reality of a bad situation.

And while you're at it, *affirm* that you do have some strengths, some resources to help you cope. Affirm, in spite of your misfortune, all you have to be grateful for. Affirm that life, while not always fair and kind, can still be *actively lived* and made meaningful.

Trust: With trust and faith, patience is born. When you believe strongly in something, you can patiently wait for it. When you fear it won't come, when your faith is frail, the wait is agonizing. But what, and whom, can you trust? Look around you. You can trust that you are not alone, that there is love for you—perhaps from your children or your family, or from someone you haven't even met yet. Or you can trust that friends will care about what happens to you. You can surely trust that you are not the first person who has had to experience a similar trying time. And so many before you made it through. It was harsh and difficult for all of them at various times, but they endured and recovered. And many will say they are better people for it. Can you trust yourself to eventually land on your feet? The more you can do this, the more patient you'll be.

And can you trust that God is good? Do you believe He cares what happens to you? Nourish your faith in an all-loving God, and patience will come your way.

Intrigued: Do you see possibilities open to you as a direct result of your misfortune? Ask yourself this question: How can I take what I've learned during this trying time and turn it into something positive, something useful, something healing for myself and perhaps for others like me?

Over fifteen million Americans currently participate in some type of support group, from the well-known Alcoholics Anonymous to lesser-known groups such as the National Spinal Cord Injury Association, Prison Families Anonymous, and the National Association for Widowed People. Every one of those groups began as a vision by someone wanting to turn their own suffering into something positive.

Don't be discouraged if your enthusiasm dries up every now and then. In difficult times it isn't easy to maintain positive feelings for long. There are no quick fixes of the heart and soul. But believe this: Nothing is meaningless unless you make it so. Doesn't it make sense to believe that since suffering has been and always will be a part of living, it must have some meaning? Can you be intrigued by the possibility that through suffering you can arrive at a more profound and beautiful understanding of what living is all about?

Endure: Yes, patience is a form of endurance. But it is a *willingness* to endure that stems from an understanding that *all pain passes in its own time.* Not in your time, my time, or a convenient time—*its own time.* "To everything there is a season . . . a time to laugh, a time to cry." You can't rush through the season of legitimate pain. You can't maneuver around it. To get over it, you need to go through it. Some days will be unbearable; others, almost kind. And when you start believing you've survived the worst of it, the next day may find you are once again in pain and inconsolable. But by choosing to endure your pain for as long as it takes, to be patient with all that is unfinished, healing will have begun.

Nearer Your Goal: Patience moves you forward. Your goal is not to solve your problems but to resolve them. Some problems can't be solved. You can't bring back someone who has died. You can't recapture a childhood. Permanent injuries can't just disappear. But all problems can get resolved. And all problems are therefore temporary. When you *re*solve a problem, it no longer has an inhibiting influence on your life. You choose to abandon *re*sentments, tap into your *re*serves, and *re*surface a better person. Once you believe that all problems are temporary and that you can resolve (that is, let go of) any lingering pain, you'll be better able to handle the wait.

Comfort: The time of patience should be a comforting time. You've been through a great deal already, and more is to come, of that you know too well. Comfort yourself. You can take comfort from the knowledge that you've made it this far. Remind yourself, especially that part of you that feels frightened or lonely, of the love others have for you and the love you've shown to others. Embrace all that you are truly grateful for. Right now. Gratitude calms an impatient spirit.

Look within and think about what *you need to hear* right this minute. I know you *want* to hear that all you've experienced was just a bad dream or that everything will work out fine, but, knowing that the situation is quite real, what do you *need* to hear? When I ask people that question, they tend to tell me similar things:

"I need to hear that I am loved no matter what."
"I need to hear that I can survive this."
"I need to hear that my children (or those I dearly love) will survive too—and that they understand."

Tell yourself, right now, what you need to hear. Comfort the unsettled places in your heart.

Easier: The pain, the fear, the ability to patiently confront life—all of it does get easier. You know that to be true because you've been there before, you've experienced how worries and hurts do subside.

"What do you need to hear?" I asked Lucy. At sixty-two she felt lost and lonely, still grieving over her husband's death a year earlier. Though she was in good health and had much to live for, including seven terrific grandchildren, her zest for life had died along with her mate of thirty-six years. And she was impatient—with her children, her grandchildren, her minister—and with the fact that her life might continue for decades more without her husband. Sometimes she wished she was dead too.

"What do I need to hear?" she repeated. She thought long and hard. "I need to hear," she finally said, "that I can go on living, go on missing Frank, without such intense loneliness and suffering. I need to hear that Frank really is waiting for me on the other side and that he really does want me to go on living. I need to hear that there are things in life I can take the time to enjoy. That's what I need to hear. Is that what you intend to tell me?"

"What I have in mind is something different," I answered. "Please close your eyes for a few minutes and picture Frank in your mind. Imagine that expression of his when he is so very happy and full of love. Now imagine the sky. You're outside, it's a day like today, and you look up. See Frank's image appear in the sky. First his face, his smiling, loving face, and then the rest of him. Imagine him filling the sky and looking down lovingly at you. And watch now as his arms reach down, wrap around you, and hold you. Feel him holding you in a warm, loving embrace. Feel his love and his happiness. Feel him, and listen closely. You know what he wants you to hear." A smile was etched in Lucy's face as she cried softly. I continued, "And when it's time to say good-bye for now, to let go, watch his image, forever happy, fade from the sky until that time when you choose once again to call him forth. Remember that whenever you need him to be with you like that, he can be."

It was several months later. Lucy was somehow less lonely and more invigorated with life. And she was patient with all that had once unsettled her so. She couldn't put into words why that was, but I believed several things made that happen.

First, she had finally come to *accept* Frank's death and the fact that she still had to do something with the time she had left to live.

Second, the exercise I did with her, I believe, helped reaffirm her *faith* in an afterlife where she would one day be united with her husband.

And she was *intrigued* by the possibilities open to her as she lived out her days. There was so much she still wanted to do and see. She knew she especially wanted to be a part of her grandchildren's lives.

Lastly she was *comforted*. Reconnecting with Frank comforted her. She let her friends and family comfort her. And she comforted herself, reminding herself how wonderful it was to have been married to Frank and how wonderful it would be when they were together again.

She found the place in her heart that had been patiently awaiting discovery. That quiet, strong place reminds us all how heartbreak, if founded on deep and lasting love, can awaken us to the real beauty and meaning of life.

Chapter 8

SOOTHING YOUR HEART IN TIMES OF CHRONIC STRESS

The Gifts of Calmness
and Self-Control

"DAD . . . DAD . . . I KNOW, DAD, but did you try getting Mom to . . . Dad, will you listen to me, please?! I can't talk to you if you keep . . . Dad, for God's sake, calm down!" Jim yelled into the telephone. He was frustrated. For the past two months his conversations with his father had gone like that. He understood his father's concerns. After all, it must be difficult to care for a wife who had become more and more helpless and disoriented. Jim's mother had Alzheimer's disease and was on a steady downhill course.

Jim's wife, Kathy, felt compassion for her husband, but she was frustrated with him too. "I keep telling you, Jim, you only make your father more upset when you yell at him like that."

"I don't yell at him, Kathy," Jim answered angrily. "But how the hell do you expect me to get him to listen? He keeps phoning me, all upset and worried about Mom, but he never listens to a thing I tell him. Why can't you understand that?"

"This is getting nowhere. Now you're yelling at me, and I'm only trying to help. Do me a favor, next time your father calls, leave me out of it," Kathy responded, walking out of the room.

It's called *emotional reactivity*. It refers to any reflexive, intense, and emotionally fueled reaction to a situation. Simply, it's an *overdone, automatic* reaction to somebody "pushing your buttons." It may be an outward reaction (yelling, crying, running away, or pounding your fists). Or it could be an inner reaction (going emotionally "numb" or being unable to "think straight" or concentrate well). It is not the emotional reaction per se that is the problem (yelling or "freezing up" might well be a perfectly normal response in some situations), it is the fact that it is automatic—that you have little or no control over how you respond.

Emotional reactivity may seem legitimate and understandable in some contexts, but rarely is it helpful. Particularly, when stress is prolonged, emotional reactivity fuels the fire of adversity. Eventually it becomes more of a problem than the problem you were reacting *to*. When you can't talk with someone about a difficulty because emotional reactivity is so high, resentments emerge and the original problem can no longer be rationally managed. Jim's father was emotionally reactive. And Jim reacted intensely to his father's reactivity. And Jim's wife, Kathy, reacted intensely to Jim's reactivity. Jim was frustrated that his father wouldn't listen to him. Kathy was frustrated that Jim wouldn't listen to her. Everybody was high-strung in a situation that called for some degree of calmness and self-control.

The ability to manage marital conflict with calmness is a crucial factor in marital satisfaction and is particularly relevant for men. According to research psychologist John Gottman of the University of Washington, during marital conflict a man's heart rate, blood pressure, and other measures of physiological arousal shoot up quickly to uncomfortable levels. Consequently men don't tolerate prolonged conflict and often resort to "stonewalling" in their conversations with a spouse. That is, they say very little and give no signs of interest in the conversation (as indicated by eye contact, nods of the head, or "uh-huh" responses). Without a solution to this impasse, wives eventually distance themselves from their husbands, feeling angry and increasing the odds that the marriage may eventually dissolve. Gottman's research also showed that when men were capable of responding to marital difficulties with greater calmness, the marriage was likely to be more satisfying.

INNER CALMNESS AND SELF-CONTROL

Sometimes misfortune stays only a short while. You unexpectedly get fired from your job, but within a few weeks you've found a better one. Someone you love is severely injured in a car crash, but forty-eight hours later you learn he will recover fully. Most people can effectively deal with a short-term crisis. They have their distraught moments, but they tap into their emotional reserves, much like a bank account saved for rainy days, and cope.

But some hardships don't go away, not for a long time. Some illnesses are chronic and debilitating. Unemployment can drag on for months. And when someone close to you dies, well, it can sometimes take years before you feel fully alive again.

Chronic stress creates its own set of problems. Researcher Shelley Taylor showed that prolonged or repeated stress can have debilitating side effects, such as increased heart disease, high blood pressure, and diminished immunity to illness. Janice Kiecolt-Glaser studied thirty-four people who were caretakers to family members with Alzheimer's disease. When compared with a control group, the immune systems of the caregivers were significantly weakened over time. Prolonged stress can wear us out emotionally and physically. But interestingly it wears out some people and not others. Why?

Some people, through a variety of ways, develop an inner calmness. They are not unemotional—they feel worried and upset from time to time—but they generally believe they have some *control* over themselves, their emotional reactions, or their situation. (They don't try to control matters they have little influence over.) Perceived control is a major factor in coping with adversity, especially when the adversity is prolonged.

A study by Ellen Langer revealed how even a small amount of perceived control can have a major impact on coping. She studied a large group of nursing-home residents. One group of residents were given a plant and told they must personally care for it if it was to survive. Additionally they were given some tips on how to relax themselves. Another group of residents, matched in age and health status with the first group, were also given a plant (with no relaxation tips), but were told that the nursing staff would take care of the plant for them. In just a few weeks the group who needed to care for their own plant were healthier and more active than the other group. More amazingly, over the next eighteen months residents with the responsibility of caring for the plant died at a rate only half that of the other group. Evidently the capacity to have some say over matters important to you can make a difference in how well you cope—and survive.

THE CALMNESS–CONTROL CONNECTION

In trying times it's okay to feel angry, sad, worried, or lonely. Being emotional is not the problem. But if your emotional reactions are "knee-jerk" and intense, or if you can't function adequately while feeling emotional, self-control has been severely diminished. And when you feel less in control, your emotions can further intensify. Finding a way to calm yourself, to soothe your heart, keeps you feeling in control—and it may help calm others down too.

Remember how Jim would get frustrated and agitated while talking with his father on the phone? His problem was not that he was sad about his mother's condition and worried for his father. His problem was his heightened emotionality in the face of his father's emotionality. Rather than trying to focus on getting his father to calm down, Jim needed to focus on his own emotional reaction, permitting his father to react any way he chose. For that to happen, Jim first needed to *accept that his emotional reactivity was part of the problem and to concern himself with changing that—not changing others*. He then practiced the following three skills to help him, *over time*, respond (not "react") more effectively:

1. Jim learned to physically relax. Research has shown how deep relaxation can help heal you, body and soul. Books such as Herbert Benson's *The Relaxation Response* and Joan Borysenko's *Minding the Body, Mending the Mind* provide step-by-step guidelines on how to meditate and deeply relax.

Jim found it most useful to relax by focusing on his breathing. Like most people, Jim didn't breathe properly under stress. His breathing was rapid and shallow. To breathe properly, he had to focus on breathing through his diaphragm. Diaphragmatic breathing occurs when the stomach puffs out as you inhale. Jim spent about twenty minutes a day closing his eyes and concentrating on proper breathing. Adapting a technique from physician Larry Dossey's book *Space, Time, and Medicine*, I asked Jim to count his breaths every time he exhaled and imagine each number falling gently to the floor, piling up one on top of the other. With practice Jim learned to feel relaxed for hours at a stretch, at a cost of about a twenty-minute relaxation exercise. And he learned to concentrate on breathing properly while talking to his father.

2. Jim tried to predict ahead of time how his father might respond. Studies show that even if people can't prevent something undesirable from happening, *predicting* its occurrence reduces feelings of helplessness (which in turn reduces stress).

3. Then Jim rehearsed how he wanted to respond to his father, using four simple but powerful techniques. First, he learned *reflective listening*, a procedure whereby the listener repeats back to the speaker his understanding of what was just said. To keep it simple, listeners are encouraged to describe the speaker's feelings in one of four ways: happy, sad, angry, or scared. So when Jim's father said to him, "Jim, your mother left the house unattended again today. What am I going to do? I'm worried about her safety!" Jim responded, "I'm not sure what you should do. You seem to be saying that you're scared Mom might hurt herself when she leaves the house all by herself. Is that right?"

Jim didn't tell his father what to do, he simply reflected back what he heard. His father, while still troubled by his situation, then felt listened to and understood.

Second, Jim practiced *empathic responding*. He tried to imagine what it must be like to be in his father's position, and he tried to communicate that understanding. So, when his father sounded worried and agitated, instead of saying, "Calm down!" Jim said, "This can't be an easy time for you, Dad." An empathic response makes a person feel not only understood but accepted too. Typically people resist changing anything about themselves until they feel both understood and accepted. By using reflective listening and empathic responding, Jim helped himself and his father calm down.

Third, Jim practiced speaking *softly* to his father. When emotions run high, compelling yourself to speak quietly can profoundly improve the tone of the conversation.

And fourth, Jim remained in a sitting position while talking with his father, especially when his father was physically present. Research indicates that in a tense situation the simple act of standing up increases the odds of angry or even violent outbursts.

Commonly, when you get overinvolved emotionally with a problem, you are underinvolved somewhere else in your life. Reinvolving yourself with those aspects of your life you've paid little attention to lately can also help reduce your emotional reactivity. Check to see if you've put aside some important aspects of your life. Could you resume your exercise program or your hobby? Might you and your spouse or some friends go out more often socially? When adversity first strikes, you just may have to put the rest of your life on hold as you cope with the sudden hardship. But eventually you must resume as normal a life as possible, even while you're still coping. Otherwise you'll deplete your resources and increase your emotional reactivity.

RELIEVING TENSION, DEPRESSION, AND HOSTILITY THROUGH EXERCISE

If you don't exercise regularly, be sure to read this section.

The benefits of regular (especially aerobic) exercise are fairly well known to the average person. But in his book *The Exercise Prescription for Depression and Anxiety,* psychologist Keith Johnsgard evaluates the impressive research evidence that shows the powerful effects of exercise on a person's emotional state. He concluded that regular aerobic exercise (at least three to four times per week for twenty to thirty minutes each time):

• Reduces the symptoms of major depression, sometimes as effectively as psychotherapy or antidepressant medication. While results can vary for different individuals (and any exercise program should be approved by your physician), the ability to have a positive influence over your own emotional state increases your sense of *control,* an important coping resource.

• Helps prevent serious depression from occurring, or at least diminishes the intensity and duration of its symptoms.

• Reliably and consistently reduces hostility. Exercise can help make you calmer and less emotionally reactive.

• Has an immediate positive impact on anxiety. The more intense the anxiety, the more vigorous a workout may be required to bring about a noticeable effect.

If you are currently out of shape (about 80 percent of Americans are physically unfit), you may resist the effort required to begin an exercise program. And if you are seriously depressed, your lethargy and pessimism (both symptoms of depression) won't help your motivation. But any exercise program can be beneficial. Start small (say, a half-mile walk) and gradually build up your tolerance (Dr. Johnsgard recommends a 10 percent increase in intensity or duration every week). Moderation is essential. Doing too much too fast is painful and costly.

In trying times, when you have too much to deal with and not enough energy or resources, you owe it to yourself and your loved ones to improve your resistance to stress—and improve your health too. Exercise can help you accomplish just that.

POSTSCRIPT: WHEN CALMING DOWN HURTS

As you calm down, you let go. You let go of anger, of anxiety, of future worries, of past regrets. Once you let go of what was, what might have been, or what could be, you come in contact with what is. But sometimes that can be unsettling.

Remember how Jim tried to cope with his father's anxiety and his mother's deteriorating mental condition? As Jim let go of his annoyance with his father, he was put in touch with a part of himself he'd really been avoiding.

All along, his *frustrations with* his father kept him from fully feeling his *sadness for* his father (and his grief for his mother).

All along, his anger obscured something he really didn't want to face: his helplessness to do anything that could solve his parents' problems for them.

All along, his arguments with his dad concealed the fact that Jim would ultimately have to work through his personal feelings of fear and grief by himself. Others, such as his wife, Kathy, may care and offer advice and support. But as Jim discovered, the more he calmed down and let go, the more he realized he was alone: No one could do his grieving for him.

If there is a lesson to be learned, it is this: The path of healing is not straight. Good days will be followed by bad, even after you believe the hardest times have passed. And once you stop fighting to change things that can't be changed, once you let go, you may (unexpectedly) grieve. "What's wrong with me? I feel so depressed. I thought I was getting *better*," you might say. But when you've lost something precious, grieving is the only way to proceed, even if it feels awful. Some people would rather fight and stay angry over unchangeable situations than grieve. To them fighting gives the illusion of control, while grieving makes them feel out of control. But grieving fully, mourning the loss, letting go—these are what's necessary for you to regain control over your life, your feelings, and your spirit.

Chapter 9

MOVING AWAY FROM
BLAME
AND SELF-CRITICISM

The Gift of
Being Nonjudgmental

❖

Heartbreak unfolds itself upon us like a shroud, graying our world and restricting our freedom of movement. Along with heartbreak comes a profound sense of loss—loss of love or loss of dreams, and often a loss of control. When heartbreak happens, our world is upended; thoughts and emotions swirl in disarray. I think the part inside us that likes to believe in magic is the same part that kindles the illusion that we can recapture control over our lives if we blame somebody, anybody, for our adversity. Often in such times the person we blame is ourself.

As long as we have someone or something to blame, as long as we can point to a "reason" why misfortune happens, we can believe that all bad events are predictable and that precautions can be taken to keep them from happening again. But there are two things unhelpful with that line of reasoning. First, it is a fantasy that we can always take steps to prevent suffering. Yes, there is much needless suffering that we can prevent, such as when we choose not to drink and drive. But much suffering, such as dealing with death, broken dreams, and broken hearts, comes from simply being human, and cannot be avoided. Also, much of the blaming that occurs is irrational and takes the form of "if only." "If only I'd had a cup of coffee with him at breakfast," one woman lamented, "he would have left for work a few minutes later and would never have had the car accident." Such reasoning presupposes that she could have known ahead of time that her husband would be involved in a car accident. As irrational as it is, it remains a common form of blaming oneself for events beyond our control. Sometimes it seems easier to feel guilty about something that is not our fault than to accept the reality that bad things can happen, often at random, no matter how carefully and how well we live our lives.*

A second and more important problem with blaming is that it distracts us from the real work ahead. Blaming and judging focuses our attention away from what we lost and away from coping. Such a distraction blunts our grief to some extent, but it really only prolongs the mourning period. Studies of people who've made it through hardships show that *they took time to face the full extent of their loss.* And eventually they abandoned guilt and resentment and forged ahead with hope and a commitment to improving their lives. *When we latch on to blaming, we seal in our pain. Recovery is not possible when pain cannot be released.*

And yet some blaming is helpful. Researchers Ronnie Bulman and Camille Wortman discovered that paraplegics and quadriplegics whose paralysis was the result of their own careless behavior (such as diving into the shallow end of a pool) coped much better than those who were the victims of someone else's behavior. In fact how well one coped

---

* According to researcher Dr. Herbert Weiner, victims of natural disasters (floods, earthquakes, etc.) usually feel no guilt about their failure to prevent the event. However, they may feel guilty for being more fortunate than other victims. Victims of man-made tragedies (violence, accidents, etc.) often blame themselves for not having avoided the tragic event.

had less to do with the severity of the loss (complete or partial paralysis) than it had to do with the circumstances surrounding the loss (who caused the accident). Victims who accepted responsibility (took the blame) for their fate maintained a sense of control over their lives and ultimately adjusted better to their condition. These victims certainly regretted their actions that led to their paralysis, but they didn't pummel themselves with guilt.

LETTING GO OF GUILT

Edna sat on the far side of the rest of the group, away from the center of attention. Group members had been sharing their stories of trying times and offering help and reassurance to one another. Everyone liked Edna. It would be hard not to. She was caring, compassionate, and, for a rather matronly and proper fifty-year-old mother of four, she had this endearing quality of blurting out a profanity or two when you'd least expect it. Everyone liked Edna. Everyone except Edna, that is.

"Don't you think you're being too hard on yourself?" a member would say to her.

"You're your own worst enemy, Edna," another would conclude.

Edna had a tendency to berate herself, to doubt her capabilities, regardless of the fact that in the two years prior to her husband's death and in the three years since, she had successfully managed the household and four teenagers alone. Five years earlier her husband, Jim, suffered a severe stroke. His recovery was slow and arduous. Despite having to work full-time to help pay their bills, watch after the children, and drive the fifty miles to the hospital where Jim was recuperating, Edna seemed undaunted. But when Jim died unexpectedly, Edna blamed herself.

"I was with him when he was dying," she said. "There must have been something I could have done that would have saved him."

"But Edna," a group member said, "you know that people often blame themselves unnecessarily when things go wrong. You've even reminded the rest of us of that when we've felt guilty."

"You don't understand," she answered. "I know I did all I could, but my best wasn't good enough. It's that simple. How can I not blame myself for Jim's death?"

The group stayed quiet a moment, reflecting on what more they could say or do to help Edna. They seemed frustrated with her, and I told them that. Someone nodded and spoke up. "Edna, you always insist on finding something to criticize yourself for. And the more we try to tell you otherwise, the stronger your criticisms become. *Won't you just stop it?*"

Of course it was not that simple. The group knew that. But out of frustration and helplessness they acted toward Edna the way many well-intentioned people eventually act toward loved ones still mired in suffering from a loss: They lose patience and insist that the person let go of their pain. But in his wonderful book *A Gift of Hope*, Robert Veninga reminds us that pain works its way out of our awareness slowly, and in its own season. "There is a season of sadness. A season of anger . . . of tranquility . . . of hope." Those seasons don't arrive and depart in orderly, predictable ways. In the throes of grief one's feelings can fluctuate rapidly and dramatically. That is the way of mourning. Still, some people can stay trapped within certain seasons, snared in winter's stark coldness, unable to recover in the warmth of a healing spring. They angrily blame others for their misfortune or they blame themselves, but there is no movement forward. They find no solace, no forgiveness, no peace of mind. Why? *Because fear has taken over.* Anger, grief, guilt, and the anguished longing for what might have been may *arise* from hurt or loss, but they *persist* only through fear. While people typically yearn for trying times to come to an end, most nevertheless fear some of the changes that will take place if they should finally let go of their pain.

Some fear a new try at love when they were betrayed before.

Some fear forgiveness. They'd rather hold on to the belief that they are bad and unlovable and have a justification for why their life is an unhappy one.

Some fear letting go of their anger if it will only give way to depression.

Some fear challenging themselves to be their best. What if their best isn't good enough?

Some fear too much closeness, or becoming too dependent on others.

Some fear loneliness. They dread the possibility they may have no one to rely on but themselves.

Some fear having to accept that things happened the way they did. They aren't prepared to alter their attitudes about themselves, others, or the world.

Some fear remembering. It's too painful.

Some fear forgetting. They feel guilty and disloyal when they realize they went almost an entire day without remembering a loved one no longer with them.

But the most troublesome fear for anyone stuck in the season of sadness, anger, or guilt is this: *the fear of their own fear reactions*. In other words, they are *afraid* of their sadness, *afraid* of their anger, *afraid* of their guilt. They are afraid of their feelings about their situation. They are their harshest critics and they say things to themselves like:

If I'm still so sad, it must mean I'm hopelessly depressed. Why can't I shake this feeling off?

My anger seems so out of control. Other people learn to control their anger; why can't I?

I wouldn't be feeling so guilty if there wasn't something fundamentally wrong with me.

It's not normal to feel what I've been feeling.

It's wrong to feel what I've been feeling.

I'll never feel better if I keep feeling this way.

The way we react to our reactions, the way we feel about our feelings, can do more to perpetuate—or resolve—our problems than anything else we do.

Maybe we're feeling depressed. But if we're depressed about feeling depressed, we've succeeded only in doubling our pain.

Maybe we feel guilty. But if we feel guilty about feeling guilty, we've again succeeded in doubling our pain.

But what if we feel depressed and instead of telling ourselves how frightening it is to feel that way, we tell ourselves something like this: *Depression is very uncomfortable and it wears me out, but I am not bad or inadequate because I'm depressed. I can do more for myself by accepting my depression as it is than berating myself for feeling it.*

So I asked Edna about her feelings.

"Like I said before," she answered politely, "I feel guilt over my husband's death."

"Edna, please listen carefully to my next question," I responded. "How do you feel about feeling guilty?" She looked puzzled. "In other words," I continued, "what is your reaction to seeing yourself as guilty?"

"I hate myself for it. I know it wears me down further and I worry how I'll take care of my children if I remain so exhausted."

Edna felt guilty about feeling guilty. That was not an unusual thing for her to do, since her tendency was to be self-critical about most things.

Many people, once they understand how their reactions to their reactions are complicating their lives, immediately change them. They realize that working themselves up over a problem usually makes the problem harder to handle. So they calm themselves, become a friend to themselves, give themselves the benefit of the doubt and permission to be human. But others, such as Edna, can't stop judging themselves so harshly. Unable to approve of themselves, they are really scared to death that no one else will approve of them either, that not one soul will truly understand them in their time of need. Their hearts ache for the comfort of being held by a loving friend, but they fear that friend won't arrive. Believing they are alone and forsaken by all others, they seal their fates by forsaking themselves.

COMFORTING YOUR INNER CHILD

Edna's judgmental tendency had its roots in her childhood. Her unrealistic guilt over her husband's death was only the most recent in a long line of self-criticisms. When she felt extremely guilty as an adult, there was a younger *childself* that was feeling guilty—and fearful of being deemed unlovable. That inner child needed comforting.

Your inner child can be that part of you that is playful, adventurous, and ever curious. She breathes with a rhythm of joy and wonder and sleeps contentedly. But if you were wounded as a child and the wounds have never fully healed, then your inner child, your *childself*, is also afraid and discontent. The more needs your childself never had met, the more oversensitive and scared your adultself becomes. Even if you were loved as a child, you probably had moments that left you shaken and frightened, moments that you never talked about or fully understood, moments that, if you did talk about them, were not taken seriously. When you face a situation that reminds you (even unconsciously) of a childhood wound, you may react with greater fear. The fear may show itself as anxiety, anger, guilt, or depression. It often takes the form of persistent self-criticism or blaming of others.

In trying times when it is already hard enough to cope, a wounded childself can restlessly dig its way into your psyche, hollow out your self-confidence, and leave you with twinges of despair.

But the childself can be healed.

I've borrowed (and slightly adapted) one exercise to help you begin the healing process from Joan Borysenko's warm and insightful book *Guilt Is the Teacher, Love Is the Lesson*. Before you begin the exercise, inhale deeply . . . now exhale slowly and completely . . . and relax a moment. Think about how you are too harsh with yourself or others. Think back on a recent time when perhaps you overreacted or underreacted to a situation. Hone in on when you were accusing instead of being nonjudgmental. Do not read any farther until you have a specific situation in mind.

You are about to travel back in time and meet yourself as a child. Let me now quote Joan Borysenko:

> In your mind's eye see the number three. . . . As you exhale let the three dissolve and become a two. . . . As you exhale let the two dissolve and become a one. . . . As you exhale let the one dissolve and become a zero. Let the zero elongate into an oval mirror, and in it you will see yourself in a scene from your childhood. What is happening? Ask your childself what he is experiencing and how he feels. Listen with great respect and love.

. . . When the child is finished, tell him what he needs to hear. . . . Take a minute to comfort him. You may want to pick the child up, hug him, or stroke his hair. Do what is needed to restore the child's sense of self, to repair the bridge that was broken. Reassure the child and give him love. Let him know that you will be back to talk again, and that he can count on you for love and understanding, no matter what. When you are ready, release the child into the mirror and let the mirror collapse into a circle. Let the circle become a one, then the one become a two, and the two become a three. Open your eyes and come back to the room.

The first time you complete the exercise, you may feel relief. You may feel closer and more loving to yourself. You may spark other insights and emotions that lead you to a deeper understanding and acceptance of yourself. Or you may feel very little. That is okay. Give yourself permission to experience the exercise as it is for you, not as it might be for someone else. I'd encourage you to repeat the exercise daily for several weeks and anytime you feel particularly scared, desperate, confused, or judgmental.

"The childhood scenes I return to have all been so similar," Edna said one day. "In all of them I make mistakes, sometimes awful mistakes, and others tell me I'm bad and just not good enough." The usual sadness in her voice had lifted. Her eyes were lighter, softer.

"In all those memories what has your inner child needed to hear from you?" I asked.

"Not that I'm without fault," she said. "Everyone here has tried to tell me I'm not at fault for Jim's death, and I've tried to explain that I am to blame, at least partly. I told my inner child that she is forgiven for anything she's done that was wrong or hurtful. I told her she is good and kind and lovable even when I—I mean she—does make mistakes.

She has always done the best she could, and that is good enough."

The gift of being nonjudgmental has always been ours. Like many such gifts, however, we need to open it up and try it on for size.

Chapter 10

OVERCOMING DESPAIR

The Gift of Meaning

❖

From the moment he left my office, I couldn't think of much else. His final few words opened up places in my heart not easily closed. About five years earlier his only son, Billy, age four and a half, died in an auto accident. The driver of the other car had been drinking, making Billy's death as utterly senseless as it was profoundly tragic.

"I could find no meaning in his death," said Bill senior. "So I had to find meaning in his life. In loving Billy I discovered a depth of love I never thought possible. I've had my days of resenting other parents who still have their kids. I've certainly been bitter. But I think I'm a kinder person because of Billy. He gave me that. And I've strengthened my faith in God. I had to, because that's who I believe Billy is with right now."

MAKING SENSE OF
LIFE'S SUFFERINGS

In the face of overwhelming suffering, with nothing left but hope's tattered remnants, we humans struggle to maintain some shred of constancy in our lives—some coherent, fundamental system of beliefs—to keep us from losing ourselves entirely. Call it the need to find a reason for living; call it belief in God's infinite love; call it what you will, but it amounts to the search, and desire, for meaning. In heartbreak and tragedy it helps to make sense of what happened, to arrive at some kind of answer to the question *Why?* And if no answer can be found, or if none is good enough (could it ever be good enough?), we need to stop asking *why* and start asking *how:* "How can I make meaningful what has happened? How can I go on to live a meaningful life?" Suffering can whittle down our dreams, our confidence, and our faith in a just world. But *when our suffering means something*, we can escape despair. Suffering is bad enough. But the meanest form of suffering is a suffering with no meaning.

Listen to John.

"After my wife died, I had no reason to get up in the morning. I was retired, so I had no job to go to. We never had children. I had some distant relatives, but basically I was alone. One day three months ago I was standing on a busy street corner waiting to cross the road. A young mother with three children came alongside of me, and one of the toddlers started running into traffic. I grabbed hold of him and pulled him back. I'll never know for sure, but I think I may have saved his life. I had to ask myself, could it be that despite the fact I saw no meaning in my life, my life had meaning for someone else? I couldn't shake that thought from my mind. And if my life had meaning for that little boy and his family, how many other strangers might it yet be meaningful for? I haven't decided how to live out the rest of my life, but I can no longer live it without it meaning something to someone."

In an often-cited study by Henry Beecher in the *Journal of the American Medical Association*, only 32 percent of a group of World War II soldiers wounded by exploding shell fragments required pain medication when their pain was severe enough to warrant a narcotic. In contrast, 83 percent of civilians who underwent similar (but unrelated to the war) surgery needed pain medication. Both groups were equivalent in age and in medical history. In many cases the tissue trauma inflicted by the civilians' surgeons was far less severe than the wounds suffered by the soldiers. But the severity and extent of the wound bore no relationship to the amount of pain experienced. According to Beecher, the intensity of the suffering and the amount of pain medication required was "largely determined by what the pain meant to the patient." Soldiers with severe injuries knew they were going home. For them, because of their injuries, the war was over. But for the civilians, surgery was fraught with anxiety. To them surgery meant time lost from work, a disruption of their daily routine, and a greater awareness of their mortality. The *meaning* attached to one's suffering seems to make a difference in the perception and tolerance of pain.

Bereaved family members cope better when a loved one's death was expected. It's hard for them, yes, but they had time to sort through some of the *why?* questions and make peace with their loved one. In contrast, when a loved one's death is unexpected and traumatic, family members struggle to cope. Not only did they not have time to prepare themselves mentally, but often their whole worldview is shattered. Their world no longer seems a safe, kind, and fair place. Meaning and purpose in life is crushed. And their God seems cruel and punitive.

If meaning can affect how we cope, how does one begin to find meaning and purpose in adversity? What is the sense of little children at play shot to death by stray bullets from violent drug dealers? Is it God's will that a hardworking father of two die from a brain tumor? And if you believe in a God who answers prayers, who intercedes in our lives, who makes miracles when a miracle is the only thing that would make a difference, then why, despite our pleas, does that God sometimes allow the innocent to suffer and the good to die young?

Making sense of life's tragedies, and putting together a life that makes sense after the tragedies, isn't easy work. But it is necessary.

MAKING TRAGEDY MEANINGFUL

PEACE TO ALL
WHO ENTER HERE

When hard times are temporary and not too severe (such as when you suffer a mild heart attack), you can more readily fit what has happened into your preexisting view of the world. Times might be a bit tough, but they make sense. Had you eaten right, stopped smoking, and exercised more, perhaps the whole ordeal could have been avoided. But when your life is violently upended, when tragedy drowns your values and your dreams, your entire worldview can become disordered and meaningless. Nothing fits. Nothing makes sense. Nothing is as it once was, or should be.

"Where is God now?" asked a Nazi-death-camp prisoner, in Nobel Peace Prize winner Elie Wiesel's haunting book *Night*. Himself a Holocaust survivor, Wiesel described an actual event where all prisoners, including Wiesel, once had to view the public hanging of three inmates, two adults and a child. The child, cherished by all, possessed a beautiful face, the face of a "sad angel." Being small, starved, and so light, it took over thirty minutes for the child to finally die on the makeshift gallows, under the watchful, weeping eyes of God's Chosen Ones.

Over ten million people died in concentration camps in World War II. One and a half million were children. How does one begin to make sense of the Holocaust? An article by psychologists Paul Marcus and Alan Rosenberg relates how some Holocaust survivors clung to their religious beliefs, though just barely, by revising their view of God. He was still All-Good, but having failed to prevent the Holocaust, He must not have been All-Powerful. Still others believed in God's power, but no longer believed He chose to intervene in man's affairs. To them the Holocaust happened not because God was dead but because God was detached and impersonal. And some lost their faith altogether, leaving it buried in a mass grave near the furnaces of Auschwitz. But all survivors, in order to somehow put their lives back together, needed to reconstruct a meaningful view of the world and of life.

Psychiatrist Viktor Frankl, also a survivor of Nazi death camps, believed that the pursuit of meaning and purpose in life is at the core of our existence. He writes in his classic book *Man's Search for Meaning* that we can discover meaning in life in three ways: through creative work, by loving others, *and by the way we respond to suffering.* "Even the helpless victim of a hopeless situation," Frankl writes, "facing a fate he cannot change . . . may grow beyond himself, and by so doing change himself." We can, it seems, respond to adversity with a resolve to somehow turn a tragedy into a personal triumph and to make the rest of our life worth living. We can be like a man Frankl writes about, a man who suffered a broken neck at age seventeen. "I broke my neck, it didn't break me," the man says. Despite the fact that he must use a mouth stick to type, he attends college. We can be like Ryan White, the boy who contracted AIDS from a transfusion and, before he finally died in 1990, became a symbol of extraordinary courage and compassion. We can be like the countless people everywhere who everyday hold their heads high with dignity despite burdens we'd not readily carry. But it isn't easy to be like them.

Peace to all who enter these corridors, who strive to find purpose in a life rocked by unasked-for suffering. Purpose and meaning can be found. But it won't be found by distracting yourself from your pain. It won't be found at your friend's house who, over dinner, kindly takes your mind off your sorrow (though it helps to know that people care). It can only be found when you go back home and open yourself up to the pain of all you've lost. Trying to discover meaning hurts before it heals. Only when you sit at a dinner table, day after day, with a place setting missing; only when you remember that this holiday season there is someone you can no longer buy a present for; only when you dry your eyes with the last precious threads of what was can you weave them into the warm fabric of what can be.

DEVELOPING A HEALING THEORY

Psychologist and respected researcher Dr. Charles Figley has worked extensively with families traumatized by loss or adversity. He helps families to reexamine what happened and why and to construct what he appropriately calls a *healing theory*. The healing theory is the family's unique and personal way of making sense of what happened and how it has affected them. And it tells them what they can expect from their future.

To be healing, the theory must offer alternative views of the adversity and its consequences—optimistic views that emphasize family strengths, humanness, faith, forgiveness, courage, and love, while not minimizing their misfortune. A healing theory is not a list of "excuses" used to "explain away" what happened. But such a theory does take into account the truth that accidents happen and that many good-intentioned people do wrong things for right reasons. (Friends and family members can hurt one another in a misguided effort to show love and caring. People hurt others more often out of fear than out of meanness.) Healing theories take time to develop. Family members, and concerned friends, ministers, or therapists, are advised to avoid quick, pat answers to difficult and painful happenings. Saying "It was for the best" or "It was God's will" may not be healing comments to a traumatized family, though many people eventually take comfort in their religious beliefs. Listen first to what their hearts have to say. Be with them as they suffer without trying to talk them out of their feelings. Remember, to discover meaning in adversity, to be able to develop a healing theory, *the pain of what was lost must first be fully experienced, not suppressed*. The pain will pass eventually, though never completely. Some forgetting will occur. But the best way to put aside one's pain, the best way to forget, is to remember.*

I'm reminded of a passage from Harold Kushner's book *Who Needs God?* A teenage girl, lamenting her boyfriend dying of cancer, hopes she never loves anyone that much again. It was an understandable response, but not a healing one. As Kushner points out, incurable diseases are a "painful outrage *precisely because* life is good and holy," not because life is meaningless. Which is the more meaningful and healing response to an untimely death: to close up your spirit in order to prevent future pain or to find the courage to love again, knowing that part of the price of that love will eventually be more pain?

In 1983 Raymond Mulhern and his associates at the Medical College of Wisconsin studied families of children

---

* It was Freud, I believe, who so wisely made that last point. However, in what context or publication he made it, I do not know.

with a terminal illness. Specifically they wanted to know what difference it made to the families if the children lived their final days in a hospital or at home (participating in a home-care program). Compared with parents whose children died in a hospital, parents who helped care for their dying child at home suffered less anxiety and depression and had fewer tendencies to develop physical problems themselves. They also had fewer subsequent marital problems and were less socially withdrawn. The siblings of patients in the home-care program were not as withdrawn, inhibited, and fearful as their counterparts. Why? My answers are speculative, but I imagine that somehow, by being at home, the last days and weeks of the child's life became even more positive and meaningful to the child and the family. Every living moment was precious. And instead of relating to one another in a sterile, noisy hospital where they had less say over what happened and restricted freedom of movement, they related in a warm, homey atmosphere where everything was appreciated, everything meant something, and nothing was taken for granted. At home, watching a rainstorm, cooking spaghetti, or removing a splinter from a hand were experiences to be cherished. By dying of an incurable disease at home, a youngster helped his family to heal.

MEANING: THE POSSIBILITY
OF PURPOSE

When on the brink of despair, meaningfulness begins as an idea, a *possibility*. It is the possibility that *in spite of* your suffering and even *because of* your suffering you will experience a quality in your life you might otherwise never have known. It is the possibility that life has more to offer you and, more importantly, *the possibility that you have much more to offer life!* It is the possibility that the God you'd once befriended is beside you still. It is the possibility of land when adrift on a troubled sea. Are you ready for such possibilities? Are you ready to take up the challenge of making your life more meaningful than it is right now? The gift of meaning is not like a serene painting that you contemplate and feel good about. It is instead a gift of lumber and nails and a hammer and saw—useless unless you build something.

Such possibilities of joy and purposefulness, even if they become realities, may never compensate for what you lost. But I think of Bill senior, who lost his only son, Billy, five years ago. In mourning his son, Bill expanded his understanding of what true and lasting love is. His memories of Billy, though painful at times, enriched his heart and strengthened his faith. To remember Billy was to affirm what was good about living, good about loving, and good about God.

So Billy's life, and death, had meaning after all. Not enough meaning to erase the pain, but enough for Bill to move forward in life with faith and hope and the capacity to keep on loving. Billy's death surely would have been meaningless if his father's spirit had died along with his son.

Often when people I work with struggle to find some meaning, some purpose, to their lives, when they live on the edge of despair groping for some sign of hope, I wonder if they'd recognize hope if they saw it. We live in a perplexing world. People sometimes seem numb to killings and human misery, yet we can sit captivated by our television sets watching men and machines working for days at a stretch in an attempt to rescue baby Jessica McClure, trapped dozens of feet down in a dry well. And our hearts swell with joy when we learn she'll be all right. Acts of courage, love, compassion, and kindness are all around us, but hard to see if we don't pay attention.

I often tell people who see little value to their lives to go out of their way each day for two weeks and do something kind for someone else. Help someone carry packages. Wait and hold a door open for an elderly couple. Bring dinner to a sick friend. Hand-deliver a greeting card to someone in a hospital who has no such cards and chat with those patients who would welcome such a visitor. Smile warmly at the harried person behind the checkout counter. Write a letter to the president of a company praising an employee who treated you well. Two weeks. That's all. That's not a lot of time to *experience the possibility* that your life can and does make a difference. Purpose in life is what you're after. And purpose in life is best defined as *putting your possibilities into practice.*

- Isn't it possible that the love you're capable of giving can make a difference in the life of someone you haven't even met yet?

- Isn't it possible that with time and support, you'll have new ideas about how to live your life—ideas that are healing and life-affirming?

- Isn't it possible that it was not God's will that such a tragedy has befallen you, and that He, too, is angry and grieving for your loss?

- Isn't it possible that your suffering is not a permanent condition?

- Isn't it possible that because of your misfortune, something very positive and good will happen in the future that never could have happened otherwise?

- Isn't it possible that the meaning of life is to make meaningful all that life has to offer and to live out your life accordingly?

The possibilities are endless.

So somehow now you must find meaning. But meaning is seldom found in spectacular palaces of grand design. It exists in small rooms, sleeps in out-of-the-way places, tended by people with warm hearts on cold nights.

And when all is said and done, you really won't "find" meaning, anymore than you "find" the air you breathe. Meaning is all around you. You must notice it, draw it inside you, and then, simply but wholeheartedly, live it as well as you possibly can.

Chapter 11

TURNING TO OTHERS
IN A TIME OF NEED

The Gift of Connectedness

❖

Rᴉᴄʜᴀʀᴅ ʙʟᴏᴄʜ, cofounder of H & R Block, was told in 1978 he had three months to live. The diagnosis was lung cancer. But in 1980 he was judged in remission and is alive and well today. During an appearance on the television program *The Hour of Power* he attributed his recovery to several crucial factors, among them a strong faith in God, nurturing an optimistic attitude, the expertise, support, and encouragement from his physicians, and the tireless efforts by his wife to bring him hope, caring, and reassurance. One of his messages was that in addition to medical technology, *relationships counted*. Coincidentally, over the past fifteen years mounting research evidence has documented how social support promotes health and can act as a buffer protecting people from the adverse effects of stress and misfortune. As Bernie Siegel said in his book *Love, Medicine, and Miracles*, "Love heals."

In a well-known report by researchers Leonard Berkman and Leonard Syme, a random sample of 7,000 residents of Alameda County, California, were studied over a nine-year period. Of the 682 people from the sample who died during that time, the best predictor of mortality was not their health habits (smoking, drinking, overeating) but their social ties: whether they were married, how many close friends they had, whether they attended church, and whether they belonged to any group or association. People with fewer ties to others died at a rate two to five times higher than people with stronger social ties. Those differences held up regardless of sex, ethnic origin, or socioeconomic status.

In the book *The Healing Brain*, researcher James Lynch wrote that no disease kills people at the rate that loneliness does. He reported that for all races and both sexes, people under seventy who were single, widowed, or divorced died at a rate two to ten times higher than those who were married. A chapter written by Meredith Minkler from the same book indicated that social support makes a difference in successfully coping with a variety of diseases including AIDS, asthma, kidney dysfunction, and migraine headaches, and in recovery rates from strokes, surgery, and certain forms of cancer.

In a study of ten thousand men in Israel, some of the effects of hypertension and high cholesterol on heart disease were counteracted when a husband felt loved and supported by his wife.

When a person in a deep coma is simply touched by another human being, the rhythm of the patient's heartbeat can change.

People really do need people. But studies show that caring for plants or pets can have healing and life-affirming effects as well. Cardiac patients who have pets to care for survive longer than patients without pets. People with hypertension significantly reduce their blood pressure when caring for a pet. Nursing-home residents with the responsibility of caring for a plant live significantly longer than residents with no such responsibility.

A study by L. Pearlin and his associates showed that for

working people who suddenly find themselves unemployed, emotional support by friends and relatives helps prevent a loss of self-confidence—which significantly reduces the risk of serious depression—although the strain of financial worries is not reduced.

High school students who reported low levels of support from family and friends lost twice as much time from school due to sports injuries than students with support.

Stable, caring relationships make a difference in health and coping. But why? Researchers aren't entirely clear, but something about *connecting* to another living being taps into inner resources. For one thing, meaningful social contact *improves the body's resistance to disease*. Also, people with strong social ties feel less helpless and more in *control* about what happens to them as a result of a caring support system. Others *commit* themselves to overcoming adversity when they have somebody they are responsible for. Having friends and family who really care also makes life more *meaningful*. Thus, improved physical immunity, a sense of control over life events, commitment, and meaningfulness undoubtedly heighten optimism and strengthen coping resources and may be the underlying cause for why social support can be such a powerful healer.

CONNECTING HEART TO HEART

James Pennebaker, in his book *Opening Up*, discussed the extensive research evidence for a phenomenon most people have experienced as true: that confiding in others eventually helps you to feel better. Confiding in others not only allows you to vent and clarify your concerns but often makes you feel cared about and valued despite your shortcomings. You feel less alone, more connected. You can probably recall times in your life when you were very elated or very sad. Didn't you *want* to talk to others then? The urge to share your joy and grief may well be universal. Yet more and more, society seems to emphasize independence rather than *inter*dependence, differences rather than similarities. It used to be only in elevators that people avoided saying hello, making eye contact, and otherwise acknowledging that others existed. Now people can live for years without ever meeting, let alone having a relationship with, their next-door neighbors.

We were meant for more than that.

Interestingly families caught in natural disasters where there is widespread destruction of a community suffer fewer emotional scars compared with disasters that strike one person or one family only. That is so in part because in a community disaster everybody is a victim, no one person feels blameworthy, and everybody chips in to help the community recover. When social connections are strong and reliable, suffering lessens.

WHEN YOU WANT TO HELP SOMEONE WHO IS HURTING

GET CLOSE, BUT NOT TOO CLOSE

Broadly speaking, you can provide support in two ways. You can offer something specific, such as advice, money, food, medical care, or shelter. This is a solution-oriented, problem-solving type of support. Or you can provide emotional support by listening, giving encouragement, using humor, talking about everyday (noncrisis) events, and so forth. While offers of food, money, or other tangible help may be necessary in some cases, caregivers with a strong desire to "do something" often underestimate the value of emotional support. In hard times just about everybody needs to know they are cared *about*, but not nearly as many need to be cared *for*. Sometimes when you've done all you can for a friend in need, the next best thing you can do is to simply make yourself available when needed. As Eugene Kennedy writes in his book *The Pain of Being Human*, the friend who makes himself available without intruding "has learned what to do when there is nothing to be done."

The benefits of social support are many, but drawbacks exist. In his book *The Healer Within,* researcher Dr. Steven Locke cited a study by psychologist David Reiss of George Washington University. Reiss observed dialysis patients over a three-year period and discovered that the patients who died came from the closest, most conscientious and involved families! Strong and sustained family closeness, far from being healing, was instead "the kiss of death." A theory given by Reiss for the finding was that the closest families were more devastated when a family member was chronically ill and that the patient died to put an end to the family's intense, ongoing suffering. Also, too much support during any type of adversity might convey to a person the message "You cannot survive without our help." *Anything, even good-intentioned offers of help, that weakens a person's sense of control or heightens a sense of helplessness may do more harm than good*. If you're not observant, even a warm, loving embrace can be suffocating to someone with a strong need to be alone. So, Rule Number One when you want to help someone who is hurting is: *Give them first the message "I love you," not the message "You need me."* This means being willing to listen to what they tell you they need and don't need. True, some people really wanting your help may not ask you for it. When that happens, ask specific questions to help you gauge if they are getting sufficient support. Instead of wondering to yourself if that person would appreciate a phone call, call and ask how many calls they've been getting and would they like any more. Ask if they've had time to cook or go shopping. If they haven't, doing some grocery shopping for them or preparing some supper dishes might be welcome.

In a crisis people's ways of coping become more rigid. Someone who likes the company of others during worrisome times but can tolerate time alone if necessary may insist on "togetherness" when suffering is overwhelming. But in the worst of times someone else might need solitude for a while to help him get his bearings. When Sam was recovering from a heart attack, the last thing he wanted was pampering and an opportunity to talk about what had happened. But his wife, Jane, felt shut out. She needed to talk, and he resisted. Actually both were troubled by his heart attack, but each managed their anxiety differently. Talking heightened his anxiety, distracting himself eased it. But lack of communication raised her anxiety, while talking about his heart attack lowered it. At such times it is best for partners to lower their expectations of each other a bit and offer to give the other some of what he or she wants. If Sam would initiate conversation with Jane more often, even though it made him uncomfortable, and if Jane would be willing to have fewer (and briefer) discussions, they would improve the odds of getting through the ordeal with little scarring. Thus Rule Number Two is: *Understand that coping styles can differ from person to person. Make a pact with family members that each one will accommodate himself somewhat to the other's needs without being demanding or critical.*

In a 1990 conference for family therapists, Barbara Gawinski reported how parents of a stillborn child need to further connect with that child in order to grieve and let go. Gawinski's comments underscore the need for emotional connectiveness as a catalyst for healing. Two out of every hundred births are stillbirths. Medical personnel used to "know" what was best for the parents of stillborn children.

Rather than further "traumatize" the parents, it was thought the best thing to do was to remove the baby as quickly as possible. But that was not the best thing to do, according to psychologist Gawinski. Now parents have the opportunity to hold their deceased child if they wish. They are encouraged to name the baby and perhaps take a photograph. Footprints, a lock of hair, a hospital bracelet, a receiving blanket—all the remembrances parents usually possess—should be made available. And it is also recommended to have a funeral for the baby. An opportunity for the family to come together in mourning helps move the parents along in their grieving process. But grieving parents of a stillborn child are not compelled to hold or name their baby. They are allowed to choose. This leads to Rule Number Three, which is: *Don't presume to know what's best for the hurting person. Be willing to listen and respect that person's feelings and desires, even if it makes you uncomfortable.* Telling another what she should and shouldn't be feeling or what she should or shouldn't be doing may turn that person away from you. Good helpers are good, respectful listeners.

DO YOU NEED A GOOD LISTENER?

Most likely. Whether your problems right now are overwhelming or manageable, having somebody around who cares enough to listen to your troubles can make a difference in your entire outlook on life. But you may have to seek that person out and risk being more open than would ordinarily make you comfortable. You have to admit you need help. And you may have to forgive people whose attempts to be helpful miss the mark. (In one study a group of bereaved persons indicated that the most unhelpful "support" they received from well-meaning friends was advice and encouragement to recover. Just "being there" and listening was most helpful.)

But do you have friends for support? In the book *To Thine Own Self Be True*, psychologist Lewis Andrews reports that about 40 percent of Americans describe themselves as suffering from shyness and isolation. One in six of us don't have even one friend in whom we can confide with confidence. Even when all is going fairly well in our lives, when tragedies and traumas are absent, it seems that loneliness can quietly dig a space in the cellars of our souls and sit there.

One nice part about opening up to others is that you don't even have to get it right for it to be beneficial. You can stammer and stutter, forget what you were about to say, cry —and the chances are good the listener will understand the essence of your message. Your story really isn't unique. Yes, the characters and scenes may be distinctive, the stage may be different, but the play is the same drama acted out by millions every day. As a psychologist I've heard a thousand diverse stories from men and women of different races, health status, and economic stature. And each story asked the same questions:

"How can I find more love in my life?"

"How can I overcome fear in my life?"

"How can I have more meaning in my life?"

It's hard enough to try to live out the answers to those questions. It's impossible to do it alone.

Chapter 12

WHAT TO DO . . .
WHAT TO DO

The Gifts of Decisiveness and Commitment

❖

"Do what you think is best. It's your choice."

Scary words? or challenging? Regardless, during trying times, even if the rest of your life gets put on hold, there is no holding back from decision-making. And every course of action you choose carries with it a new wave of decisions. The decisions you make may grow old, but they will never fade away, for no one is free from having to live out the consequences of their decisions. You can decide to postpone choosing. You can decide to let someone else make the hard choices for you. You can choose never to choose. But those are your decisions.

Most of us aren't fully prepared to make the kinds of decisions required of us during hard times. We need help. So we pray, talk to family, friends, or experts, and do the best we can with the information we obtain. But it can still be confusing and scary. I remember the first decision my wife and I, as brand-new parents, had to make for our three-day-old son as he was about to be discharged from the hospital. Instead of choosing which outfit he would wear home, we were told by the pediatrician, "Your son has a high fever. We think it might be meningitis. Can we have your permission to do a spinal tap? We'll need your signatures." Many decisions are burdens, whether you're ready to make them or not. As it turned out, my son did have a mild form of viral meningitis. He recovered quickly and was home within five days. (My wife and I recovered a few days later.)

Choice-making is essential for healthy coping. In a difficult situation, having options, even limited ones, heightens your sense of control. The belief that you have some (even minor) influence over the course of events in your life can profoundly affect your ability to persevere, especially in the face of setbacks. In one study hospital patients who recovered sooner and with fewer complications had also been rated by their physicians as being difficult patients. Evidently, instead of passively accepting their treatment, these patients asked more questions, challenged the efficacy of some procedures, and generally made a bit of a nuisance of themselves. They weren't obsessed with controlling their treatment, but they were *involved*. They chose not to sit on the sidelines. Counselor and author Earnie Larsen reminds us that there are always options, always choices available to us. In the game of life it doesn't matter what your score is at halftime. And as long as you are alive, Larsen says, you're still at halftime. What are your choices for the second half of the game?

COMMIT TO CHOOSE, THEN CHOOSE TO COMMIT

You have some tough decisions ahead of you. Will you remain in your marriage and try to improve it, despite your unhappiness? Will you finally leave the job you've hated for fifteen years? Will you forge ahead with your life even though someone you loved will no longer share it with you? Will you take an active role in your cancer treatment or will you let the doctors do all the work? Will you give up on God or go looking for Him?

Will you face the hard questions or will you ignore them?

Sometimes when so much has been so hard for so long, choosing to get out of bed and face another day can be a monumental decision.

Still, your first major step in coping is taken when you *commit yourself to choosing*. A commitment to choice is the determination to take an active role in overcoming your difficulties. It is a commitment to decision-making. It is the will to be a player, not an observer; a survivor, not a victim. Author and minister Robert Schuller defines any problem as "a decision you haven't made yet." The moment you decide what course of action to take, a problem is no longer a problem; it is then both a challenge and an opportunity.

When Glenn wondered whether he should invite his newly widowed mother to live with him and his wife, Jean, Jean told Glenn, "Whatever you decide is fine with me." Had Jean *truly* made a personal choice? Or was she evading the responsibility of making a decision by letting Glenn have final say? One way to tell: Will she resent Glenn's decision later on? Anytime you blame another for an unhappy situation you find yourself in, somewhere along the line you probably abdicated your responsibility to make a personal choice.

Once you've committed to choosing, to being an active participant in coping, you must *choose to commit* yourself to the choices you've made. You must persevere and give it all you've got. People committed to a cause don't retreat at the first sign of difficulty. They hang in there. Setbacks, while disappointing, do not discourage them. But to commit, you must have a goal in mind. And the value of the goal must outweigh the value of maintaining the status quo.

The toughest choice for couples in counseling, for example, often comes after they've made progress in mending their relationship and one of them lets the other one down. Do they view the setback as temporary and understandable or as a serious sign of a relationship on the decline? Without a commitment to improving their relationship, such couples can feel defeated rather easily. True, even the most committed couples may eventually decide the marriage cannot be saved. But when commitment is thin, so, too, are the odds of rebuilding a satisfactory relationship.

THE ATTITUDE OPTION

It is as true in tough times as it is in kind times: Being good, loving, honest, faithful, forgiving, committed, or optimistic (or for that matter, being bad, unloving, dishonest, unfaithful, unforgiving, uncommitted, or pessimistic) always involves some degree of choice to be so. Certainly it is easy to show love when you are offered love, and difficult to be forgiving when betrayed. But circumstances alone do not dictate how you will respond. You are not a robot. You possess the power to make a conscious and determined effort to rule your own actions and emotions. In times of great misfortune you may *feel* helpless or victimized, but does that mean you must remain so? *Times may be tough, but you still have options.* A client of mine once compared life to a game of poker. "If you get dealt a bad hand, you don't blame the dealer. You just do the best you can with what you've got," he said. "But if you keep getting dealt bad hands, over and over," he continued, "something is wrong. Then maybe you can blame the dealer." I agree with him to a point. Some people will try to cheat you and make your life more difficult than necessary. But you abdicate power over your life the moment you take the position that someone else must change in order for you to be better off. What if they won't change? You always have options. You don't need aces to win at poker. A pair of deuces will do just fine if you play them right. And nobody is forcing you to remain in a dishonest poker game, right?

Norman Cousins, in his book *Head First*, tells the story of a thirty-year-old man named Pedro falsely arrested for drug smuggling. Innocent, and unable to post bail, he rapidly lost weight and grew despondent waiting in jail for his trial to begin. He also had rheumatoid arthritis, a condition that can worsen under stress, and while incarcerated his joints became so badly inflamed, he could barely walk. After the trial began, the real criminal—who was nearly identical in appearance to Pedro—was apprehended, and Pedro was released. But his ordeal had ravaged him. He had reason to be bitter, reason to be depressed. But with the help of Norman Cousins he *chose* to focus on more positive goals: to restore his faith in human beings, to feel loving, to develop a purpose in life, to laugh again. In time he gained weight, his depression lifted, his arthritic pain steadily reduced, and he returned to his job. He was dealt a pair of deuces, but eventually won the game.

Just as with Pedro, all of what has happened to you, all the hurtful and unfair events, get filtered through something that only you possess: your attitude. While it is true that attitudes can prompt you to behave in certain ways, *your behavior more powerfully shapes your attitude.* This means that by *willfully choosing to behave in ways that run counter to your attitudes, you can change those attitudes.* You have the choice to act in ways that will ultimately improve your attitude. Thus, instead of despairing over questions such as "Do I love her enough to stay married?" or "Do I have what it takes to succeed?" or "Is there any hope for my recovery?" you have the option to ask yourself instead, "Will I show her love and caring anyway?" "Am I willing to take the next step necessary in order to have a chance at success?" "What is one thing I could do today that might improve my odds of recovering?"

Times may be tough, but you still have options. When you want to strengthen the personal qualities required to help you land on your feet during difficult times, first answer these two questions:

1. What would someone who is feeling more hopeful (determined, patient, forgiving, committed, creative, etc.) be thinking and doing that is different from what I'm thinking and doing?

2. What would be the next step I could take today to make progress in thinking and behaving more effectively?

Remember, you have the ability to choose your reaction to what happens to you. Will your response be positive or negative? Constructive or destructive? Hopeful or cynical? Consider the following list of options. Just for today I can choose:

- To visualize a positive outcome rather than imagine the worst

- To celebrate the good things I have rather than feel entitled to more

- To recommit myself to overcoming these hard times

- To act like a survivor, not a victim

- To take charge of things I have control over and let go of things I can't control

- To find at least one positive effect of this adversity

- To trust that with faith and effort this difficult time will give my life more meaning

- To accept that bad events have happened and that bad events are temporary

- To be mindful and appreciative of something I usually take for granted

- To believe that God has a plan for my life that is good

- To seek out the companionship of loved ones and take comfort that I am not alone

- To feel good about feeling good

- To give myself the freedom to continue to make choices

There is no doubt in my mind that by willfully choosing to think and act in a positive, goal-directed manner, you can alter the course of events in your life. Sadly, you can't erase the tragedy that may have stricken your heart. But you can soften its blow. You can soothe your spirit. And you can pick up the pieces and rebuild your life so that once again, or perhaps for the first time, you can feel more joy than sorrow, more contentment than restlessness, more hope than despair. Will you transform your life overnight? I'm sure you already understand the answer is no. But you can transform the night into light. You can look ahead and imagine the gleam of a new day. If every day you envision the possibility that you can feel better, that your life can still be full and meaningful, and take at least one new step that very day toward your goal, you'll move farther away from where you are now.

AN UNUSUAL CHOICE?
CHOOSING TO SUFFER

Choosing to suffer is not necessarily a sign of masochism. In fact most of us choose to suffer many times a week because we intuitively understand that suffering can have value and purpose. We choose to suffer a little whenever:

We put someone else's needs ahead of our own

We give hard-earned money to charity

We listen and care about a friend's problems

We postpone getting what we really want

We are honest with ourselves and admit personal weaknesses

We see a wrong and try to right it

We say we are sorry

We discuss the feelings we fear discussing

We remember someone close to us who has died

We try even though we know we might fail

We are understanding about someone else's misunderstanding

We try to do the right thing even when we can't be sure what the right thing is

We try to heal a relationship that hurts

We give our children more freedom

We forgive

If we can see some value, some purpose, some goodness in suffering in small ways, might we not see some meaning to suffering deeply even if the suffering is unfair and unasked for? We don't have to know what the meaning might be, but we can choose to be open to it, to look for it, and to be faithful to the idea of it.

One man I know looked back on his life of fifty years with nothing but shame and regret. He never achieved the success in the business world he'd imagined he would. But more sadly, he regretted the many mistakes he'd made as a father—how he put his job first and his family last—and how he'd never appreciated and loved his wife the way she deserved. "I'm a failure," he concluded. "And since my children are all grown, it's too late to do anything about it."

Too late? Not by my way of thinking.

"Henry," I said later, "there are two essential lessons parents need to teach their children. One is how to love themselves and others enough to make a positive difference in this world. But the second lesson is equally important: how to admit mistakes and right wrongs, how to handle setbacks and defeat. Essentially the second lesson is how to commit oneself to living a purposeful life, a life with integrity, despite personal weaknesses, hard times, and failures. You have remorse for how you've conducted your life so far. If there is any meaning in your suffering now, it is that it gives you the opportunity to teach your children how to handle hardships and personal regrets with dignity, commitment, and compassion." A tear came to his eye. A moment ago his suffering was a reaction to a poorly lived life. Now it gave him purpose and made his life more meaningful.

Being widowed for over a year, Marge discovered she had more compassion now for lonely people. It was a small consolation perhaps, but then again compassion is not a gift to be taken lightly.

Suffering can have value.

One of the amazing things about choosing to suffer is that it can make a difference even when logic tells you that choice is irrelevant. When you know you are suffering anyway, such as when a loved one dies, what sense does it make to "choose" to feel what you're already feeling? Isn't that simply playing a head game? Well, for one thing, your mind doesn't readily distinguish between what is objectively true and what you tell it is true. For example, while watching a frightening movie, adrenaline will flow and you'll respond with anxiety even though there is no danger. Similarly, when you choose to suffer, even if the suffering was forced upon you and you had no choice in the matter, you are taking perceived control over a situation that once seemed entirely out of your control. Helplessness seems to intensify pain. Perceived control reduces pain somewhat. Many angry and impatient drivers stuck in a long traffic line would rather veer off to an alternate route, even if tolerating the wait would result in a shorter drive time overall. Doing *something* usually feels better than doing *nothing*.

Research shows that people who feel overwhelmed with negative, intrusive thoughts and feelings regain strength and perspective by devoting some regularly set time during the day to contemplate their distressing feelings (that is, instead of trying to distract themselves from their pain, they make a conscious choice to experience it). That time of day should be scheduled (the earlier in the day, the better). The rest of the day is set aside for more usual activities. After several days people discover they have more choice over when and where they will grapple with their painful feelings and no longer feel completely helpless when a wave of anger or sadness comes over them. At such times they say to themselves, "I understand these feelings will come over me unexpectedly, but I can put them aside for now and focus my attention elsewhere."

So when Marge, still grieving over the death of her husband, *chose* to feel angry and sad at her loss, something happened. By choosing instead of fighting the feelings, they lessened in intensity. She still hurt a great deal, "but somehow it was a bit more bearable."

Some pain cannot be fended off. If you try to run from it, you won't outdistance it. You can't talk yourself out of it. When you lose something precious to you, when your world gets uprooted, you will suffer. At such times, when no amount of comfort can make the pain go away, then willfully choosing to suffer—to accept and embrace your feelings—helps you to pick up the pieces and eventually move on with your life.

Chapter 13

EMBRACING WHAT
YOU HAVE LEFT

The Gift of Gratitude

❖

On cold nights, in hard times, gratitude can comfort you, like a warm blanket for a troubled and weary traveler. It cannot remove the ache from loss or discouragement, but it can soothe you, leave you more content, more reassured that life's beauty and goodness haven't forsaken you completely.

Gratitude sometimes comes easily during adversity, as it would if you learned that a loved one had survived a horrific accident. And certainly you'd be grateful to hear that the cancer you have is treatable and that complete recovery is likely. When there are miracles, when there is relief, gratitude flows in gushes from your heart. When you finally hear that matters will work out okay, it's natural to feel thankful.

But what if you can't be sure how things will work out? Or what if the worst has already happened?

"Be grateful. It could have been worse," some people tell you. "It will be a blessing in disguise," say others. And still more remark, "Be thankful for what you have left. At least you still have your health (or your family . . . your daughter . . . your job)." Such words may be wise and true and possibly consoling, but, if spoken too soon, before you've had the opportunity to face the enormity of what has happened to you, they may wound, not heal.

While it's usually helpful to look at the bright side during adversity, trying to feel grateful too quickly for the good things you've been given may also prematurely halt any necessary grieving if you've suffered deep losses.

You must be sad, or mad, or scared before you can be glad again.

It's okay to feel ungrateful, to be angry over the loss you didn't bring about or deserve. Feeling ungrateful now doesn't mean you will always feel that way. (And nobody wants to remain bitter forever.) But right now you may be hurting a great deal, and for me or anyone else to tell you to cheer up, to focus only on that which is good and give thanks for what you still have left, is to miss an opportunity to show compassion.

Anytime our words or actions convey to others the message *You shouldn't feel the way you do*, we do not understand them, and they are lonelier for it.

CAN YOU BE GRATEFUL AND UNGRATEFUL (ANGRY) AT THE SAME TIME?

Yes. Rather than being a confusing experience, regard it as a necessary and welcome next step on the path to healing. When you are hurt, very angry, or scared, you tend to focus solely on the darker, more painful feelings, as if the pain was all there was. But there will be times—a moment here, a moment there—when happiness, contentment, or gratitude flickers in the shadows of your pain. And for that moment you smile. Sometimes, at first, those peaceful moments can be cruel reminders of what was, and you can actually feel bad about feeling good. Many people grieving over the tragic death of a loved one often feel guilty for those unplanned moments of contentment or solace.

"I feel disloyal," one man told me after the death of his wife. "Knowing that I can feel good somehow diminishes what she must have meant to me. I mean, if I *really* loved her and needed her as much as I always thought I did, shouldn't I be unhappy all the time now that she's gone?"

I wanted to talk him out of his feelings, to help him to understand that it's not unusual to think the way he does and that it wasn't a sign of disloyalty. That might have made *me* feel better, but it might have made him feel misunderstood—or worse, discredited. So instead of trying to change him, I sought to understand.

"You're telling me that for you to have moments of peace or gladness is to be disloyal to the memory of your wife," I answered, reflecting back my understanding of what he'd just told me.

"Yes . . ." He couldn't finish his sentence. He started to sob, but at the same time tried to hold himself back; his deep sighs and emotional heaves thus came in awkward fits and starts and made him feel, I imagined, all the more self-conscious. I waited. Since he was still deeply saddened over his wife's death and was feeling guilty for the fleeting moments of comfort he's felt since her death, I suspected he felt guilty for other things too. Since my goal was not to talk him out of his feelings but to understand them, I asked him about any other guilt he may have been experiencing.

"I'm wondering if maybe you're not just feeling sad about your wife's death," I finally said. "You seem to have other regrets. Is that right?"

It was. He was sorry for the kind of things many people feel sorry about at such times. He hadn't told her he loved her nearly as often as he knows he should have. He'd taken her for granted. He'd resented some of her small habits, which seemed so petty now. And he needed to know in the depths of his very being that somehow she understood and had forgiven him.

So I asked him about their early years together, their first apartment, their grand and youthful expectations, her young face. I asked about their children; he spoke of the times the kids made them proud and the moments they made them cry. He spoke about the good times, the unnerving times, the times they lived on hot dogs and potatoes and still managed just fine.

And here and there, while speaking, he would smile. He didn't realize it then (for it was but a whisper in his soul), but he was feeling grateful. He was remembering what was good—the happy times, the times of commitment during hardship, the caring, the sacrifices, all the times that mean the most to those with loving hearts—and he was remembering with gratitude.

Gratitude teaches you how to smile again. And by smiling, you open up a place in your heart for gratitude to sleep forever.

LEVELS OF GRATITUDE

The first level of gratitude was just discussed: to remember with love the good things you may have recently lost.

A second level of gratitude is to appreciate what you still have left. Since your natural tendency is to focus on the threat or loss—and minimize all else—your perspective is distorted. You have a type of tunnel vision. Being able to broaden your attention to the gifts of your life that you still possess keeps your perspective in balance.

You may have lost a leg or an arm, or your vision or your hearing, but you still have your heart and soul.

You may have lost a loved one, but not the effects of that love.

You may have lost custody of your child, but not your responsibility as a committed parent.

You still have people who care about you. You have your intelligence, your common sense. You may have lost hope or love or the will to persevere, but you haven't lost the *promise* of them in the future. Such losses need never be permanent. All problems are temporary. And while you may have wasted much time, be grateful you still have time left. Not as much time as you had yesterday, or five minutes ago, but time still remains to be used as you see fit.

It helps to remember and grieve over your loss. But it's just as helpful to be grateful for what you still have.

THE THIRD LEVEL OF GRATITUDE

The third level is the most difficult and comes only with wisdom and experience, and even then I suspect only with the grace of God. In level one you were grateful for all that was good that you've sadly lost. In level two you were grateful for all the good that you have left. In level three, however, you become grateful for everything, the good *and the bad*. Especially the bad. In level three there is an understanding that the bad can be a teacher, that goodness can, and often does, come from it, and that it is all part of the awesome gift of your life.

Think back on several different painful moments in your life. Perhaps you were betrayed or rejected. Maybe you wanted to get a certain job, go to a specific school, but didn't have the credentials. Think of the setbacks and heartbreaks you experienced. Maybe you remember your divorce. Think of the losses you didn't deserve. With the passage of time, most people discover that *precisely because certain bad things happened, their life took an unexpected turn that eventually resulted in very positive changes—changes that never would have occurred had the negative event never occurred.* As one woman told me, "I'm not certain what a 'bad thing' is anymore. At the time I'm sure it's bad and it does feel awful. It can feel wrong and unfair. But after, usually long after, I discover that blessings came from it."

Blessings from misfortune? A brush with death often teaches you how to live. A broken heart can leave you more appreciative of a committed love, more sensitive to the fears and hopes of a beloved other. A loss of self-esteem may help you face yourself honestly, perhaps for the first time, the foundation for any legitimate feeling of self-worth. You can't learn bona fide forgiveness until you've been betrayed. You can't fully comfort a friend in his sorrow unless you remember a time when you needed comforting. You can't quite discover the full depth of meaning and dignity to your life until you witness some suffering and try to ease it, find a hollow heart and try to fill it, or behold a child's spirit and try to honor it.

And you probably can't grow in your relationship with God until you've felt let down by Him.

The blessings may never compensate you for what you lost. But they help give comfort to your suffering. They help add meaning to your life. Deanna Heath of Mt. Pleasant, Michigan, suffered five miscarriages before giving birth to a healthy son, and as she went into labor with her second child, a baby girl, something went terribly wrong, and the baby was born dead.

Several months later Deanna learned her best friend had lung cancer and would die within a matter of weeks. And only two years passed before Deanna's twenty-eight-year-old brother died in a work-related accident. The two-month-old son he left behind, Deanna's nephew, was diagnosed with leukemia a few months later.

"After my daughter died, I began keeping a list of all the changes that came from that loss," Deanna said. "My aim has been to find the gifts along the way, the gifts my daughter brought me, and the gifts my friends and family have given." Deanna's list of gifts is now quite long. Among the most notable is her position as counselor for Hospice of Central Michigan, helping terminally ill cancer patients and their families. She also leads support groups for parents coping with the death of a child.

Right now you may be unable to imagine that anything good could come from what you've been experiencing. But in times of despair, consider that possibility, and consider it well. And if you doubt that possibility, all you need do is recall your past hurts and discouragements and ask yourself, "In some way aren't I grateful that I went through what I did back then?" Often enough your answer will be yes.

Chapter 14

"HOW WOULD YOUR FATHER HAVE HANDLED YOUR PROBLEMS?"

The Gift of Your Heritage

❖

Iᴛ ᴄᴀɴ ʙᴇ ʜᴀʀᴅ to feel really good about yourself when you come from a family you're not especially proud of. You can be successful and relatively happy in life, but if you haven't come to terms with your heritage, you may be in a weakened position in times of stress. Decades of work by eminent psychologist Ivan Boszormenyi-Nagy suggest that when you can't find anything good to say that might reflect the esteem of your parents, you worry in the depths of your soul if there is a reason to esteem yourself.

Some families do great damage to their members. Most do the best they can, but that's not always good enough. So one of the requisites for being an emotionally healthy adult is to make peace with your parents and to find something in your heritage to draw strength or comfort from. How do you begin such a task? By looking deeper into your background rather than shying away from it. By going to family members and asking questions about certain relatives and certain events. Keep hunting until you discover something you can care about. When you notice yourself feeling compassion for a family member, or pride, you've hit paydirt.

But begin with the belief that there is more to your family background—more that is good—than you've ever realized.

In my work as a psychologist I rarely hear stories about people's parents that include anything more than shallow, stereotyped descriptions. (Mothers fare better than fathers, since men have tended to remain more on the periphery of their children's lives.) Whether a man complains about his father's aloofness or fondly recalls his dad's strength of character, or a woman sighs at how her mother never really understood her, the portrayals often lack depth. People see their parents in only one or two dimensions, rarely choosing to capture in their mind's eye what they've sometimes sensed stirring in their hearts. "There must be more to my parents than I know," they say quietly to themselves. Intuitively people sense a beat of passion and depth in their mothers and fathers. But such intuition, like a lover's whisper in the night, is oftentimes hard to hear and easily ignored when one does not wish to become aroused. People consider their parents' strengths *or* weaknesses—but seldom both, and then rarely with any penetrating insight. In many a person's life his parents—indeed his heritage—remain a riddle. That is not only a sad commentary on parent-child relationships, but it helps to explain why some adults can't seem to get a grip on certain problems in their life.

In short, we tend to use our parents as a frame of reference for how to live and love, behaving in ways that either resemble their ways or designing a new form for ourselves. Parents become blueprints, the basis from which we make decisions (often quite unconscious) on how to construct our lives and resolve our problems—no matter what the parent-child relationship was like. So when clients come to my office unable to cope well with long-standing difficulties, I eventually ask them this question: *"How would your father or mother have handled your problems?"*

DRUMBEATS TO
A FATHER'S HEART

"My dad would have given in to her a long time ago," Ted said, responding to the question. "My father was basically a good person, don't get me wrong, but he was much too passive. He never took a stand about things that mattered. If he was having the same kinds of problems with my mother that I'm having now with Lynn, he would have stopped fighting with her just to get it over with. If the truth be known," he said reluctantly, somewhat embarrassed, "my dad was a wimp."

Ted and Lynn's relationship was often more turbulent than smooth. It was not so much that they disagreed about most things—such as how to make pot roast and how to discipline the children—but they did so with a belligerent "I'm right, you're wrong" attitude. Differences were not only unaccepted but pelted by hailstorms of criticism and self-serving logic. On Lynn's birthday Ted purchased a popular self-help book, modified the title, and handed Lynn her copy of *I'm OK, You're Not So OK*. It was meant to be humorous, but it was also a perfect description of how he viewed their relationship.

"I don't know, Paul," Ted began one session. "Maybe a divorce is the best thing. That's not what Lynn wants, but neither is she willing to see my way on a few things."

"You told me last time, Ted, when I asked how your father would have handled things, that he probably would have found a way to stop the fighting—"

"He would have *given in*—I believe those were my words," Ted interrupted.

"That *is* what you said," I conceded. We were both right actually, but I figured it would have been a therapeutic error (not to mention a losing battle) to start an "I'm right, you're wrong" interchange with Ted. "I guess I can't help wondering," I continued, "if your unwillingness to let Lynn have her way on some matters, or at least compromise with her, has something to do with your opinion of your father."

Ted thought about my words. "You mean, am I hardheaded about things because I don't want to be a wimp like my father?" He caught my drift better than I thought he would. For the first time since I'd known Ted, he was speechless, actually pondering a notion without needing to come up with an automatic, usually defensive, answer. "Maybe you've got something there," he admitted.

"Please think about it more, Ted," I said. "Being adamant about a point of view can be a good thing at times. It just becomes a problem for anybody the moment they're inflexible in their responses to difficulties. Your dad's response to problems never varied," I added. "He always gave in. But your response to problems doesn't vary either: You never give in. In that regard you and your dad have a lot in common."

Ted began changing shortly thereafter. It was no longer possible for him to respond reflexively to Lynn with his "I'm right, you're wrong" attitude. He'd stop himself, sometimes in mid-ramble, questioning whether he really wanted to take such a strong stand or whether he was simply attempting not to be like his father.

"How would your father have handled your problems?" Some questions are drumbeats, *poom-poom*ing in the corridors of our minds, never really letting us get a good night's sleep until we've come to some kind of terms with them.

A related question is *"Which qualities of your father (or mother) are qualities that you would hope to have and which qualities of his (or hers) have you wished to change for yourself?"*

You cannot respond to that question honestly without unearthing your mixed feelings about your parents. Some people constructively resolve their ambivalence by accepting their parents as human—as possessing both strengths and weaknesses. They understand that their parents did the best they could. They forgive them for what needed forgiving and love them all they can. Good or bad, they find something in their parents or their heritage to be proud of. But for those whose ambivalence is not resolved, whose feelings seem mixed and at times painfully contradictory, an honest answer to the above question reveals more about themselves than it does about their parents.

"My father was a kind man," Ted later revealed. "Sometimes it was difficult for me to tell when he was being genuinely kind or when he was just being passive and unassertive. But other times it was clear to me: Dad had a kind heart. That's one way I've wanted to be like him."

"How do you think you've fared?" I asked.

"Not very well," he answered. "I've certainly been unkind to Lynn through the years."

"Perhaps," I said later, "the part of you that wants to be more like your father could find a way to show more kindness. And the part of you that wants to improve on his ways could show more flexibility."

"Perhaps," he said with a smile.

Ted's ambivalence toward his father showed itself in the way he treated Lynn. His inability to come to terms with his father's passivity was wreaking havoc in his marriage.

Stephanie hadn't yet seen her mother in the fullest possible light either. She kept her mother on a pedestal. "I'm in awe of my mother," she said to me. "Maybe if I had half her stamina and ambition, I'd have made something of myself."

Stephanie was an engineer for a multinational computer corporation. And her job made her miserable. Over the course of eight years she'd been promoted several times and received high marks for her performance, but you'd never know she was a success by talking with her.

"I don't find the work exciting anymore. I don't know

what's wrong with me. Some days I just dread the thought of going to the office."

"How would your mother have handled your problems?" I asked one day.

"Mom would have persevered. She'd have viewed the bad days as temporary and plowed ahead until her mood changed." Stephanie's mother was a widow who, despite rough going when her young husband died, saw the hard times through with hope and conviction.

"It seems you admire your mother's capacity to withstand tough times and persist in her efforts despite sometimes difficult odds," I said. "You'd like to possess those qualities yourself. But are there any qualities of hers you'd like to change for yourself?"

"None that I know of," she said quickly. Then with a bit of a laugh, "Actually the very qualities I admire her for I think I'd want to be different for me. Persisting at being an engineer hasn't been satisfying. You know, I've always secretly wanted to be a writer."

"Sounds to me that the main difference between you and your mother is not one of stick-to-it-iveness. You've demonstrated your capacity to hang in there by remaining eight years in a job that's not for you. But your mom stuck with something she deep down believed in. You've ignored what you believe in and stuck to something you don't care for."

"I never thought about it that way," she said pensively.

"So, let me ask again. How would your mother handle the problem of being in a job situation that made her miserable?"

"She'd have given it a fair shot, but if it still made her unhappy, she'd have found something else."

"How much longer do you need to stay on your job until you believe you've given it a fair shot?" I asked.

"You know, I've often toyed with the idea of going to

journalism school," Stephanie responded. "I bet I could work half-time on my job while enrolling at the university."

Stephanie was on her way. In her case her mother was actually a positive role model. People who cope well during trying times often report that recalling how someone they respected handled certain adverse situations helps them with their own coping. Positive role models or not, proud heritage or not, we all tend to incorporate some of our parents' coping styles into our psyches. When our attempts at coping seem to fail us, it is a good idea then to consider just what impact, if any, our parents' styles have on our efforts.

ONE FINAL QUESTION

I've written about your heritage, but there is still your legacy to consider. A generation or two from now *you* will be part of the heritage that new family members must come to terms with. Will how you handled things make a difference to them?

Chapter 15

ACCEPTING OTHERS
AS THEY ARE

The Gift of Tolerance

❖

$\mathbf{M}$OST OF US, at various times in our lives, are bundles of contradictions. Perhaps we prize our calm, collected, analytical side, but experience sudden emotional flare-ups. Or we set meaningful goals for ourselves, but then place obstacles in our own path. We wish a friend good luck in some endeavor, but feel a little pleasure if he should fail. We seek to be understood, but refuse to understand the person who can't, or won't, understand us.

It is the discontented heart, seeking contentment, that is sometimes disquieted in the presence of another's serenity. It is the procrastinator who is often intolerant of another's dawdling.

And this inconsistency is normal, although it can also be troubling. It happens because none of us is perfect. It happens because even the most insightful person doesn't quite have his or her act together. It happens when we insist we be somebody we aren't yet able to be. It happens when we don't fully accept ourselves, our imperfections, and the imperfections of others.

In good times we tend to be more tolerant of imperfections and differences. But under duress imperfections may seem intolerable. Yet it is during such times that our ability to be tolerant and accepting is needed most.

"DO YOU REALLY CARE ABOUT ME?"

The standard cliché heard in psychologists' offices and Twelve Step programs goes something like this: "You can't change other people, so only try to change yourself." (An ironic proclamation, considering it is heralded by people in the business of helping others to change.) Still, there is great wisdom in that tattered cliché. It is really meant to declare that *the persistent effort* to get someone to change is useless and can be counterproductive. When I see two people locked in a power struggle, I know it is no longer differences of opinion that truly divide them; rather it is their continued efforts to get the other one to change that is preventing the desired change.

Wil and Debra were married for eight years. Several years ago Wil began a concerted effort to get Debra to take what he believed should be a greater interest in the family instead of her career. He was weary of her late hours and frequent business trips. At first he was polite in his requests for her to change. Then he got angry. A pattern emerged where threats and yelling were followed by angry withdrawal and silence. Debra not only disagreed with Wil's accusation that she didn't care about him or their children, she soon viewed his mood swings as evidence of his lack of caring for her. They polarized. But no longer was it her work schedule that divided them. Each felt terribly hurt and angry that the other could be "so uncaring, so selfish."

Then something happened. Beyond being angry, Wil became depressed. He stopped trying to get Debra to change. His cease-fire wasn't another angry withdrawal, a ploy to get her to reconsider. He simply, and sadly, gave up and began believing that perhaps the relationship could never be any more than it was now. Then something else happened. Debra noticed his sadness, believed it to be genuine, got worried, and approached him. "Maybe you've been right about some things, Wil," she told him. "My career is important to me, but so are you and the kids. Maybe we can work something out."

Now she's ready to change! Wil thought to himself. *Why did she have to be so stubborn all this time? Maybe I don't want to try to work things out anymore. . . .*

Wil viewed Debra's change of heart as too little too late, instead of realizing her attitude was *a reaction to a fundamental change in the style of their interaction.* It was precisely because he had given up trying to get her to change that she moved closer toward him and light appeared in the window of their relationship. They were at a crossroads. If each could learn to *tolerate* the other's opinions (that is, stop trying to get the other to change) and *care* that differences between them were painful to each other (that is, have compassion), the odds of them working matters out satisfactorily would be greatly enhanced.

Before anyone can sincerely change, he or she first needs to feel affirmed and understood. Too often people feel devalued. Persistent efforts to change someone usually fail when nowhere in the efforts is it *sincerely* communicated, "I care about you, I accept you, and I understand your misgivings about what I need from you."

"BUT SHOULD I SETTLE FOR LESS?"

There are many things that should not be tolerated, such as abuse and cruelty. To accept someone as they are doesn't mean you have to put up with harmful acts. The gift of tolerance is not derived from an "anything goes" mentality. But it allows for mistakes, forgiveness, and the opportunity for personal growth.

Anytime you need someone else to change in order for you to be happy, your intolerance builds. In troubled relationships dissatisfied spouses typically blame each other for their unhappiness. They become less and less tolerant of the other's ways. But viewing a partner as "the problem" misses a crucial aspect as to why the problem still exists: Couples often reinforce in their partner the very behaviors they find objectionable.

Examples:

• Mary pursues her husband, Ed, for more time and affection. He backs off, feeling smothered. The more she pursues, the more he withdraws, and the more he withdraws, the more she pursues.

• Mark felt his wife, Angie, spent too much time with her children from her first marriage and not enough time with him. At first she made some adjustments to accommodate him, but eventually she resented his "infantile attitude." The more she showed resentment, the more he felt unloved and the more he insisted she spend less time with her children.

• Phil is sloppy; Tina is fastidiously clean. The more she cleans, the less he concerns himself with tidying things up. The less he cleans, the more she feels compelled to do so.

There can be no "overfunctioner" without an "underfunctioner," no "domineering style" without a "submissive style." From this perspective, then, intolerance of another is a sign of inadequate responsibility to oneself. *The less you take proper care of your own needs, and the more you require others to meet those needs for you, the more intolerant you'll become when others fail to meet those needs.* As psychologist Gus Napier points out in his book *The Fragile Bond*, spouses (or those in any kind of partnership) are more controlled by their own dependency than they are by their partner's behaviors.

GUIDELINES TO TOLERANCE

Detach

Detaching (but not withdrawing completely) from an emotionally intense struggle rarely seems to be the common-sense thing to do. "If I stop trying to get her to change, she'll never improve!" said the mother of a twenty-four-year-old daughter who regularly smoked marijuana and occasionally used cocaine. But detaching may be the wisest thing to do. By detaching you break away from the automatic push-pull of a dysfunctional relationship and focus on taking better care of yourself. Go for long walks. Go back to church. Visit with friends more often. Reawaken a tired romance. Become involved in a challenging and satisfying project. By unhooking yourself from your struggle with another and directing more energy into personal areas you'd like to build or strengthen, your anxiety will be less of an intrusion into your life. (Ironically you then increase the chances the other person will make a change for the better, since he no longer has to justify his actions to you.) And when that other person provokes you (and he surely will), do what a colleague of mine advises: Learn to stop being a "missionary" and start being an "anthropologist." This healthier approach involves making mental notes and observations about your partner's behaviors, so that you can protect yourself when necessary, rather than trying to "convert" him.

Care

Don't abandon or reject the other person, but do establish boundaries. You don't demonstrate caring by putting up with abuse or any offense that reduces your capacity to care for yourself. Effective detachment is not avoidance of that person, nor is it just another way of showing anger. In detaching you continue to *care about* that person. Particularly, should you detach and become less needy in the relationship, you can anticipate your partner becoming more anxious and troubled for a time. When Mary cut back on pursuing Ed for affection and involved herself with friends and a computer course at the local college, Ed got nervous and began pursuing her. It would have been a mistake for Mary to say something like, "Too late, Ed. You had your chance." Instead she appreciated and responded to his advances, yet *continued* to see friends and take college courses.

Invest Properly

As a psychologist I'm sometimes asked how I can spend my days listening to, and untangling, people's problems without becoming depressed or frustrated myself. It wouldn't be possible for me to do my job well unless I followed this rule: I am never more invested in the need for people to change than they are in trying to change. I may care deeply about them, offer an abundance of hope, encouragement, and insight, and be willing to go all out for them, but I gauge my degree of emotional investment so that it is always one notch below their level. I might like it if they change, but I must not need them to change more than they need themselves to change. It would be like pulling dead weight. When I am more invested in (translation: more anxious about) someone changing than they are, progress grinds to halt. Changing is not easy work. It becomes impossible if the therapist (or overinvolved family member) absorbs all the anxiety inherent in the work involved.

Ask yourself this question about any chronically dissatisfying relationship you may be in: Are you more worried about the other person changing than he or she is? If so, reduce your degree of investment in needing that person to change by reinvesting that energy into more personal areas of growth (i.e., yourself).

You also need to learn to tolerate higher levels of a loved one's pain if you are to be of any genuine help to him when he needs you. This may sound cold-hearted, but when you rush in to douse the fires of another's pain, you may prevent him from developing his own capacity to cope with suffering. Tolerating higher levels of a loved one's pain is not indifference. On the contrary, it demonstrates a willingness to suffer with him rather than a need to talk him out of his suffering. Telling loved ones not to be sad when they are or to act stronger when they can't (in an effort to help them —*and you*—feel better) does little to comfort or aid them. It may even prompt them to feel guilty for being unable to respond the way you want them to. In tolerating their pain you'll be able to listen better. They will then more likely feel understood and cared about more profoundly. And if more help from you is genuinely required, you'll be much more likely to know what really is needed after having listened so well.

TOLERANCE . . .

. . . Is sometimes turning the other cheek, but it is never a failure to be true to your deepest and best self.

. . . Is often a quiet suffering, a willingness to put up with something difficult, knowing that others may never fully appreciate your level of discomfort.

. . . Is not for all moments, for every circumstance; but it may well be for these moments, for this circumstance.

. . . Often provides a perspective you'd never have envisioned had you been impatient and intolerant.

. . . Allows for acceptance of others, for if tolerance is the lesson, those others must be your teachers.

. . . In its purest form is a showing of love.

As with love, forgiveness, honesty, and all the great gifts of the human spirit, tolerance demands that you take a risk. Tolerance is founded on faith; and faith, by definition, is founded on belief. So the tolerant person, as well as the loving or forgiving person, must act on faith, knowing that sooner or later that same tolerance may cause him to suffer. Not all acts of love, forgiveness, or tolerance are rewarded. You may show tolerance and then be repudiated. Does that mean you should hold back? Is tolerance meaningful only when you risk having to suffer? Evil should not be tolerated, but how do you recognize it? Answers to such questions are not straightforward. While our civilized society aims for standards, morality seems to shift in political winds. We're not always sure what's right anymore, or what we should tolerate. Some of what's tolerable today was intolerable yesterday and may not be tolerable tomorrow. Some people call that progress. Others see it as a sign of a civilization on the decline. What do you choose to tolerate in a world where terrorists are called freedom fighters, some killings are called merciful, and some wars are holy?

The gift of tolerance is precious and fragile. Like all such gifts, please handle it with care.

Chapter 16

FINDING PEACE OF MIND IN A SEA OF HARD FEELINGS

The Gift of Forgiveness

❖

MID-WINTER, EARLY **1991.** The war against Saddam Hussein was two weeks old and U.S. troop casualties had been few, miraculously. But the headlines that day came not from Baghdad but from Buffalo. I watched the middle-aged couple on television talk about what had just happened to them and how they were coping. Losing a child in war, or for any reason, is always awful. But in a twist of fate their son was killed not by Iraq's guns but by "friendly fire." Tragically and accidentally he was killed by someone on his own side. The parents, deeply sad, were also, movingly, deeply proud. What would they do if they could meet the U.S. serviceman who killed their son by mistake? They would "embrace" him. They'd want him to "talk out" his feelings; after all, imagine how devastated he must feel. And they would not blame him. Somehow, in their suffering, it seems they also felt compassion, acceptance, and understanding—necessary ingredients for a forgiving heart, but often hard to stir together when one's world has been swiftly and harshly uprooted.

I do not know what the dead soldier's parents felt toward Saddam Hussein. But during a great loss most people look angrily for someone to blame (even themselves if need be) and find it difficult to rid themselves of their bitterness. At such a time there is no forgiving attitude, no desire to reconcile, especially when the one who caused the tragedy shows no remorse. And that is not only a normal response, it is a necessary one. For if you are to ever get beyond your anger and sadness, at least enough for you to move forward in a life revived with purpose, you must first weep and rage over your loss.

GENUINE FORGIVENESS IS RARELY EASY

Forgiveness is one of those virtues that, like charity, people see as valuable and necessary—until they are called upon to make a sacrifice of their own. To genuinely forgive after suffering a deep hurt or loss is one of the hardest things to do. An unkind remark by a good friend may be quickly forgiven. But to forgive brutality, betrayal, abandonment, violence, or injustice, to forgive the person or God who in one swift movement wiped out your reason for living, is to squeeze the last ounce of love out of an already crushed heart. While forgiveness is glorious and holy and healing, the first step on that healing journey may well be anguishing. Forgiveness hurts. But no more, perhaps, than what is risked with any act of love.

Genuine forgiveness is not motivated by fear but by caring. It is not done for approval, to avoid rejection, or to appease others. It is not a "peace at any price" policy. If offered with a casual "Let's forget about what happened" attitude, without a willingness to take a hard look at what actually did occur, the forgiving act may not have the strength to endure. While understanding and empathy help mold a forgiving attitude, true forgiveness is not built on strong sentimentality and sympathy at the expense of justice and dignity. Justice and dignity are absent if, in the name of forgiveness, you ignore or minimize serious offenses.

With forgiveness there is a leap of faith, a willingness to trust, when previously that trust was betrayed. The level of trust may not be as deep as it once was, but it matters to you that it deepen over time.

With forgiveness you show love and compassion to the person who hurt you, rather than bitterness and revenge. And that's difficult.

With forgiveness you never forget what happened, but neither do you wallow in the memory. Instead you make peace with your past, embrace the present, and look forward to your future.

FINDING FORGIVENESS

SIX GUIDELINES

A young couple discovering for the first time their love for each other see only goodness in each other's heart. Another couple, with a love grown cold over years of mutual isolation and resentment, see only selfishness in each other's heart.

For each of those couples, and for all of us, there is a truth: We see what we look for. In hard times if you want a reason to justify staying angry or guilty or depressed, you needn't look very far. Any of us, if we bend our sights to the direction of pessimism, fear, or hatred, will soon see only those things. So during misfortune and adversity we must instead bend our wills toward that which is optimistic and loving if we are to make any headway in recovery.

The first guideline to finding forgiveness is to realize that *forgiveness begins as a decision.* No question about it, forgiveness is a process of will-bending. It is choosing the path of forgiveness even though you don't feel like forgiving. Listen to Pamela:

"I wanted our marriage to survive. I kept waiting for that one day when I'd wake up and suddenly feel forgiving. His affairs were wrong, his lying was wrong, and my anger felt right, but I didn't want to feel that angry anymore. It hurt too much, and it made living together intolerable. But the forgiveness feeling wouldn't come. I waited and looked for it, and it wasn't there."

Pamela's rage at her husband's betrayal was normal and understandable. But however justified it was, she eventually realized that her anger ran her life. No longer happy and vivacious, she was guarded, suspicious, and quick to accuse. It is often at this point, when you know your anger is justified but you're ready to get beyond it, that forgiveness becomes a possibility. It can sting. It may not seem fair to be forgiving when you didn't deserve the heartbreak. It hurts to hold back from getting even. It's scary to begin trusting when your trust was once betrayed. But you need to understand that *you can choose to be forgiving and still feel angry and uncertain at the same time.* Over time your anger will lessen and your faith in others will strengthen, but anger and a forgiving attitude may coexist.

When Pamela realized that forgiveness began as a decision, not a feeling, she asked herself, *What would I be doing differently in my interactions with my husband if I held a more forgiving attitude?* She concluded that she wanted to go on more "dates" with her husband—they used to enjoy going to dinner and a show—and she chose to focus more on her husband's good qualities. She also understood that while she'd still tell him when she felt jealous and angry, she'd do so in a manner designed not to accuse and wound but to inform. For Pamela it was a good beginning.

A second guideline in finding forgiveness is to understand that *you may be withholding forgiveness as a way of exercising control* over a situation you previously had little control over. When bad things happen and your world turns upside down, you need to gain some sense of control in order to cope. Refusing to forgive can give you that sense of control. It's your way of shaking a fist at the forces that hurt you. You no longer feel powerless. But unless you eventually find other ways to get some control, withholding forgiveness can prevent you from finding what you almost certainly want: serenity, joy, and a sense of meaning in your life.

Withholding forgiveness also stifles your grief, which is undesirable in the long run. Staying angry, bitter, and blaming—all outward focuses—shrouds your anguish over having suffered a great loss. And until you can fully embrace the extent of your loss, grieving is stunted. So instead of focusing on how others are to blame, consider these questions: What exactly did you lose? Was it love? esteem? hope? faith in a just world? (Remember, some things, such as trust and hope, need not be permanent losses.)

It hurts to feel so sad, I know. But grieving is a vital part of recovery. And bitterness, like ice forming in a creek, slows the flow of progress.

A third guideline is to understand that you can nurture a forgiving attitude by *taking responsibility to make your own life satisfying in as many areas as possible:* your family life, your friendships, your occupation, your leisure time, and your physical and emotional health. Many people, unhappy with their lives, hold on to anger and resentment over past injustices as a way to justify why their lives are so unfulfilling now. "If it weren't for you," they say, "I'd . . . have a better job . . . socialize more . . . see my parents more often . . . own the house I've always dreamed of." Perhaps. But even if you began at a disadvantage or were treated unfairly, you're better off placing more emphasis on doing something constructive about your life than preoccupying yourself with a blaming and nonforgiving attitude. You don't have to feel forgiving before you can decide it's worth it to spend more time improving your life and less time fostering resentment.

The fourth guideline to finding forgiveness comes into play when you wish to mend a broken relationship. Here *you must evaluate your role in the troubled relationship.* When chronic problems exist, you are likely responsible for some of the difficulties. Even if you didn't cause the problems at first, you may have unwittingly perpetuated them by virtue of how you tried to cope. For example, Louise resented her husband, Tim's, overinvolvement with his job. Tim believed if he was ever to move up the corporate ladder, it was necessary to make his career a priority for the next several years. "I'm doing this for us," he tried to explain unsuccessfully. The more overtime he worked, the more Louise demanded time spent together. But the more she demanded, the more he resented her for "not understanding" and the more he preferred time spent at work than with her. Soon any moments they did spend together could not be enjoyed. After eight months of this tug-of-war, neither felt forgiving and they blamed each other for their difficulties. For Tim to feel forgiving, he needed to accept the fact that his unwillingness to budge from his position had fueled the fires. And he needed to understand that Louise was hurt, not so much because he was overinvolved with his job but because in arguing his position he dismissed her feelings as childish and irrelevant. For Louise to be forgiving she needed to accept the fact that by essentially giving Tim an ultimatum to choose between his job or her, without expressing any caring or compassion for how he was feeling, she had helped put them both in a no-win position. Admitting your own mistakes and focusing more on how much love you can give—not how much you can get—improves the odds that problems will be short-lived.

The fifth guideline is to understand that *you may have to forgive some people for past hurts before you feel ready to completely forgive others for present hurts.* Yes, you may feel angry when your spouse seems distant and cold, but it might be hurting so much because one of your parents also treated you that way. If you haven't made peace with your parents, you will have inflated expectations of your partner.

The sixth guideline is this: *While it helps in the forgiveness process to have an understanding of what motivated others to hurt you, such an understanding may never be complete.* Don't insist on "getting to the bottom" of what happened. Consequently you may have to accept that those who hurt you, however wrongly, were probably managing their lives the only way they knew how. Most people hurt others out of anger, fear, or ignorance. Ask yourself, *As smug or indifferent to my pain as the other person might be, would I want to trade my life for his? Would I want to conduct my life and my relationships like he does? Probably not. His punishment is that he must live with himself and the consequences of his behavior.*

Finally, when you wish to find forgiveness but can't imagine how, when you're struggling to replace fear and resentment with hope and caring, when you secretly wonder if you are forgivable, people with positive religious beliefs often look to God. They ask for His help. Many tell Him they are ready to do what He wants, not what they might prefer. And they ask to be forgiven for ways in which they've been hurtful. Remember, as great as the act of forgiving another is, its power to heal flows from your recognition that you are not above needing to be forgiven yourself.

THE "I FORGIVE YOU"
EXERCISE

This exercise is a variation on a technique suggested by Harold Bloomfield in his book, *Making Peace with Your Parents*. But the exercise is useful no matter what the relationship.

Imagine the person you need to forgive is sitting directly across from you (even if that person is yourself). Say aloud the words "I forgive you." Pay attention to the thoughts that immediately follow those words. For example:

I forgive you. . . . But you don't deserve it.

Again, repeat the phrase and notice the thoughts that follow.

I forgive you. . . . But I'm always the forgiving one.

I forgive you. . . . And you'll never appreciate the sacrifice this is for me.

I forgive you. . . . Why did you hurt me the way you did?

Keep repeating the phrase *I forgive you* while closely monitoring the thoughts that immediately follow. If you repeat the phrase about ten times, you will probably experience one of two things. First, you may discover that your angry and hurt feelings lessen in intensity. (You may be surprised at how considerable the reduction may be.) Second, you might discover that one phrase keeps repeating itself in your mind after you say, "I forgive you." If so, that repetitive phrase likely represents a stuck, unresolved issue for you. For example, one man found himself repeating *I forgive you. . . . But our relationship will never be what I'd hoped it would.* From that repetition he realized that to forgive (in this case his parents) he'd also have to let go of any hopes he secretly had that they would admit their own mistakes one day and welcome him back as a valued and cherished son. That saddened him. And he now understood that one reason he had taken a nonforgiving stance with his parents was to block the grief that would come from accepting the likelihood that his parents would never love him the way he wanted.

It can be helpful to repeat this exercise regularly. It provides you with ongoing feedback about your progress and suggests clues to issues you may need to further address.

It seems difficult enough some days to love your friends. So the notion of forgiving your enemies—well, isn't that next to impossible? Next to impossible, yes. But not impossible. If you have ever forgiven anybody for anything, or know what it is to be truly forgiven, then you understand just how possible forgiveness really is. But it takes effort, prayer, grace, and a willingness to suffer, alone or with your God, the agony and uncertainty about whether you're doing the right thing.

Chapter 17

BUILDING YOUR
SELF-ESTEEM

The Gift of Self-Love

❖

YOU HAVE TO BELIEVE you matter if you expect to cope through these tough times.

You have to believe you matter, that you're worth fighting for, if you expect to help loved ones through these tough times and if you hope to persevere when the going gets rough.

You have to believe you matter before you can find a meaning to your suffering and a purpose to your life.

You have to believe you matter.

Why? Because your level of self-esteem determines to what degree you view misfortune as psychologically threatening. The higher your esteem, the lower your perception of psychological threat—*regardless of the adversity.* Also, your level of self-esteem determines how long and hard you'll persevere when complications and setbacks arise. Research clearly shows that people who believe they possess the skills necessary to cope persist longer in their efforts. And finally your level of self-esteem determines how quickly you'll bounce back after suffering some tragedy or loss. Few people come through trying times unscathed, but those with higher self-esteem are more resilient to the effects of stress.

POSSESSING HIGH SELF-ESTEEM

When your self-esteem is high you radiate integrity, competence, and compassion. You say what's on your mind in a clear, respectful, straightforward manner. You take responsibility for your feelings and actions rather than blame others. People always know where they stand with you. You acknowledge your imperfections, are willing to take risks, and view life's hardships as challenges to overcome. You are spontaneous without being reckless. You know how to give without expecting others' approval in return. You've learned the art of caring-without-rescuing; you know when to step in and when to step back when someone needs to fall on his or her face. You accept compliments graciously, but never take yourself too seriously. You are interested in what other people think about you, and are typically well liked, but your self-esteem does not depend on being approved of and well liked. Clear about who you are and the values you hold, and not inclined to be self-conscious, you don't confuse your feelings and attitudes with those of others. Not in constant fear of rejection, you feel free to let others be themselves. Consequently you are a superb listener and are keenly empathic. You make few, if any, excuses and don't pretend problems are no big deal when in fact they are. Like everybody else, you are dependent on others to some extent for love, affection, and attention, but you know you can take care of yourself when you choose. When you feel anxious and needy, you don't whine or manipulate others into meeting your needs. Instead your warmth and upbeat nature make you fun to be with. Others then want to meet your needs.

But possessing high self-esteem won't make you immune to anxiety, especially when times are hard. You can possess strong self-esteem and still awaken one day feeling blue, pessimistic, unsure of yourself, and lonely. The difference between people with high and low self-esteem is not the amount of doubt and fear they possess. But people with higher self-esteem are more resilient. They experience negative emotions, but they bounce back. They get hurt at times, but they also know how to roll with the punches. They land on their feet more quickly.

Too often, when adversity has tested the limits of one's endurance, someone with a moderate level of self-esteem will say, "I always believed I was self-assured, but after what's happened, I think I was mistaken. No one with a strong self-esteem would feel the way I've felt recently." That's unfortunate. That person feels worse not because his self-esteem is in fact low, but because he believes it is low.

Most people feel good about their abilities in several areas of their life, but possess some doubts about their abilities in other areas. That is not an indication of having weak self-esteem. A realistic assessment of one's strengths and weaknesses indicates sturdier esteem. A person with low self-esteem magnifies her weaknesses and failures, compares herself unfavorably to others, and tends to view anxiety-producing events in black-and-white: "Either he loves me or he can't stand me. . . . I'm either a success or I'm a failure. . . . I'm either competent or I'm incompetent." Such a rigid style of coping is bound to lead to despair and further loss of self-esteem.

A relationship failure almost always lowers self-esteem, if only for a short while. Especially if you were the one "rejected," it can be hard to feel lovable and attractive. Consequently, in order to protect themselves from the view of having been abandoned, nearly two thirds of the people getting a divorce claim to be the one who initiated it. Many divorcing partners also blame their spouse for the failed marriage, likely because it is too painful to one's self-esteem to admit personal failure in something as important as a marriage.

COMPONENTS OF SELF-ESTEEM

Two primary components of self-esteem are perceived *competence* and perceived *worthiness.* How strongly, or weakly, you regard your overall competence and how strongly, or weakly, you regard your worthiness will determine your level of self-esteem. Broadly speaking, the combinations of these two components are listed below, ranked from highest to lowest in the reflection of self-esteem:

1. Strong belief in competence/strong belief in worthiness

2. Weak belief in competence/strong belief in worthiness

3. Strong belief in competence/weak belief in worthiness

4. Weak belief in competence/weak belief in worthiness

If you believe strongly that you have the necessary skills to cope and function well and that you are a worthwhile person (number 1, above), your self-esteem will be high and you will manage adversity as well as can be expected. Even if you experience a rather devastating trauma, such as the untimely death of a spouse, the odds are you will recover with fewer scars and maybe even emerge a stronger person in the long run.

Conversely, if you have little faith in your coping skills

and question your value as a person (number 4, above), stress will be arduous indeed. This, by the way, frequently typifies people during a divorce. Many divorcing people seriously question whether they are attractive and lovable anymore, which is an indication of diminished self-worth. They also doubt their skills in making a new relationship work (diminished competence). Noncustodial parents (usually the fathers) tend to worry about their adequacy in their new role as a part-time parent. Statistically more women than men are worse off financially after a divorce, and many women fear they lack the skills necessary to be financially secure. Consequently one's self-esteem may not only be damaged during a divorce, but with diminished esteem it is more difficult for such a person to cope as effectively afterward.

Having a weak sense of competence and worthwhileness sometimes characterizes people in other situations too, such as when dealing with lengthy unemployment or a chronic, debilitating illness.

In this success-oriented society it is possible to have a moderate amount of self-esteem despite few successes and many failures (a weak sense of competence) *if you strongly believe in your worth as a person* (number 2, above). When you believe you have value just as you are, you are more likely to keep trying to improve your competence in areas important to you and therefore increase the odds you'll eventually become more successful. The person who regards himself as having personal value and worth is open to learning the necessary skills needed to feel more successful and competent without fear of looking bad. However, since most people believe you have to *do* something in order to *be* somebody, it's uncommon to find someone with few skills or successes who nonetheless possesses a moderately strong self-esteem. During adversity, moments exist when one's skill level seems impoverished. One psychotherapist I know, competent in stress management, felt her own coping skills buckle when her child was in a serious car accident. Actually she was coping better than she realized, but from her viewpoint "what helped me most was the love and support of my family, not my personal coping abilities." Seeing herself as a loving mother and beloved by others (a strong sense of worthiness) sustained her esteem and kept her from faltering, despite the fact that her personal coping skills were limited when dealing with her child's injury.

Many people sadly fit the mold of being highly successful and competent (number 3, above) but still believing deep down in the hidden places of their hearts that they are nothing. The more worthless they feel, the more goals they may try to accomplish, but their gratification is fleeting. Somehow nothing they do feels good enough. They hold good jobs, have nice homes and families, but drag themselves to the office every day feeling tense and mildly depressed. They look around and see others who seem to be more successful, more happy, more fulfilled and say to themselves, "What's wrong with me? Why do I feel so empty? Something is missing, but what?"

A man, seventy years old, reflected on his life, a life that was "a succession of disappointments. I can scarcely recollect a single instance of success in anything that I ever undertook." In fact the man was John Quincy Adams—congressman, senator, and later the sixth president of the United States (as quoted by John F. Kennedy in his book *Profiles in Courage*). How is it that someone with every reason to feel satisfied with his accomplishments belittled his obvious successes and repudiated his self-worth?

FACING YOUR FEARS
THE KEY TO SELF-ESTEEM

Psychologists Richard Bednar, Gawain Wells, and Scott Peterson, authors of *Self-Esteem* (in my view, the finest scholarly text to date written on the topic), believe that self-esteem is largely determined by an individual's self-appraisals. The authors go on to say that self-appraisals are generally positive when individuals *face their fears*, but they are negative when individuals *avoid* facing their fears. Generally speaking, people who attempt to cope with threatening situations head-on, even if they don't always succeed, appraise themselves later as courageous, fairly competent, and responsible individuals (strengthening their self-esteem), whereas people who avoid facing threatening situations later appraise themselves as cowardly and incompetent (which weakens their self-esteem).

For anyone, choosing to face a threatening situation creates anxiety and self-doubt—very uncomfortable feelings. But perseverance, in the presence of strong anxiety, enables people to think highly of themselves (and enables others to think highly of them too). Avoidance of a threatening situation reduces anxiety in the short run but heightens one's sense of inadequacy. To avoid facing a threatening situation, individuals often deny or distort the seriousness of the threat and underestimate their coping skills. Personal growth, and therefore self-esteem, is stunted when denial and pretense replace awareness and honesty.

Too often people with lower self-esteem rely on others' approval of them to feel better. But sadly the lower a person's self-esteem, the more likely he will put on a facade to win approval and the less likely he is to take seriously another's positive appraisal of him. "If they only knew the real me," one man lamented, "they wouldn't be so approving." Consequently people with low self-esteem get trapped in a vicious cycle of:

1. Needing approval

2. Putting on a false appearance to win that approval

3. Having to therefore doubt the credibility of any approval they subsequently receive, which leads to

4. The need for more approval

When you put on a facade to win approval, you neglect your innermost needs and yearnings—and only you can be fully responsive to those needs. In one study by researchers Jeanette and Robert Lauer, it was found that couples successfully married for over fifteen years valued their partners' needs to fulfill their innermost longings. These partners fell in love with each other all over again as they watched each other grow and challenge themselves.

EMILY'S STORY

Emily had a hard life. She was raised by an alcoholic mother, and by the time she was twenty-two Emily herself was an alcoholic. After ten years of a marriage rocked by the effects of her drinking, Emily devoted herself to Alcoholics Anonymous and began a program of recovery. Today, three years later, she is sober. But her marital problems worsened after she joined A.A., and six months ago her husband finally left her for another woman. Both she and her husband intend to fight for custody of their eight-year-old daughter, but Emily worries she may be unable to support her daughter financially. Emily also feels guilty that her years of drinking not only contributed to a failed marriage but provided her daughter with a home life "that no child should experience. I should know. I grew up in a household like that."

Emily's self-esteem needed strengthening. Proud of her accomplishments in recovery from alcoholism (a positive self-appraisal), she stayed with the A.A. program to develop her coping skills further. She requested a change from part-time to full-time work at her sales job, something that added to her daily stress somewhat but helped alleviate some of her financial concerns. "Working longer hours is definitely more taxing, but I like viewing myself as a survivor." (Still another positive self-appraisal.) To improve her physical health and socialization, she joined an aerobic-exercise program at the YWCA. ("I'm worth it.")

"I have many moments when I still don't feel very valuable to anyone. This is an area where my faith in God has helped me. When I'm not feeling very lovable, I remind myself that God truly loves me, that He is rooting for me. I must admit that thinking about God this way was a small consolation at first. But soon it became a very meaningful part of my attitude about myself. I also believe that He has forgiven me. I'm still working on forgiving myself."

One final way Emily chose to improve her own sense of esteem was to "every day do something that will help boost someone else's self-esteem." That was not as easy a task as it might seem. Casual, ordinary compliments about someone's appearance or dress may be pleasing but may not enhance their esteem. To accomplish her goal, Emily found ways to tell people how they have made a positive difference in her life or in the lives of others. She told one A.A. member, "Whenever I doubt I can achieve a lasting recovery, I think of you. I think of the many hardships you've been through and how you've persevered and stayed on the road to recovery. Thank you for that." Positive affirmations of the value of another's life can be powerful boosters to a sagging esteem.

Celeste and Cory Tate know how to boost a hungry person's self-esteem. Eight years ago the Tates started Gleaners, a food bank that collects unsold food from supermarkets (food that ordinarily would have been thrown away—a yearly waste of $27 billion in America) and distributes it in Gleaners' own stores to needy people.* Emphasizing self-esteem and self-reliance, Gleaners distributes food to thirty thousand people each month. It is not a handout—customers must pay two dollars for every bag of food they buy or else donate some of their time to the organization. The recipients feel valued by the Tates and can respect themselves as well.

Everyone wants to feel valued by others. When you were young, your self-esteem was greatly influenced by the manner in which you were treated by your parents. But there were countless moments when your self-esteem glowed in response to personal accomplishments too. Can you recall how you felt the first time you pedaled a two-wheeler without falling? Or the first time you spelled your name? Or hit a home run? Or maneuvered a sled down a snow-laden hill? Have you ever seen how thrilled a baby can be when she takes a step for the first time? Such accomplishments are satisfying even without an audience. They make a child feel powerful, competent, and challenged. In such moments the child values herself. Those moments should not fade away with age. Especially when times are dark and difficult and demanding, reaffirm your worthiness, face some of your fears, appraise yourself positively, and give yourself the gift of self-love.

* This information obtained from *Noetic Sciences Review* 17 (Winter 1990–91):37.

Chapter 18

WANTING TO DO
WHAT'S RIGHT

The Gift of a Clear Conscience

❖

To this day I can't recall all of the details, probably because the news story forced me to think about things I didn't want to consider. Evidently a man, a father, walked into the hospital room where his young son slept and quietly, seemingly lovingly, cradled the boy in his arms one final time before shutting down the machines that were prolonging the boy's life. For the boy, whose medical condition was terminal, death came quietly, wrapped in a father's embrace.

The man was quickly arrested. I don't know if what he did was right. I do know my heart filled with compassion for him as I heard his story. I imagined him in those agonizing, lonely moments before he was clear about what he would do. I imagined him wanting to do one last protective, healing, and fatherly act, to deliver his son's spirit from pain to a God and a heaven he believed was waiting.

Should a court of law proclaim him guilty, I doubt he will abandon his belief that he did the right thing. And should the same court judge him innocent, I suspect he'll be relieved but not vindicated. Doing the right thing cannot be judged solely by the outcome or others' opinions. *Any deci-*

sion must necessarily be made without knowing for sure whether it really is the right one, and therein lies the agony and the loneliness of making it.

Do you continue to try to make a troubled marriage work or do you decide it's over and move on with your life?

Do you have the abortion or not?

Do you quit a secure but unsatisfying job for something less secure but potentially more rewarding?

Do you keep assisting your "irresponsible" adult child or do you let him fend for himself?

Do you place your parent who can no longer care for herself in a nursing home or do you bring her into yours?

Even after you make the decision and embark on the "right" course of action, loneliness can shadow you. In those quiet moments of solitude only you know how it felt to have struggled with the choice. Hopefully, friends and family help support you, but you must make the final decision about what to do. *You and only you can accept responsibility for your choices.*

THE STRUGGLE TO KNOW AND DO THE RIGHT THING

Ron is scared. After several years of repeatedly repairing a marriage that kept breaking apart, he and his wife of eleven years finally agreed to end it.

"If there is any peace of mind from this decision," Ron said, "it is that at least now I know where we stand. I think the hardest part of trying to work things out was our nagging doubts, our inability to hold on to the faith that we'd succeed. It's not easy to keep working at something you really don't believe in."

A lanky forty-two-year-old, younger-looking than his

age, Ron was the proud, though weary, father of five. When he and Audrey decided that their third child would be their last, they never figured on triplets. Ordinarily he'd still find ways to speak warmly of Audrey if for no other reason than that she, too, was the proud and weary mother of five children. But right now Ron was hurt and angry.

"She's discreet about it—I mean, she never throws it in my face—but she made it clear that her boyfriend occupies a large part of her life. What do I do about that?" he asked, not expecting me to answer. "Sure, she has to get on with her life, but doesn't she know what it's like for me to have to knock on the door of what used to be—still is, technically—my house and see evidence that he's been there?"

I nodded slightly, not wanting to interrupt him but to let him know I understood. This was the first time he'd expressed his anger, and I wanted him to continue. Up until now he'd been matter-of-fact about the divorce, barricading his feelings behind a facade of rationality.

"The thing of it is," he pointed out, "that she wants me to accept her affair and, for the sake of the kids, not make it an issue in court. But if it were me having the affair, you can bet she'd make it an issue if she believed it would ensure her getting custody or more money from me."

"It feels very unfair to you, Ron," I offered, not yet wanting to challenge his assumptions about his wife but to clarify his concerns instead.

He labored to keep his composure, unable to look at me. And with a hoarse whisper he added, "I worry so much about how all this is affecting my kids. If I battle with Audrey, and I think I have a right to, the kids will suffer. That's the bottom line. They're already worried and frightened over the separation. I don't want to do anything that will make it worse for them. But if I tolerate all Audrey's doing, I can't help but feel I'm going down without a fight, that I'm letting her get away with something. Shouldn't my kids know that their mother is out of line and that their dad has backbone?" He shook his head slowly, dejectedly. "All this scares me," he concluded. "Where is the rule to tell me what to do?"

Ron grieved for a failed marriage. He grieved especially that his children had to suffer because of it, and it pained him imagining his wife in bed with another man. But his deepest anguish was not being sure how to handle it in the right way—the way that would ultimately be best for his children. He wanted to do the right thing, yet no solution seemed right enough.

I believed Ron when he said he wanted to do what was right. His willingness to agonize over his hard choices suggested to me his depth of caring and commitment to his children. But that's not how many other parents approach a situation like Ron's. Too often when divorcing parents assure me they'll negotiate the breakup in a manner "that serves the best interests of the children," my stomach tightens. I think it's their use of the phrase *the best interests of the children* that corrodes my faith. It is a pat phrase, well worn and too easily uttered with the emotional distance that often accompanies words that are supposedly the right things to say. Like the common "Let's get together for lunch sometime soon" spoken by casual friends, the promise lacks depth. The intent may be good, but it's understood there will be no follow-through as long as anything else gets in the way. Most, if not all, divorcing couples *want* to do the right thing for their children. But *doing* the right thing requires more than desire. In fact when wanting is all they can muster, parents will likely end up doing the wrong thing: that which is hurtful.

Coping with divorce is difficult under the best of circumstances. Feelings of hurt and resentment can linger long after the papers have been signed. The parents struggle to try to do what's right, to walk the fine line that separates cooperation and compromise on the one side and self-protection on the other. But the truth seems to be this: *The difference between wanting to do what's right and actually doing it is the difference between believing strongly in something versus being willing to die for it.*

In trying times such as a divorce it's impossible to do the right thing without experiencing a kind of death. There must be some torment, some sacrifice, and *there is always the agony of never being one hundred percent sure that your actions were proper and good.* For parents that last agony can be the most burdensome when, in their hearts, they wish to avoid adding unnecessarily to their children's suffering. But trying times pain the soul precisely because the ordinary, everyday rules we conduct our life by no longer seem to offer a clear light to guide and protect us during the storm. Doubt fogs our vision. And even if the light shines through, our convictions often have to withstand the pounding from others who don't agree with our beliefs and who won't like us for carrying them out. When we suffer the anguish of doing what's right, we die a little in the process and are never quite the same again. We know it's all for the best, but it's hard to truly understand that at the time.

Ron knows how it is to die a little. He anguished over whether or not to challenge Audrey's adultery in a court of law or keep the peace to protect the children. He didn't know what the right thing was. But *his willingness to grapple with his uncertainty was his first step toward doing the right thing.* Ron refused to dismiss the dilemma as minor and its consequences as out of his hands. Divorcing parents who give a nod in the direction of "the children's best interests" but who quickly get involved in hostile exchanges with each other have lost sight of their responsibilities and their children, no matter how much they maintain otherwise. It's understandable how such matters can sometimes get out of hand. But the legitimate struggle to do the right thing requires us not to look outward for blame but inward for answers—and for much-needed grace.

"Ron, some people might think this is an unreasonable question—and perhaps it is—but I'm hoping it will help," I said. "Imagine it is twenty years from now. Your children, all grown, want to tell you something. 'Dad,' they say, 'we never told you this before, but we want to thank you for how you handled the divorce twenty years ago. It made a difference.' What had you done, Ron, that they are now thanking you for?"

Ron thought a moment. "They're thanking me for finding a way to remain on friendly terms with their mother—at both the time of the divorce and during the years after." He took a deep breath, sighing audibly. "I think it may not be necessary to fight her in court," he offered. "If only she'd be just a little more sensitive to my feelings, we wouldn't have to turn the divorce into a war. Maybe I should talk again with Audrey," he concluded.

Doing the right thing requires us to inhibit our knee-jerk impulses. Whether it's punching walls, screaming at the family, quitting a job, or reflexively "making nice" in order to keep a relationship boat from rocking, under stress the right thing is rarely that which is done automatically.

When waters are calm and everybody is happy and agreeable, doing the right thing can be easy. It's easy to show kindness when others show consideration. It's easy to forgive when others seem genuinely remorseful. Financial risks can be made with peace of mind when one has plenty of money to cover the loss. But when wave after wave of injustice and heartbreak crashes in on you, doing the right thing becomes a test of personal integrity.

Adversity need not be extreme for you to struggle with doing the right thing. My mother-in-law, Beverly, recently retired from decades of public school teaching. "In the past year," she said, "it's been difficult for me to teach the kids honesty, because I'm not sure I believe in it anymore. It seems that dishonest people get ahead in this world while the ones who try to do what's right get abused." Despite the fact that it was more difficult for her to teach honesty, she taught it anyway. And it was that effort, when doubts were strong, that made her teaching all the more meaningful and good, and in her own way heroic.

A PERSONAL STORY

During the twenty-second week of pregnancy with our third child, my wife learned that the results of a special test (one that she almost decided not to take) indicated a problem. Our baby might have spina bifida, a condition that can cause retardation, paralysis, and even death. After a routine sonogram offered no additional information, another sonogram was scheduled—this time conducted in a medical center by a physician specially trained to detect physical abnormalities in the developing fetus. We were told that if no defects were apparent, the chance that the baby would still be born with some deformity was twenty percent. We then agreed to an amniocentesis, which would further detect the presence of any abnormalities.

The nearly two weeks spent waiting to have the tests performed and analyzed had been solemn ones. Not only were our imaginations working overtime ("What if the baby is profoundly retarded?"), but something the nurse had told my wife stung our consciences. "If the tests do show some deformity in the fetus," she said, "you will be nearly twenty-four weeks along in the pregnancy. That's as much as the law allows if you wish to get an abortion. You'll have little time to decide what you want to do."

What we wanted was for the baby to be all right, not to have to get an abortion. But suddenly, nothing was clear anymore. It was as if the values we believed in had all been suspended and there was no absolute rule to latch on to. We both believed that to have an abortion would be wrong for us. But we also wondered. What if the baby was so deformed and retarded that it would have to spend its entire life lying in a crib in some institution? What if the deformities, while not severe enough to warrant the baby living elsewhere, still drained my wife and me emotionally and financially? What would the effect be on our two other children as their whole world turned upside down? How could we be sure our decision would be the best, not merely for ourselves, but for all concerned?

In the days that followed, my wife and I talked about the situation. We never planned our discussions. They happened while preparing dinner, when we greeted each other at the end of the workday, and late at night when sleeping was impossible. The more we talked, the less panicked we felt.

I remember saying I might opt for an abortion if we knew for sure our child would have to be institutionalized its entire life. I remember my wife placing her hands on her belly, feeling the baby kick inside her, not at all sure she could have an abortion under any circumstances. I remember praying, "God help us to make the right decision," adding a line I'd heard others speak, a line I'd never really uttered before, "but Your will, not ours, be done."

There was no sudden mystical revelation. I felt no immediate relief. In fact I felt a bit like a coward—having passed the buck to a Spirit that some people would say doesn't exist—and a bit of a fraud to think I could truly decipher God's will. Still, an answer came, quietly, with no trumpets or fanfare. *There is a divine plan for our lives that is for the good*, I reminded myself. That was the answer. If I believed that such a plan existed, and I did, then it mattered little whether the baby was born healthy or not.

We decided to follow the pregnancy through.

Several days later we received good news: All test results were within normal limits. As best as anyone could tell, our baby would be fine. But two days later all was not fine. "We almost missed it," said the genetic counselor over the telephone. "It's such a rare thing to find." She went on to explain that a chromosomal analysis revealed a problem with the baby's first chromosome. Apparently a portion of it had detached, then inverted, then reattached itself to the rest of the chromosome.

My mind swirled. It was only seven A.M., my wife had already left for work, and I was trying to think how I'd explain all this to her. "Since the chromosomes contain genetic material," the counselor continued, "the concern is that some of that material may have gotten lost when part of the chromosome broke off. That would mean the baby might develop with certain genetic information missing."

There was no way to tell for sure if indeed there was any gene damage. Nor was science advanced enough to tell us what the deformity, if any, might be. Would the baby be missing a finger? An eyebrow? Would there be a heart defect? A sensory defect? Might the brain not develop properly? There were no answers. All they could say was that in ten percent of cases like this, babies were born with some deformity.

We would still go ahead with the pregnancy. A ten percent chance of deformity meant a ninety percent chance of perfect health. Pretty good odds. I made the analogy that if I developed cancer but was told I had a ninety percent chance of complete recovery, I'd be ecstatic. And I reminded myself that even if the baby wasn't healthy, perhaps I could one day use my knowledge of psychology and develop a program to help families with similar burdens. That notion didn't evaporate my fears, but it did help me to feel more positive and made the whole ordeal somewhat more meaningful.

In retrospect, what my wife and I experienced as we tried to do the right thing and cope successfully was very similar to what most people experience during trying times when they, too, strain to do what is right.

First, *there was a willingness to struggle with the issues*, to ask hard questions and feel miserable feelings rather than make a quick decision just to get the whole matter over with.

Second, *there was a crisis of faith*, a time when old values and beliefs rose up and handed us their resignations, leaving us seemingly alone with the task of choosing. Before now abortion was not something we'd have even considered, but there we were considering it. And moments of "Why did You allow this, God?" however brief, added to our confusion.

Third, *there was an appeal to a Higher Power*, a willingness to say, "We need help. We can't make this decision without You."

And fourth, *as long as we could be extraordinarily honest with ourselves, we noticed answers coming from within—answers that nudged us inexorably in the direction of what felt good and loving and hopeful and positive.*

Did we do the right thing? We believed so. With the suffering of uncertainty came the gift of a clear conscience. But as psychiatrist and author M. Scott Peck points out, "Our unconscious mind is always one step ahead of our conscious mind." We can never really be certain that our actions, however well thought out, are motivated more by instinct than by reason, more by fear than by love. All we know is that we can't know for sure.

"However, if your will is steadfastly to the good," Peck continues, "and if you are willing to suffer fully when the good seems ambiguous, then your unconscious will always be one step ahead of your conscious mind—in the right direction. You will do the right thing. But you won't have the luxury of knowing it at the time."

Postscript: On March 26, 1990, Julia Christine Coleman was born. Two years later she is by all appearances healthy. Had we not experienced the ordeal described above, I doubt this book would ever have been published.

Chapter 19

FINDING SOMETHING
TO BELIEVE IN

The Gift of Faith

❖

WHAT'S LEFT to believe in when your whole world has turned upside down?

Is it possible to affirm a faith that your life is a precious gift and that God is alive (let alone that He is good) when tragedy has crushed your reason for living? When loneliness casts its shadow upon you, when depression haunts you, when it hurts too much to stay awake, but sleep cannot be counted on for much relief, can faith find a place in the spaces of your soul?

Faith is surely something of a miracle, for it is born rarely in triumph, when hearts beat strong, but in tragedy, when hearts lay broken. Yes, faith can thrive in good times. But typically faith becomes a meaningful force in people's lives only when misfortune strikes, when hope has fallen into disrepair. People may say, "Thank God," when all is well, but they pray to Him, argue with Him, have a relationship with Him, and as often as not begin to deeply believe in Him, when all is hell. Talk to people with a sturdier faith and you'll find they've not had easier lives. Like bone, faith often grows stronger after it's been broken (though it may take a long time). Faith is surely something of a miracle.

THE FAITH FACTOR
WHAT DO YOU BELIEVE IN?

During trying times your degree of faith can make the difference as to whether you give up or persevere. The spiritual dimension to your faith—which includes your belief in a power greater than yourself, or perhaps the notion of some divine plan in your life—no doubt can be a powerful and positive force.

But there is a human dimension to your faith too. The human dimension reflects your judgment as to your capabilities to cope (or to the coping capabilities of those people you're relying on to help you). When you ask yourself, "Do I have what it takes to make it through this?" or "Are resources available to me?" you are assessing not just your coping skills but your faith in being able to use them effectively. Extensive research by psychologist Albert Bandura at Stanford University has repeatedly shown that possessing high "self-efficacy"—strong confidence that you can perform necessary coping behaviors—is a powerful determinant of successful coping. In other words the more confident you are about your ability to cope, the more likely you will be to persevere and eventually cope well.

Just how, or if, the human and spiritual dimensions of faith work together to improve coping is not well understood, largely due to the complications in reliably defining and measuring one's spiritual faith. People with the same degree of spiritual faith may have different ways of expressing it. And people with no spiritual or religious beliefs can and do cope quite successfully. However, the work of esteemed researcher Aaron Antonovsky allows for some speculation about the human and spiritual dimensions of faith.

What Antonovsky calls *a sense of coherence* is a person's feeling of confidence that his or her world is fairly predictable and that there is a high probability that things will work out as well as can reasonably be expected. According to Antonovsky, people with a stronger sense of coherence cope better than people with a weaker one. This sense has three components, which I believe allow the spiritual and human dimensions of faith.

The first component is *comprehensibility*. It refers to the perception that the world is ordered, consistent, and clear—that it makes sense and is predictable. The more orderly and predictable your world and what is happening to you in it, the more ably you will cope.

Many of life's problems can render your world less predictable. For example, couples struggling to improve an unsatisfying relationship often experience setbacks in their progress. Once progress becomes unpredictable, and once positive changes are regarded as temporary and unreliable, partners can easily become cynical and pessimistic. Such a loss of faith may cause partners to give up rather than persevere. People suffering a serious illness such as cancer may have to endure months of treatment before they have any clear indication that remission is likely. It's hard to cope when you can't be sure what the outcome will be. At times of hardship and uncertainty, embracing higher spiritual principles can anchor your free-floating anxieties and make your world a bit more meaningful and comprehensible.

Orel Hershiser, who pitched the 1988 Los Angeles Dodgers to a World Series championship, suffered a serious arm injury in 1990. In a recent issue of *Life* magazine,* he spoke

* From an article entitled "Who Is God?" *Life* magazine, December 1990, p. 57.

of his deep faith in God and the comfort of prayer. Does he possess a faith that his arm will eventually heal? Sometimes he believes that can happen. But Hershiser says he possesses the "broader faith" that his life will still be okay whether or not he ever pitches again. His faith made his life more predictable and his misfortune therefore more acceptable.

The second component of a sense of coherence is *manageability*. Your world is manageable when you believe you have the resources necessary to deal with whatever life throws at you. Such resources come from yourself, others, or from your God.

"I refuse to go through life taking a backseat," says Luanne Maloof of Poughkeepsie, New York. "My faith is a predominant part of my life now. I made coping with my cancer a spiritual journey." Luanne's ordeal began in September 1989, when a series of often painful tests such as a bone-marrow biopsy concluded she had Hodgkin's disease, an aggressive but often curable cancer of the lymphatic system. For Luanne radiation therapy followed chemotherapy. Corrective surgery followed that. She is now in remission, and regular checkups and monitoring continue to this day. Married and only twenty-nine when the diagnosis was made, how has she managed? "I swim three times a week to rebuild my lung power and lessen my bone pain," Luanne explained. "I keep a daily journal to better understand my emotions. I draw. I meditate. I take long walks on the beach and have conversations with God." And when she lost her hair to chemotherapy ("I was told my hair was beautiful, but that I was more beautiful than my hair") she opened Bobby-Lu's Hair & Wig Salon, devoting her time to helping other cancer patients who've lost their hair. With strong faith in God, her doctors, and herself, Luanne Maloof believes that physical healing is not the essential ingredient in overcoming cancer. "Some people with cancer will die from it, but those who feel spiritually healed have over-come it."

The stronger your resources and the more manageable you believe your life is, the less it matters when problems confront you. Just ask Luanne.

The last component of a sense of coherence is *meaningfulness*. Life is more meaningful when problems are viewed not simply as threats and burdens but as challenges. The possibility that you can grow physically, psychologically, or spiritually by confronting certain hardships helps make the tragic times more meaningful, and more bearable. "At first it scared me," said one father, discussing his fears of seeing his children less after his divorce. "Then I realized that when I am able to be with them, I'll be with them fully. I see this as an opportunity to become a better father, a more involved father, than I might have been if the marriage had survived." The opportunity to become a better father gave meaning to his ordeal.

For many people a primary function of their religious faith is to provide meaningful guidance. They believe that experiences such as suffering, loss, and betrayal can be made meaningful when out of suffering comes compassion, out of loss comes gratitude, and out of betrayal comes forgiveness.

Some believe that God cares but does not intervene in human affairs. Others believe that, for divine and un-fathomable reasons, God sometimes intervenes and answers some prayers but not others.

And some believe that if you can make your life more meaningful despite suffering, loss, betrayal, and unanswered prayers, then who is to say you have not been touched by the hand of God?

DOES FAITH MOVE
MOUNTAINS?

SOME
RESEARCH EVIDENCE

In his book *Recovering the Soul*, physician Larry Dossey discussed research on the power of prayer. In perhaps the most remarkable study cited, cardiologist Randolph Byrd randomly assigned 393 patients, admitted over a ten-month period to the San Francisco General Hospital coronary care unit, to one of two groups: either a group prayed for by a home prayer assembly or a group not prayed for by such an assembly. Neither the doctors, nurses, nor patients knew which patients were in which group. Each patient had between five and seven people praying for him or her. The results? Patients in the prayed-for group were five times less likely to need antibiotics. They were three times less likely to acquire pulmonary edema, a condition where the heart does not pump properly and the lungs fill with fluid. None of the prayed-for patients required an artificial airway to be inserted in their throats to assist in breathing, while twelve of the non-prayed-for members needed such assistance. Fewer members of the prayed-for group died, but not enough to make a statistically significant difference.

Were such results miraculous? Not by scientific standards. But had the same results been obtained by a new drug or surgical technique, Dr. Dossey claims the results would have been hailed as a breakthrough. Such experimental findings do not prove the existence of God (no experiment or analysis could ever make such a definitive proof), but they underscore the increasing importance that faith and belief can have in the healing process.

With regard to physical disorders and illnesses, your degree of faith in the treatment you are receiving can sometimes be a powerful determinant in the rate of your recovery.

Traditionally, medical researchers have tested the effects of a new treatment drug by comparing its potency with that of a placebo—an inert substance or procedure, often a sugar pill, that has no known therapeutic effects. If patients responded equally well to the placebo as to the new drug, the new drug was considered to be of no value. But even when a new drug outperformed a placebo, the startling truth was that in many research studies *some patients benefited therapeutically by ingesting only a sugar pill*. Belief, and only belief, caused physical changes. Such things aren't supposed to happen.

WHEN YOUR FAITH LETS YOU DOWN, WHAT'S LEFT TO FILL YOU UP?

Maybe your faith wasn't strong enough. Perhaps if you believed more strongly in God, the universe, your doctor, or yourself, things would have worked out. You can hear the timeworn admonition scolding you, "O ye of little faith," and you blame yourself for the tragedy that has befallen you or someone you love.

Maybe it's not yourself whom you blame. Instead you blame God. And you resent those who tout a "think positive" or a "keep the faith" approach to life. Surely they must be misguided, you feel.

It is typical to look for someone or something to blame. Most of us believe that when something goes wrong, somebody made a mistake and is blameworthy. And by having someone to blame we don't feel so powerless.

But accidents do happen.

And disaster can strike at random.

And people who shouldn't die, do.

And medications don't always rid the body of disease.

And the best person for the job doesn't necessarily get chosen.

And faith alone is not always sufficient, or even necessary.

If by embracing a spiritual faith you've convinced yourself that life will be fair, you've embraced a fantasy. Faith does not promise you fairness, or good health, or escape from all that is human. But it does help provide meaning to your pain and comfort in your grief. Faith helps you to be a little less afraid and to accept that bad things can happen to good people (and that good things will happen to bad people).

When your faith lets you down, you have two options: Abandon it or struggle to deepen it. In Bernie Siegel's *Love, Medicine, and Miracles,* his exceptional cancer patients made a positive shift in attitude and faith when they went from asking "Why me, God?" to "Try me, God!" They didn't allow their faith to die when an unasked-for illness came their way. Rather, in the face of their illness, they acted to deepen their faith—not only in God but in their doctors and their own ability to help heal themselves.

Those with a deeper faith rarely, if ever, pray for material favors. But they do pray for strength to cope with whatever comes their way, just as Luanne Maloof did. They understand that not getting what one wants can often be to one's benefit and that valuing *all* life has to offer has its merit.

And they understand, because they've been there, that it's hard to appreciate such a philosophy when tragedy and hardship first appear on your doorstep.

Chapter 20

FAITH DREAMING
DREAMS

The Gift of Hope

❖

THERE IS SOMETHING spiritual and healing in hope.

Hope pleases us. It restores our determination and sense of optimism. An unseen, untouchable force, it eases our suffering, calms our fears, and holds our hand when it needs to be held. Hope tries to tell us that in the end everything can still be good and worthwhile, even when life hurts. It is a light, a warmth, that we sometimes feel drawn to.

But hope sometimes seems to be an illusion—unreal, or too far away to have any real effect. It can seem dim and distant, and we wonder sometimes if hope creates as much suffering as it heals. "Every time I hope, I ache," one woman told me, wondering if her husband would ever fully recover from the devastating effects of his head injury. "In order to hope, I have to feel. I have to accept things I refuse to accept. I don't want to hope anymore. I don't want to feel anymore. I want to forget. I want this all to be over. Can't you understand?"

Many of us pay little attention to hope until we have nothing else to grasp. Hope (like God) can be a last resort and, as such, can be resented. (We often resent those things that make us more aware of our dependencies and limitations.)

Hope can fill us with joy and enthusiasm. But it appears to let us down at times too. When hoping is followed by disappointment, we may still hope. We may hope even harder. But how long can we have faith in hope when disappointments build, when the stark reality of our situation is at odds with what we desperately need it to be?

Hope is often a paradox. Sometimes only when we completely give up hoping does true hope become possible. When you've lost all hope that a loved one will survive; when absolutely no shred of hope exists for a dream to be fulfilled; when loss, true and anguishing loss, is now a reality; a new kind of hope, small and insignificant at first, can nestle like a sleeping child on your breast. It is the kind of hope that whispers tenderly to mourners maybe a year or so after the death of a loved one; it is the kind of hope that lonely couples caress long after a romance has withered; it is the kind of hope that people suffering from a terminal illness softly embrace.

It is the hope that one's life can still be good and meaningful despite tragedy and loss.

It is the hope that joy and peace of mind are still real possibilities, however remote they seem now.

It is the hope that hope still lives.

In the final therapy session with a married couple I'd been seeing for ten months, I asked them, as is my custom, why therapy worked so successfully for them. The day I'd first met them they were depressed and despairing. Therapy was the final ritual they felt duty-bound to try, though their expectations were low. "What worked for me," the husband answered, "was hope. You gave me hope. You told us in our first meeting that as long as the two of us were here to work on our marriage, you would not give up on us. I remembered those words when everything seemed futile, and they gave me the encouragement to keep trying."

In studies too numerous to mention it has been found that hopeful and optimistic persons are more successful, persevere when difficulties emerge, are happier and healthier (emotionally and physically), and generally live longer compared with pessimists. Despair, helplessness, and pessimism are self-fulfilling. The more you believe that nothing you do matters, that you have little positive impact on the misfortunes in your life, the more quickly you'll give up the fight—practically ensuring defeat and depression.

In one often-quoted study, researcher Roger Ulrich compared the recovery rates of forty-six patients who underwent gallbladder surgery. Half of the patients were assigned to a recovery room with a view of trees and foliage. The other half were assigned to a room with a window that faced a brick wall. Patients in the room with the pleasant view had a briefer hospital stay, required less pain medication, and made fewer complaints than the patients with the view of the brick wall. What was it about viewing nature that contributed to an improved recovery? Peacefulness and relaxation probably had some effect. But I suspect another crucial factor was hope. Beholding a beautiful scene of nature may have instilled a sense of optimism in the patients, a belief that the world was waiting for them to take their place among the active and involved members of society.

The power of hope to help you cope and recover from adversity should not be underestimated.

THE UNDERPINNINGS OF HOPE

When you are scared, really scared, there is something unconvincing about hope. It feels phony, unrealistic, akin to wishful thinking. Cheery, upbeat words of encouragement from friends and loved ones, however hopeful sounding, may even add to your misery at first. *Before you can appreciate positive advice and sunny forecasts, you need to feel understood at a heartfelt level.* Listen to Susan:

"When I was sure my husband wasn't coming back, that our marriage was really over, some friends told me he didn't deserve me. They reassured me, 'You're still young, Sue. You have plenty of time to get remarried.' Somehow they only made me feel worse. I wanted to believe my future was bright, but all I could focus on was how scared and angry I felt. My friends didn't seem to understand. I felt more alone, more isolated, than I would have if they'd said nothing at all. Then I met this woman at a support group. After the first meeting we chatted for a few minutes. She told me she understood what I'd been going through because her husband ran out on her just like mine. She told me she felt afraid and angry for a long time afterward. And you know what? I immediately felt better, more hopeful, after talking with her. She understood. And she had survived. Then I began believing I could too."

When you believe that someone really understands you, even though you're scared, hope takes root in your heart. When you know that your feelings make sense, at least to one other person, you don't feel so alone or without options. *The felt sense of being understood is an essential underpinning of hope.*

A second underpinning of hope is *faith.* The more faith you have that you possess the resources to cope and the more you believe you can rely on spiritual strength to help you, the more hopeful you will be. Faith in yourself, your family, your country, your healers, or your God, prevents you from feeling helpless. You believe someone is always available to rely on. As long as you do not feel helpless, you will not feel hopeless.

Part of the job of increasing your faith is to learn about others who've experienced the kind of misfortune you are now experiencing and learn from them. For example, parents of learning-disabled children or children with other handicaps often subscribe to pertinent newsletters and journals to keep abreast of the latest information. Cancer is still a dreaded disease. But Richard and Annette Bloch, coauthors of *Fighting Cancer*,* write that cancer is "the most curable of all chronic diseases." Richard Bloch should know. Thirteen years ago he was told he had three months left to live. Two years later he was completely cured of the lung cancer that was expected to kill him. The Blochs go on to report that there is no type of cancer (not even the most deadly) from which some people have not recovered. Such information helps restore faith and nurture the hope that recovery is possible.

The third underpinning of hope is *committed work.* You must actively work at keeping hope alive by doing all you can to cope with your situation effectively. Nick Buoniconti, former pro linebacker with the Miami Dolphins, wrote in a magazine article how he resigned his position with a Fortune 500 company after his teenage son, Marc, was left completely paralyzed by a football injury. Working full-time to raise funds for the Miami Project to Cure Paralysis, Nick Buoniconti helped the Miami Project grow from a handful of researchers to over sixty scientists, with twenty-five laboratories and a yearly budget of six million dollars in only five years. It has become the world's largest center

* This book, along with other relevant publications, is available free of charge by calling the National Cancer Institute at 1-800-4-CANCER.

for spinal-cord-injury research. And Marc Buoniconti, paralyzed from the neck down, hasn't abandoned hope. He is a dean's-list student at the University of Miami and president of his own record company. Marc's personalized license plate reads, I'LL WALK, and speaks to the hope and optimism of scientists at the Miami Project, who no longer accept the long-held belief that paralysis is irreversible. To them the once-impossible—spinal cord repair—is now a hopeful possibility.

The final underpinning of hope is *meaningfulness*. Meaningfulness can be attained when you nurture the attitude that even if your loss, injury, or misfortune will have long-lasting or even permanent effects, your life can still be rewarding and purposeful, particularly if there is something larger to give yourself to (such as your family, your community, your country, your God, or others in need). Consider what happened to Candy Lightner, divorced and a mother of three, as she revealed to interviewer Bill Berkowitz in his book *Local Heroes*. Candy's daughter, Cari, was killed by a drunk driver. In her initial grief, Candy wanted revenge. She wanted the man who killed her daughter to be severely punished. But she also had a "philosophy of life . . . that something good always comes out of something negative." She believed that by allowing her daughter's organs to be donated, at least some good would come from the tragedy. But someone from the hospital told her that because her daughter's body was badly mutilated, an organ donation wouldn't be possible. Shaken but undaunted, Candy Lightner, a housewife with little formal education, went on to found one of the largest and most successful nonprofit organizations in the country: MADD, Mothers Against Drunk Driving. Due to Candy's courage, tenacity, and the unfailing hope that her daughter's death could save lives, MADD's three-hundred-plus chapters now take credit for the more stringent laws against drunk driving and a shift in the nation's attitude. More and more Americans now deeply believe that driving drunk is morally wrong and totally unacceptable.

No matter what your loss or adversity, if you can trust that someone *understands* your pain, if you can nurture the *faith* that you have the resources to cope, if you *commit* yourself to overcoming your difficulties, and if you believe that your life can still have *meaning* regardless of what happens, hope will thrive, and so will you.

BUILDING AN OPTIMISTIC ATTITUDE

When you're feeling depressed and pessimistic, can you learn to be optimistic? Respected researcher and psychologist Martin Seligman of the University of Pennsylvania is positive you can. In his book *Learned Optimism*, which details his acclaimed research in the area of helplessness and depression, Dr. Seligman has demonstrated that *how* people think about their problems can worsen or improve their coping efforts. When something bad happens to people with a pessimistic explanatory style, they believe that it's their fault (they take on more blame than necessary), that the effects will be long lasting, and that the event will affect a wider area of their life. In contrast, when something bad happens to people with an optimistic explanatory style, they believe that it's not their fault (or they accept responsibility for only their share of the blame), that the negative effects will be temporary, and that they will affect only a specific area of their life. Stated simply, pessimists see misfortune as being caused *personally* and as having *permanent* and *pervasive* effects. Optimists don't overblame themselves, and they view the misfortune as temporary and with limited negative effects. Consequently optimists tend to cope more successfully during adversity.

According to Seligman, failure or loss is much more likely to result in a serious depression when the person experiencing the failure tends to be pessimistic. Someone with a more optimistic stance may well be sad and disappointed, but he or she will recover quickly without serious depression.

THE ABC'S OF OPTIMISM

Most people believe that when they have strong emotional or behavioral reactions to a loss or misfortune, it was the Adversity ("A") that led to the emotional Consequence ("C"). But in fact it was the Belief ("B") about the adversity that really led to the consequence. Adversity led to Belief, which led to Consequence.

When Larry was fired from his job ("A"), he felt scared and depressed ("C"). But his anxiety and depression was more a consequence of his beliefs ("B") about being fired. "I'm incompetent," he told himself, adding, "I'll never get a job with this pay and I'll have to sell my house. My wife will never understand." Such negative thoughts would make anyone feel depressed and defeated. When Larry understood how his thinking was impeding his ability to cope, he learned to Dispute ("D") the pessimistic line of reasoning. "Yes, I was fired," Larry told himself, "but I know I am competent because I've done well on that job for years." (When Larry looked realistically at all the evidence—a helpful way to dispute pessimistic thinking—he realized he was in fact quite competent to do his job.) "But I haven't been happy there, and that was why I performed poorly and eventually got fired," he continued. (Larry discovered a more accurate, alternative reason for why he lost his job. Listing alternative rea-

sons to explain why something bad happened is a second helpful way of disputing pessimistic thoughts.) "Criticizing myself is keeping me from doing what I have to do, which is finding a new job that I'll enjoy. Money may be tight at first, but we have some money in savings, so we'll manage." *(Again, he assesses all available evidence.)* My wife will be worried, but she's always supported me in the past. I'm sure she'll do so again now."

By thinking that the negative effects of his unemployment (loss of income, loss of esteem, marital stress) would be temporary, Larry felt more encouraged, more optimistic, and far less depressed. His situation hadn't changed—he was still unemployed—but his attitude about it changed.

Do you get discouraged easily? Are you feeling helpless and depressed? The first step to nurturing optimism is to assess your explanatory style, that is, determine whether or not you're thinking pessimistically. If you are, dispute your pessimistic beliefs. What is the evidence for your negative proclamations? Does evidence exist to contradict your pessimism? Are there alternative reasons that can help explain what happened that leave you feeling more optimistic? Don't exaggerate your losses. Emphasize your talents and gifts. Appreciate and be grateful for what you have. Remember, all problems are temporary, and even permanent losses need not have permanent effects.

REFRAMING YOUR "WHAT IF'S"
THE GIFT OF HOPE

I know, and you know, there will be suffering ahead for us all. And even when we're spared from it personally for a time, we read about it in the newspapers and watch it unfold on the television news. We see it etched on the weathered faces of people we pass on the street.

Some suffering goes unseen, hidden in the hearts of people too lonely or too frightened to share it with someone who would care. Some suffering is needless, brought on by man's inhumanity to man. But much suffering is inevitable if you live long enough and love hard enough. Life is the most precious of gifts. It allows us the opportunity, over and over, to love fully and deeply and to be fully and deeply loved. But life so often hurts so terribly.

I write of hope because it is the stuff of our souls. It is one of the qualities that distinguishes us from lower animals and makes us God's kin. It keeps us dreaming, creating, persevering, and overcoming. It protects us from the storms of despair. And it nudges us to smile, however slightly, even during life's grim moments.

You may understandably cry, "What if I can't . . . what if I fail . . . what if you leave me . . . what if the worst happens?" But what if instead you believe:

- That all your problems—every one—will be temporary.

- That in spite of your trials and tragedies you can be acquainted with resources you never knew existed.

- That even if your loss is permanent, you can hold out the hope that *today* holds promise for some happiness.

- That you can make your suffering meaningful and go on to live a meaningful life.

- That people who have hurt you, most of the time were doing the best that they could given who they were. They hurt you because they were weak, not because you were unlovable.

- That you can make a positive, powerful difference in the life of someone you haven't even met yet.

- That you may more fully embrace life and its beauty as a consequence of the hardships you are now facing.

- That forgiveness is always possible.

- That God loves you, is with you right now, cares about your suffering, and has a plan for your life that is for the good.

What if you believed such words? Then you would know hope, and despair would find no resting place in your heart.

If there is a mixed blessing to hope, it is this: Genuine hope compels you to remember at a time when you may ache to forget. You cannot hope for healing without remembering that which has made you suffer. But you will not hope for long without also remembering some of what's been good and glorious and loving and meaningful in your life.

Of such things do not forget.

SOURCES

Ader, Robert (ed.). *Psychoneuroimmunology*. New York: Academic Press, 1981.

Andrews, Lewis M. *To Thine Own Self Be True*. New York: Doubleday, 1989.

Antonovsky, Aaron. *Health, Stress, and Coping*. San Francisco: Jossey-Bass, 1979.

———. *Unraveling the Mystery of Health: How People Manage Stress and Stay Well*. San Francisco: Jossey-Bass, 1988.

Bandler, R.; Grinder, J.; and Satir, V. *Changing with Families*. Palo Alto, Calif.: Science and Behavior Books, 1976.

Bandura, Albert. "Human Agency in Social Cognitive Theory." *American Psychologist* 44 (September 1989):1175–84.

Bard, M.; and Sangrey, D. "Things Fall Apart: Victims in Crisis." *Evaluation and Change*. Special Issue (1980):28–35.

Beavers, W. Robert. *Psychotherapy and Growth: A Family Systems Perspective*. New York: Brunner/Mazel, 1977.

Bednar, Richard L.; Wells, M. Gawain; and Peterson, Scott. *Self-Esteem: Paradoxes and Innovations in Clinical Theory and Practice*. Washington, D.C.: American Psychological Association, 1989.

Benson, Herbert. *The Relaxation Response*. New York: William Morrow, 1975.

Berkman, L.; and Syme, S. "Social Networks, Host Resistance, and Mortality: A Nine-Year Follow-up Study of Alameda County Residents." *American Journal of Epidemiology* 109 (1979):186–204.

Berkowitz, Bill. *Local Heroes: The Rebirth of Heroism in America*. Lexington, Mass.: Lexington Books, 1987.

Bloch, Richard; and Bloch, Annette. *Fighting Cancer*. Kansas City, Mo.: R. A. Bloch Cancer Foundation, 1985.

Bloomfield, Harold. *Making Peace with Your Parents*. New York: Ballantine Books, 1985.

Borysenko, Joan. *Minding the Body, Mending the Mind*. Reading, Mass.: Addison-Wesley, 1987.

———. *Guilt Is the Teacher, Love Is the Lesson*. New York: Warner, 1990.

Boszormenyi-Nagy, Ivan; and Sparks, Geraldine. *Invisible Loyalties*. New York: Brunner/Mazel, 1984.

Bozarth-Campbell, Alla. *Life Is Goodbye, Life Is Hello: Grieving Well Through All Kinds of Loss*. Minneapolis: CompCare Publishers, 1982.

Breznitz, S. "The Effect of Hope on Coping with Stress." In M. H. Appley and R. Trumbull (eds.), *Dynamics of Stress*, pp. 295–306. New York: Plenum, 1986.

Brown, Fredda Herz. "The Impact of Death and Serious Illness on the Family Life Cycle." In B. Carter and M. McGoldrick (eds.), *The Changing Family Life Cycle: A Framework for Family Therapy*, pp. 457–82. New York: Gardner Press, 1988.

Bulman, R.; and Wortman, C. "Attributions of Blame and Coping in the Real World: Severe Accident Victims React to Their Lot." *Journal of Personality and Social Psychology* 35 (1977):351–63.

Buoniconti, Nick. "Beating the Odds on Paralysis." *Spotlight Magazine* 14, no. 13, New Jersey/Rockland/Hudson Valley Edition. November 1990, p. 47.

Cobb, S. "Social Support as a Moderator of Life Stress." *Psychosomatic Medicine* 38 (1976):300–14.

Coleman, Paul W. *The Forgiving Marriage: Overcoming Resentment and Anger and Rediscovering Each Other*. Chicago: Contemporary Books, 1989.

Cousins, Norman. *Head First: The Biology of Hope.* New York: E. P. Dutton, 1989.

Csikszentmihalyi, Mihalyi. *Flow: The Psychology of Optimal Experience.* New York: Harper & Row, 1990.

Curran, Dolores. *Traits of a Healthy Family.* New York: Harper & Row, 1983.

Dohrenwend, B. S.; and Dohrenwend, B. P. *Stressful Life Events.* New York: John Wiley & Sons, 1974.

Dorian, B. J.; Keystone, E.; Garfinkel, P. E.; and Brown, G. M. "Immune Mechanisms in Acute Psychological Stress." *Psychosomatic Medicine* 43, no. 86 (1981).

Dossey, Larry. *Recovering the Soul: A Scientific and Spiritual Search.* New York: Bantam, 1989.

———. *Space, Time, and Medicine.* Boston: New Science Library, 1982.

Everstine, Diana Sullivan; and Everstine, Louis. *People in Crisis: Strategic Therapeutic Interventions.* New York: Brunner/Mazel, 1983.

Figley, Charles R. "Catastrophes: An Overview of Family Reactions." In C. R. Figley and H. I. McCubbin (eds.), *Stress and the Family: Volume 2. Coping with Catastrophe,* pp. 3–20. New York: Brunner/Mazel, 1983.

———. *Helping Traumatized Families.* San Francisco: Jossey-Bass, 1989.

Frankl, Victor. *Man's Search for Meaning: An Introduction to Logotherapy.* Boston: Beacon Press, 1968.

Friedman, Edwin. *Generation to Generation: Family Process in Church and Synagogue.* New York: Guilford, 1985.

Gawinski, B.; Patterson, J.; and Louw, D. "Infertility, Miscarriage, and Family Therapy." Presentation at the 1990 Annual Conference of the American Association for Marriage and Family Therapy. Washington, D.C., October 1990.

Glenn, N. D.; and Weaver, C. N. "The Contribution of Marital Happiness to Overall Happiness." *Journal of Marriage and Family* 43 (1981):161–68.

Gottman, John. "Growing Up Married: Men and Commitment—The Psychophysiology of Marriage." Paper presented at the Annual Convention of the American Association for Marriage and Family Therapy. San Francisco, 1989.

Gove, W. R. "Sex, Marital Status, and Mortality." *American Journal of Sociology* 79 (1973):45–67.

Horowitz, M. J. *Stress Response Syndromes.* Northvale, N. J.: Jason Aronson, 1986.

Hunt, Morton. *The Compassionate Beast.* New York: William Morrow, 1990.

Jampolsky, Gerald G. *Goodbye to Guilt: Releasing Fear Through Forgiveness.* New York: Bantam Books, 1985.

————. *Love Is Letting Go of Fear.* New York: Bantam, 1981.

Johnsgard, Keith. *The Exercise Prescription for Depression and Anxiety.* New York: Plenum Press, 1989.

Justice, Blair. *Who Gets Sick?: How Beliefs, Moods, and Thoughts Affect Your Health.* Los Angeles: Jeremy Tarcher, Inc., 1987.

Kabat-Zinn, Jon. *Full Catastrophe Living.* New York: Delacorte Press, 1990.

Kalellis, Peter M. *On the Other Hand: Deciding What to Do About Indecision.* Allen, Tex.: Argus Communications, 1980.

Karpel, Mark (ed.). *Family Resources.* New York: Guilford, 1986.

Kennedy, Eugene. *Loneliness and Everyday Problems.* Garden City, N.Y.: Image Books, 1983.

————. *The Pain of Being Human.* Garden City, N.Y.: Image Books, 1973.

Kennedy, John F. *Profiles in Courage.* New York: Harper, 1956.

Kent, J.; Coates, T.; Pelletier, K.; and O'Regan, B. "Unexpected Recoveries: Spontaneous Remission and Immune Functioning." *Advances* 6, no. 2 (1989):66–73.

Kerr, Michael; and Bowen, Murray. *Family Evaluation*. New York: W. W. Norton, 1988.

Kiecolt-Glaser, J.; Garner, W.; Speicher, C. E.; Penn, G.; and Glaser, R. "Psychosocial Modifiers of Immunocompetence in Medical Students." *Psychosomatic Medicine* 46 (1984):7–14.

Kiecolt-Glaser, J. K.; Fisher, L. D.; Ogrocki, P.; Stout, J. C.; Speicher, C. E.; and Glaser, R. "Marital Quality, Marital Disruption, and Immune Function." *Psychosomatic Medicine* 49 (1987):13–34.

Kiecolt-Glaser, J. K.; Glaser, R.; Shuttleworth, E. C.; Dyer, C.; Ogrocki, P.; and Speicher, C. E. "Chronic Stress and Immunity in Caregivers of Alzheimer's Disease Victims." *Psychosomatic Medicine* 49 (1987):523–35.

Kisher, G. R.; and Figley, C. R. "The Relationship Between Psychiatric Symptoms of Crime Victims and Their Supporters: Evidence of the Chiasmal Effects of Co-victimization." Unpublished manuscript, Purdue University. Cited in Charles R. Figley, *Helping Traumatized Families*. San Francisco: Jossey-Bass, 1989.

Kobasa, Suzanne. "Stressful Life Events, Personality, and Health: An Inquiry into Hardiness." *Journal of Personality and Social Psychology* 37 (1979):1–11.

Krauss, Pesach; and Goldfischer, Morrie. *Why Me? Coping with Grief, Loss, and Change*. New York: Bantam, 1988.

Kubler-Ross, Elizabeth. *On Death and Dying*. New York: Macmillan, 1969.

Kushner, Harold. *When Bad Things Happen to Good People*. New York: Schocken Books, 1984.

———. *Who Needs God?* New York: Summit Books, 1989.

Langer, Ellen. *Mindfulness*. Boston: Addison-Wesley, 1989.

———. *The Psychology of Control*. Beverly Hills, Calif.: Sage, 1983.

Langer, Ellen; and Rodin, J. "The Effects of Choice and Enhanced Personal Responsibility for the Aged: A Field Experiment in an Institutional Setting." *Journal of Personality and Social Psychology* 34 (1976):191–98.

Larson, Earnie. "To Get the Right Answers We Must Ask the Right Questions." *Marriage Encounter* 19, no. 7 (September 1990):20–23.

Lauer, J.; and Lauer, R. "Marriages Made to Last." *Psychology Today*, June 1985, pp. 22–26.

Lazarus, R. S. *Psychological Stress and the Coping Process.* New York: McGraw-Hill, 1966.

Lehman, D. R.; Wortman, C.; and Williams, A. "Long-Term Effects of Losing a Spouse or a Child in a Motor-Vehicle Accident." *Journal of Personality and Social Psychology* 52, no. 1 (1987):218–31.

Lewis, J.; Beavers, W.; Gossett, J.; and Phillips, V. (eds.). *No Single Thread: Psychological Health in Family Systems.* New York: Brunner/Mazel, 1976.

Linn, B. S.; Linn, M. W.; and Jensen, J. "Degree of Depression and Immune Responsiveness." *Psychosomatic Medicine* 44 (1982):128–29.

Locke, Steven; and Hornig-Rohan, Mady. *Mind and Immunity.* New York: Institute for the Advancement of Health, 1983.

Lynch, James. "The Broken Heart: The Psychobiology of Human Contact." In Robert Ornstein and Charles Swencionis, *The Healing Brain.* New York: Guilford Press, 1990.

Marcus, Paul; and Rosenberg, Alan. "The Holocaust Survivor's Faith and Religious Behavior: Implications for Treatment." *Psychologists Interested in Religious Issues Newsletter* 15, no. 3 (1990):11–18.

McCubbin, Hamilton I.; and Figley, Charles R. (eds.). *Stress and the Family: Coping with Catastrophe.* New York: Brunner/Mazel, 1983.

————. *Stress and the Family: Coping with Normative Transitions.* New York: Brunner/Mazel, 1983.

Medalie, J. H.; and Goldbourt, H. "Angina Pectoris Among 10,000 Men: Psychosocial and Other Risk Factors as Evidenced by a Multivariate Analysis of a Five-Year Incidence Study." *American Journal of Medicine* 60 (1976): 910–21.

Melnechuk, Theodore. "Emotions, Brain, Immunity and Health: A Review." In M. Clynes and J. Panksepp (eds.), *Emotions and Psychopathology*, pp. 181–247, New York: Plenum, 1988.

Minkler, Meredith. "People Need People: Social Support and Health." In Robert Ornstein and Charles Swencionis, *The Healing Brain*. New York: Guilford Press, 1990.

Mulhern, R. K.; Lauer, M. E.; and Hoffman, R. G. "Death of a Child at Home or at the Hospital: Subsequent Psychological Adjustment of the Family." *Pediatrics* 71 (1983):743–47.

Ornstein, Robert E.; and Sobel, David S. "Bare Your Soul and Beat Disease." *Prevention*, pp. 32–33, July 1989.

Pearlin, L. I.; Lieberman, M. A.; Menaghan, E. G.; and Mullan, J. T. "The Stress Process." *Journal of Health and Social Behavior* 22 (1981):337–56.

Pelletier, Kenneth R. *Mind as Healer, Mind as Slayer.* New York: Delacorte, 1977.

Pennebaker, James W. *Opening Up: The Healing Power of Confiding in Others.* New York: Morrow, 1990.

Pennebaker, James W.; Barger, Steven D.; and Tiebout, John. "Confronting Traumatic Experiences and Health Among Holocaust Survivors." *Advances* 6, no. 4 (1989):14–17.

Quarantelli, E. L. "An Assessment of Conflicting Views on Mental Health: The Consequences of Traumatic Events." In C. R. Figley (ed.), *Trauma and Its Wake: The Study and Treatment of Post-Traumatic Stress Disorder* (pp. 173–218). New York: Brunner/Mazel, 1985.

Roskies, E.; and Lazarus, R. S. "Coping Theory and the Teaching of Coping Skills." In P. Davidson (ed.), *Behav-*

ioral Medicine: Changing Health Lifestyles, pp. 38–69. New York: Brunner/Mazel, 1980.

Scarboro, Glenn. "The Delusion of Differentiation: Notations on a Family Process." In Peter Titelman (ed.), *The Therapist's Own Family*. New York: Jason Aranson, 1987.

Schuller, Robert. *Believe in the God Who Believes in You.* Nashville: Thomas Nelson, 1989.

———. *Tough Times Never Last But Tough People Do!* New York: Bantam, 1984.

Schuller, Robert A. *Getting Through the Going Through Stage.* Nashville: Thomas Nelson, 1986.

Seligman, Martin E. P. *Learned Optimism.* New York: Alfred A. Knopf, 1991.

Seligman, Martin E. P.; and Schulman, Peter. "Explanatory Style as a Predictor of Productivity and Quitting Among Life Insurance Sales Agents." *Journal of Personality and Social Psychology* 50 (1986):832–38.

Selye, Hans. *Stress Without Distress.* New York: Lippincott, 1974.

Siegel, Bernie. *Love, Medicine, and Miracles.* New York: Harper & Row, 1986.

Simonton, O.; and Simonton, S. "Belief Systems and Management of the Emotional Aspects of Malignancy." *Journal of Transpersonal Psychology* 7, no. 1 (1975):29–48.

Sinnett, N.; Sanders, G.; and DeFrain, J. "Strong Families: A National Study." In N. Stinnett, J. DeFrain, K. King, P. Knaub, and G. Rowe (eds.), *Family Strengths 3: Roots of Well-Being*. Lincoln: University of Nebraska Press, 1981.

Smedes, Lewis. *Choices: Making Right Decisions in a Complex World.* New York: Harper & Row, 1986.

Sobel, David. "The Placebo Effect: Using the Body's Own Healing Mechanisms." In Robert Ornstein and Charles Swencionis (eds.), *The Healing Brain: A Scientific Reader*. New York: Guilford, 1990.

Stearns, Ann Keiser. *Coming Back: Rebuilding Lives After Crisis and Loss*. New York: Ballantine, 1988.

Strong, Maggie. *Mainstay: For the Well Spouse of the Chronically Ill*. Boston: Little, Brown and Company, 1988.

Suls, J.; and Mullen, B. "Life Events, Perceived Control, and Illness: The Role of Uncertainty." *Journal of Human Stress* 7 (1981):30–34.

Taylor, Shelley E. *Health Psychology*. New York: Random House, 1986.

Ulrich, R. S. "View Through a Window May Influence Recovery from Surgery." *Science* 224 (1984):420–21.

Ursin, H.; Baade, E.; and Levine, S. (eds.). *Psychobiology of Stress: A Study of Coping Men*. New York: Gardner Press, 1978.

Watzlawick, Paul; Weakland, John; and Fisch, Richard. *Change: Principles of Problem Formation and Problem Resolution*. New York: W. W. Norton, 1974.

Weiner, Herbert. "The Concept of Stress in the Light of Studies on Disasters, Unemployment, and Loss: A Critical Analysis." In Michael R. Zales (ed.), *Stress in Health and Disease*. New York: Brunner/Mazel, 1985.

Wiesel, Elie. *Night*. New York: Hill & Wang, 1960.

Wikler, L.; Wasow, M.; and Hatfield, E. "Chronic Sorrow Revisited: Parent vs. Professional Depiction of the Adjustment of Parents of Mentally Retarded Children." *American Journal of Orthopsychiatry* 51, no. 1, pp. 63–70, 1981.